THE LONG ARM
OF AMERICA

BOOKS BY MARTIN CAIDIN

THE LONG ARM OF AMERICA
THIS IS MY LAND
OVERTURE TO SPACE
BLACK THURSDAY
COUNTDOWN FOR TOMORROW
THE LONG NIGHT
RENDEZVOUS IN SPACE
THE LONG, LONELY LEAP
MAN-IN-SPACE DICTIONARY
THE NIGHT HAMBURG DIED
SAMURAI!
THE POWER OF DECISION
SPACEPORT U.S.A.
THUNDERBIRDS!
BY APOLLO TO THE MOON
ZERO!
AVIATION AND SPACE MEDICINE
RED STAR IN SPACE
THUNDERBOLT!
A TORCH TO THE ENEMY

GOLDEN WINGS
MAN INTO SPACE
TEST PILOT
THE MOON: NEW WORLD FOR MEN
AIR FORCE
THE SILKEN ANGELS
BOEING 707
CROSS-COUNTRY FLYING
THE ASTRONAUTS
THE WONDER OF FLIGHT
WORLDS IN SPACE
WAR FOR THE MOON
I AM EAGLE!
THE ZERO FIGHTER
VANGUARD
LET'S GO FLYING!
ROCKETS BEYOND THE EARTH
X-15: FIRST FLIGHT INTO SPACE
ROCKETS AND MISSILES
JETS, ROCKETS AND GUIDED MISSILES

THE LONG ARM
of America

THE STORY OF THE AMAZING HERCULES AIR ASSAULT TRANSPORT AND OUR REVOLUTIONARY GLOBAL STRIKE FORCES

by

MARTIN CAIDIN

Drawings by Fred L. Wolff

NEW YORK: E. P. DUTTON & CO., INC.
1963

THIS BOOK IS FOR RALPH H. McCLARREN

CONTENTS

		PAGE
	Author's Foreword	xi
	Prologue	3
I	Checkmate	18
II	How Big Is a War?	28
III	The Flexible Blueprint	41
IV	Squat, Square, and Rugged	58
V	Genetics of a Giant	65
VI	Slide-Rule Philosophy	80
VII	The Proving Ground	98
VIII	Test Pilot's Roundtable	112
IX	Bite a Bigger Chunk of Air	131
X	The Weapon	159
XI	The Longest Arm	190
XII	Hit 'em Harder!	215
XIII	The New Warfare	243
XIV	The New Warfare—Part II	258
XV	From the Flight Deck	280
XVI	Angels with Steel Wings	301
XVII	Assignment: Anywhere	316
	Epilogue	356
	Index	363

ILLUSTRATIONS

Photographs

	PAGE
Unearthly energy of a nuclear cloud	20
Preparing to refuel over the Pacific	51
The first Hercules	62
P-38J Lightning flown home despite heavy damages	71
Lockheed's internationally famed Constellation	75
Lockheed Neptune at South Pole	75
F-94C Starfire interceptor	77
C-130E Hercules production line	87
The YC-130 on a flight test	101
Practicing formation flights with new assault transports	114
C-130B cruises with two engines shut down	135
Maintenance crew at work on Hercules' engines	144
The Hercules has engines of tremendous power	149
Deep furrows dug by Hercules wheels	163
Rough-field tests	167
Hercules takeoff from rough, sandy field	169
Anti-tank weapon is chained to floor of Hercules	172
Heavy equipment air drops	175
Cargo-capacity test	179
Loading up for advanced field trials	179
Cargo hauled by parachute from the open ramp	185
Massive load clears the cargo ramp	186
Pallet-loaded jeep is pushed into Hercules	188
TAC Commander General Walter C. Sweeney, Jr.	193
Bullpup missile blasts away from F-105 Thunderchief	195
Phantom II fighter	195
"They were able to fly in a manner they'd never dreamed of"	197
The crews moved fast	200
Super Sabres of TAC in CASF Bravo	206

PAGE

Hercules roll into the loading area of an Army base — 208
They wait to board their paratroopers and other soldiers — 208
Air Force technicians board special alert bus — 209
Airman on CASF alert bids wife and daughter good-by — 210
"There goes Daddy . . . *again*" — 211
Refueling miles over the middle of nowhere — 213
Red Alert! — 216
Major General Maurice Preston telephones from Airborne
    Command Post — 218
The secret TAC Command Post — 220
At TAC Command Post — 221
Weather conditions are shown in situation reports — 221
"Instant response" is keynote of Hercules operations — 223
The Hercules gives unprecedented range of vision — 226
"Waves of Hercules thundered over Panama. . . ." — 228
Paratroopers pour from Hercules — 229
"Ready to load!" — 232
C-130E Hercules — 237
Over the drop zones — 246
Fresh off the drop zone — 249
General Walter C. Sweeney, Jr., and General Paul D. Adams — 256
Yanking a huge truck out of the transport — 260
A mechanic of the Air Commandos — 266
Paratroopers prepared to leap from C-130 Hercules — 275
Major Wilmer S. Wallick at controls of Hercules No. 297 — 283
In the copilot's seat is the author — 283
First Lieutenant James S. McReynolds, copilot — 284
Everything is "right on the button" — 286
Spinners ringed with ice — 286
Captain Alfred C. Bowman, Jr., navigator — 288
Hercules of the U.S. Marine Corps — 299
Hercules crew in the Congo — 305
Congo natives unload flour from Hercules — 308
United Nations personnel help battered U.S. pilot — 308
C-130 roars over Asian village — 310
C-130A Hercules ready for mass-effort airlift operation — 314
Hercules booms upward from its ski tracks — 322
After a ski landing in Greenland — 322
Snow sleds are pushed to cargo ramp — 325

PAGE

RCAF Hercules in Far North	326
Over Antarctica	327
Unloading in Pensacola Mountains, Antarctica	329
Navy Hercules is unloaded without stopping	330
Unloading a 23,000-pound cargo package	330
At the Pensacola Mountains	333
At the South Pole Station	333
Navy Hercules at McMurdo Sound	334
After 2,600-mile flight in Antarctica	337
Takeoff from rough grass strip, Peru	347
On the "other side of the Andes"	348
Refugee Tibetan orphans being moved into Hercules transports	350
During a photo-mapping mission	353
The "Four Horsemen"	357

Drawings

The world-famed *Winnie Mae*	67
Lockheed Sirius	69
First of the Electras	69
Hudson bomber	70
Job fulfilled by the Hercules	121
Not one accident attributed to Hercules' engines	147
"You make a controlled *crash*-landing . . ."	161
Troops march into the Hercules' hold	171
Takeoff with rocket boost	174
Landing tests with ski-equipped Hercules	176
Rescue mission	181
Flight deck of C-130B	227
"Hardware facilities" of Hercules	233
The C-130E	235
Operating from jungle and forest strips	240
Formation air drop	247
Mass paratrooper drop	253
Extraction technique using "people pallet"	262

	PAGE
Hercules in electrical storm	291
Hercules tanker and Crusader fighters	298
Preparing to chop power	343
The huge StarLifter	360
Assault missions for the Hercules	360

AUTHOR'S FOREWORD

ONE MAN does not—because he cannot—write a book like *The Long Arm of America* by himself. To be sure, it is his long attendance to his typewriter that presents the final product in book form, and the words are, he hopes, properly connected so as to portray the stream of events and at the same time convey their deeper significance. But right there is the key to it all—"to portray the stream of events." The current runs deep and broad, and the contributions to its flow come from many hundreds and even thousands of people.

These are the people who worked with me toward the final goal of portraying a monument to American industry—the Hercules—and who sustain the intense pattern of movement in the cockpit, in the hangars, in the flight operations rooms, in the design offices where slide rules move silently and begin the first steps of a bright new chapter of the future. There are too many faces and too many names to recall here in this limited space, and never would it be possible to do justice to them all.

There are the Offices of Information of the United States Air Force, the Army, the Navy, the Marines, and the Coast Guard; officers and men of the Tactical Air Command and the 19th Air Force; of Strike Command and the 839th Air Division in Tennessee along with the 322nd Air Division in France. . . . There were willing and able contributors at Langley, Seymour-Johnson, Sewart, MacDill, Evreux-Fauville, Wiesbaden, Tempelhof, Kindley, Lajes, Newfoundland, Rhein-Main . . . in a dozen countries, a hundred old friends and several hundred new ones. All these people gave unstintingly of their time and effort and, it should be noted, wore their pride and their feelings on their sleeves, to my everlasting gratitude for such free and uninhibited assistance.

Thus the effort to produce the final product has had a kaleidoscopic quality, rather than being an ordinary research and study program to amass material. The book is much more alive than that—it is a reflection of men. The author's many hours in the Hercules, the wonderful hours of flight and of feeling the response and sensitivity of the great machine, are also part of the many threads used in weaving the final fabric of this story.

Individuals and groups, friends and strangers, the identified and the faceless, made this book possible. And there were those who made a long and very special effort—among whom I readily count First Lieutenant Douglas A. McCoy, USAF, of Headquarters, Tactical Air Command; my good friend and associate Henry A. Curth, who with me came closer to the edge of disaster, in a violent storm, than either of us likes to remember; Lee Rogers, Chess Abernathy, and the extraordinarily cooperative people of the Lockheed-Georgia Company. And above all, perhaps, Colonel William G. Moore, Jr., USAF, Commander of the 314th Troop Carrier Wing at Sewart Air Force Base, Tennessee—and the many crewmen who revealed to me in flight and in performance the heart of the Hercules.

It is out of the question to include here all the names—but of my gratitude to one and all there is no doubt.

MARTIN CAIDIN

THE LONG ARM
OF AMERICA

Prologue   THE WIND COMMANDS
the rain from the night sky with maddening persistence. For many
hours an unremitting downpour has covered the great military air
base near the small town of Evreux, France. The concrete ramps are
pools of water; the open earth is a bog of wet coldness.

The rain spatters harshly on broad wings, splashes down from
high tails, and runs across glass and plastic. It pervades the clothing
of armed guards slogging in discomfort from one enormous machine
to the other. The machines stand unresponsive to the liquid punishment. Four winged giants rest in one parking area. A half-mile
away, eight others cluster along the concrete ramp. At another, only
one stands beneath the rain.

Inside long buildings edging the perimeter of Evreux-Fauville
Air Base the floors and walls are greasy with the wet cold. Men
sleeping in these rooms are uncomfortable, for the dampness is a
film of beaded moisture around metal fixtures, within clothing—
everywhere.

Each room is 16 by 16 feet. None of the walls is thick enough
to keep out the spattering rattle of water tumbling from broken
drains onto concrete. It is the kind of sound that grates on the
nerves even through the numbness of sleep.

Outside these rooms, beyond the mist-enshrouded runways, only
60 miles beyond the great aircraft, there lies the City of Light.
Beautiful, gleaming Paris . . .

It might as well be a million miles away, for all that the men in
these rooms care. Theirs is a world removed from it by greater
distances than the measurement of miles. They live within an oasis.
It is an island of their country, an element of the United States to
which distance is a meaningless figure. It exists in a relationship
of time to other places in the world—time in hours and minutes as
a wing slices through the air. So many hours and minutes to here,
so many more or less hours and minutes to there, or there. The
miles mean nothing at all.

The web of time is spun by the relationship of distant events. On
this same evening, but hours earlier, one of those events began to

reach out to this airfield only 60 miles across the soil of France from Paris.

It is not much of an event as measured in geological terms. The crusty skin of the planet shifts—not much: the thickness of a hair, as measured in planetary terms. But to man . . .

To man, and to his works, this minute shrug of the terrestrial crust appears in a different, more meaningful form. It is noticed first in a large town sprawling across Middle Eastern hills. The response to this shrug is a low, building growl of thunder. It rises from the caverns of the subsurface. With its passage there comes the continued movement of the terrestrial shrug.

The hills also shift. Not much—only by several feet. On the planetary scale, it is nothing.

In the community, it is stark terror. To man, the earth seems to lift up, to poise for a fraction of a second, and then to shift violently to one side. The low growl becomes a crashing, terrifying roar. It is earthquake—the spasmodic twitch of a planet that spells disaster and death, horror and agony, to tens of thousands, perhaps hundreds of thousands of people.

The earth shrugs—and thousands of men, women, and children perish. Many thousands more are cut, maimed, bruised, gashed, injured lightly or injured seriously. In the towns and villages beyond this one that is stricken worst of all, buildings rock and teeter. Water supplies are lost as their buried conduits crack and the water drains away into the earth, beyond recall.

There is pain, injury, death, and terror. There is fire, disaster. There is the threat of added death and agony. There is the threat of epidemic.

Unless help from the outside can be rushed in to combat the effects of the earthquake.

Help in specific form. Help spelled as medicine, food, water, portable power supplies, field hospitals, doctors and nurses, and the thousand and one things needed to apply to the great and raw wound of disaster. Help is needed; the call goes out.

It winds its tortuous path by radio, undersea cable, telephone. It moves through channels of government. It travels with greater speed than is normal, for riding every word is that beseeching plea to help those still alive, that their numbers may not be added to the swelling ranks of the dead.

The cry for aid moves around the world. It leaps continents and oceans, and then begins to spread out to other points even more distant in space and time.

It reaches out to a dark, cold, wind-lashed, water-soaked spread of concrete, grass, buildings, and great metal airplanes, only 60 miles from Paris. It arrives at Evreux-Fauville Air Base, and it triggers a spreading series of responses.

Nailed atop the door of one of the looming hangars is a sign faded by wind, rain, sun, and time. Nevertheless, it is a sign still legible, a sign of identification. One can make out the lettering that reads "839th Air Division." This is one of the "homes away from home" for this air division, which hangs its biggest sign back in Tennessee. Here at Evreux there are 16 great airplanes of the division, on overseas duty. They are here for many reasons. One of those reasons is imperative at this particular instant.

A man—cold, tired, wishing he were back in Tennessee with his wife and his children—sits behind a wide, austere desk. It is not really a desk; it is a surface of boards hammered together to form what serves as a desk. The floor beneath the feet of the man—a captain—is damp and cold. The walls are a cold gray-blue color. The lights in the ceiling are bright and unfriendly.

The captain lifts a receiver from a telephone. For a moment he pauses, studying again the notes he has scribbled from another telephone conversation which, only seconds before, swept any ideas of sleep or rest from his mind. Then, quickly, he dials three numbers.

In Building Number 195, a telephone in a hallway buzzes—telephones in France do not ring; they emit a croaking buzz more disturbing than the ring. The sound reaches through the steady noise of the rain. It pushes through a closed door and pierces the sleep of a man. With unusual suddenness he throws back his covers and swings his feet to the floor. Only for a second does he pause as the clammy surface meets his feet. Then he is up and moving quickly into the hallway of the old French barracks. He picks up the phone, grunts his name into the speaker.

In seconds he is completely awake and alert. He drops the phone back to its cradle and walks across the cold floor to another room. Urgently he shoves open the door and awakens the occupants. They are the rest of his crew . . . the men on Alert Status.

"It's a bad one," he says in greeting. "Somewhere in the Middle East."

The words come out in choppy fashion. "First reports claim at least 5,000 dead. Maybe twice as much. We're to move out—" he glances at his watch—"in exactly 52 minutes. Let's go."

"*Let's go. . . .*"

The response to the shifting of the earth's crust, many miles away, is in motion.

The three men dress quickly. They have no time to shave, just enough for a quick spray of cold water over the face. They pull on flight suits and jackets, jump boots and other flight gear. Some clothes and toilet articles are thrown into a small handbag. The men seize other bags, bulging with flight charts, radio charts, data vital to flight across a dozen different lands and seas.

The three men walk quickly to the end of the long building. The rain slices sharply at them as they open the door and expose themselves to the wind. Cursing, they run to a waiting vehicle.

Minutes later, several miles away in Flight Operations, the crew —pilot, copilot, and navigator—are hard at work. There are flight plans to receive, navigator's courses to plot, code identifications to mark, and the thousand other small but interwoven items of preparing a mission. The pilot receives additional information on the earthquake and its effects, and learns the course he will fly.

They will depart from Evreux for a run of 320 miles to Rhein-Main in Germany. They will slide out of the rain-soaked darkness onto the slippery concrete runway of Rhein-Main, and taxi quickly to a waiting hangar. Here the cavernous belly of their winged machine will gape wide, and men will roll into the airplane an entire field hospital—complete with equipment, doctors, medical aides and nurses, operating tables, power units, oxygen equipment, medicines, and the other assorted paraphernalia of saving lives.

Rhein-Main will disappear behind them as they move swiftly with their precious cargo to Incirlik Air Base at Adana, Turkey. Here there will be more cargo and more specialists to load into the machine, fuel for the tanks, additional orders for the crew, and another hasty departure. It is 320 miles from Evreux to Rhein-Main, 1,300 miles from Rhein-Main to Incirlik, 800 miles more to their destination—to broken bodies and spilled blood and stricken children.

The flight crew plot the intricacies of their movement through the rain-filled skies. As they do so, on-duty personnel in Flight Operations transfer code names and numbers to machines and begin to punch out sequences of information. Hundreds and thousands of miles away, at different sites across Europe and down into Africa, other machines clatter to life, keys respond to electrical command and stamp out the messages.

The three men are concerned only with the immediate problems of their flight: how much fuel is to be carried, the center of gravity of the great airplane, cruising altitude and speed, radio and coded frequencies, and other technical items to be woven into their duties. In the pit of their stomachs there is another need, but that will remain forcibly subdued. At this time of night, by the strange quirks of austerity programs, there is no place on this great airfield for this crew to eat breakfast before they fly. It is a small thing, but an aggravating burr to the men who slog through the rain to their airplanes.

Time passes swiftly and the men waste none of it. From Flight Operations their alert vehicle pounds through the rain and the puddles. They drive to a gate where a suspicious, cold, and unhappy airman awaits them. A .38-caliber revolver rests within easy reach on his hip. He studies the men, examines their identification, jots down their names, and passes them through.

The truck roars to a wide concrete oval where brilliant lights reflect rain and water. The lights play on a great silver aircraft. It is an assault transport, a powerful and rugged machine known to surprisingly few Americans. This is the Hercules, an unlovely brute assigned the impersonal title of C-130B by the United States Air Force.

As modern aircraft go, the Hercules is unlovely and more. It seems designed without regard to aesthetic appeal. The wing rests straight across the top of the huge, cavernous fuselage. It is not the sleek, sweptback wing that most Americans identify with the modern age of flight. And, strangely, it has four powerful jet engines— but they are geared to wide-bladed propellers. The plane rests on a bulky housing of landing gear in thick pods which accent a look of clumsiness. Its nose is wide and unstreamlined, preceded by a thick, black, and bulbous mass containing intricate radar equipment. It has enough flight deck windows to meet the needs of two or three great jet airliners, and they blink in the reflections of light, like an insect of titanic proportions. In the glare of lights and rain, the tail soars up and almost out of sight into the encroaching darkness.

The Hercules is an unlovely brute . . . but her men love every inch of her stout metal frame. For there is no other machine in the world that can stand, or fly, or perform with this brilliantly conceived craft.

Thunder assails the ears of the three men as they run from the alert vehicle to a door in the side of the airplane. Ground power equipment roars loudly; gas turbine equipment shrieks with an unholy cry as power feeds into the innards of the Hercules. The men ignore the sound, clamber up the steps into the belly of the airplane. Then they ascend a steep, short ladder, and enter into another world.

What is unlovely outside becomes a modern wonder within the nose. The Hercules does not have a cockpit, the normal housing for crew, controls, and instruments. Instead, with sounds muted suddenly by thick, padded insulation, the crew moves into a wide and spacious flight deck. Here are four wide seats, racks and panels and consoles of instruments and controls, a thousand blinking and gleaming lights, and a tier of roomy sleeping bunks.

They waste no time in looking about them. The need for speed is their impetus, time is their enemy. To go through the sequence of events necessary to bring this great machine to life, the crew must move in a swift, integrated orchestration for approximately 15 to 20 minutes. Three men await the three officers as they arrive at the Hercules. There is a loadmaster, whose task it is to assure that all cargo, loads, and passengers are secure within the belly of the craft before it begins to move; at this moment he has little to do, for the cavernous hold remains empty of cargo. There is the scanner, connected by interphone to the flight deck, who visually checks the starting operation of the four powerful engines and assists the loadmaster.

And there is the flight engineer, a sergeant of experience and exquisite skill at his duties. He sits in a wide seat behind but between the pilot and copilot, and he ministers to a bewildering array of instrumentation—controls, switches, gauges, and dials—all his actions coordinated with those of the flight crew. He does not handle the actual controls by which the machine will respond to the demands of the pilot, but he flies this craft as much as any other man. To fly one of these giants is to achieve splendid coordination among several men, and the entire performance suffers without this integration.

There are 164 separate and precise steps to follow on the checklist of imbuing Hercules with life. The normal procedure will not, cannot, be followed now. When the great airplane is kept on Alert Status, the flight engineer keeps his machine "primed and cocked." He anticipates, and prepares well ahead of the flight crew's arrival, the things which they must do.

Exactly 176 seconds—*by the clock*—after they strap themselves into their seats, the crew of the airplane feed movement into the machine. In less than three minutes the airplane is moving away from its parking ramp, heading toward the point of takeoff on the runway. The huge propellers bite the air with a deep, thrumming sound, the cry unmistakably that of the Hercules moving out. Water sprays and splashes away from the moving behemoth, and the Hercules rocks from side to side as its propellers chew at the air.

The airman standing guard steps outside his small hut. Unconscious of the rain, he watches the airplane disappear in the wet darkness until only the flashing red beacon is visible. *Something* is up; the crews do not leave at this time of night without an emergency call. He steps back into the guard hut, lights a cigarette, glances at his watch. Two minutes later he nods with satisfaction.

Thunder builds up from miles away; it rolls through the distance, changes pitch, then thrums down from overhead. He catches a glimpse of the flashing beacon lights. . . .

Then he turns his head to see other flashing beacons, this time headlights on the airfield perimeter road, rushing away through the rain, away from the airfield.

The vast stirring is full-blown now. The Alert Status aircraft is gone. Another crew moves into immediate standby. But the 839th Air Division at Evreux is only a tenant with 16 aircraft; the majority of the division has remained back at Sewart Air Force Base near Nashville, Tennessee. The 839th's airplanes are on rotational duty for several months at Evreux; they are guests of the 322nd Air Division, which calls Evreux home. And now the alert spills down and fans out through the smallest element of the 322nd.

Engaged in the operation of Evreux-Fauville Air Base and the entire C-130 Hercules system of the 322nd and its tenant elements of the 839th are a total of 18,449 people. The division operates approximately 90 great airplanes, which at any moment may be anywhere along a total of 67,000 route miles, operating from any one of 52 major airfields.

They range from Pakistan to Norway, Karachi to Seville, London to South Africa. It is a complex, intricate, continuous functioning of men and machinery.

Every now and then something unusual happens. A brushfire war flames hotly, a dam collapses, or—as in this instance—the earth shrugs its mantled shoulders. And then it is necessary to interfere with the careful functioning and to interrupt the meticulous programming.

As the first Hercules vanishes into the rain and darkness of the early morning, Air Police vehicles fan out through the countryside surrounding the air base. Their purpose is to awaken and alert to their duty call the crews of the 322nd's Hercules aircraft. The airmen wind along country roads, twist through neat farm lanes, roll cautiously through the narrow streets of small, silent towns.

Why not simply use the telephone for this alert? Again, influencing our national operations about the world, there is the matter of austerity, a balancing of funds available as against expenses considered. In the French countryside, it costs the United States $62.50 simply to install one telephone in the home of one officer or airman who lives away from the Evreux air base. The cost of maintaining a telephone is many times that in the United States. Accountants juggled figures, arrived at totals, and shook their heads in economic despair. The funds to be allotted to telephones could perform more valuable services elsewhere, decreed the budget-makers, and so the crews who live widely scattered throughout the local countryside must be awakened and alerted to duty by these fast-roving Air Police teams.

Some of the crews live 45 minutes away from the base. Assuming a round trip of one and a half hours, and at least ten minutes to awaken a man, to have him pack hurriedly, and to bid his wife and children a sleepy farewell, plus minor delays, it will be two hours before the outlying crews are on assignment to aircraft, preparing to move out.

Thus a system of staggered alerting is used. The nearest crews are the first to report on duty. The others follow suit, and their times of arrival are integrated with the operations plan. If the mission is immediate delivery of emergency hospital units, or if there is a need for air evacuation, then the alert airplane must be rolling—as this first Hercules was on this morning—within one hour of its call. "Normal alert" provides a time margin of two to three hours' interval in which to get the crews assigned to specific duties, provided with orders and flight clearances, and taxiing out to the runway.

Before the sun rises above the horizon—a moment noted by the clock rather than any sighting of the sun through the thick clouds and undiminished rain—the alert Hercules has landed at Rhein-Main, loaded its precious medical force, and is airborne and en route to Incirlik.

Before the run rises, 16 more Hercules are in the air, rushing toward the earthquake disaster area. Before the sun rises, an additional nine Hercules are landing at different bases throughout Europe and the Middle East, diverted from normal flight assignments, dumping their cargoes and loading on emergency supplies.

By the time the administrative personnel of Evreux-Fauville Air Base arrive at their offices for their morning coffee and their first work assignments 40 giant aircraft are moving the means of survival to a place in the Middle East where the dead are lamented and the injured struggle for life.

Several thousands of these people will live. Their angel of mercy is a huge, unlovely brute that will fly thousands of miles to their aid.

Very few of them will know the giant by name. Very few will care. They have their own words of thanks, in their own language.

Thus it is that the Hercules is known by many names, to many people, in dozens of lands about this earth. To each and every one of them, the Hercules is an extension of a land few of them have ever seen, a land mostly unfathomable to their limited breadth of experience. To them the Hercules represents the United States, a physical evidence of a land countless miles distant across the oceans and over the clouds.

Hercules—her men, her desperately needed cargo and supplies, and sometimes even her weapons—represents to them the long arm of America.

This is the story of that stupendous reach.

It is much easier to say where the Hercules has *not* flown than it is to recite a list of geographical locations which have known the sight and the sound of these amazing giants. If the writer were to perform the latter task, he could do so simply by copying down the name of virtually every nation on this planet.

So it is easier to say that the Hercules has not flown through the Soviet Union east of Moscow (it has flown to that city) or through Red China and—well, that is it. The Hercules *has* flown to every other part of the world, from the Arctic to the other end of the globe, where permanent operations are conducted at the South Pole, has girdled the equatorial regions and visited the lands in between.

Ours is a day and age of miracles. We are enthralled with the awed description of sunset on the earth from the unmatched vantage of 100 miles above the surface. We ponder in justifiable wonder pictures of the other side of the moon. And we listen to the warbling song of an electronic messenger sending us its priceless information from above the surface of a world tens of millions of miles away.

Closer to home, we shrug at supersonic flight, and then respond to this aerodynamic marvel with a curse as the supersonic lash shakes our homes and rattles our dishes. Energy becomes a meaningless term after we have learned to live, albeit uneasily, with the loose latch of Pandora's thermonuclear box.

We are surfeited with the marvelous and only mildly interested in the miraculous. Yet we have forgotten, it seems, that it is actually the everyday and the prosaic by which we live. It is not the bright flame of a technological wonder, nurtured by the tender loving care of thousands of technicians and living only for a brief moment, that turns the wheel of events of our world. Rather, it is the day-by-day application of force, in many different forms, in the affairs of men, that dictates to us the manner in which we shall live our lives.

We have glimpsed an operation under way at Evreux on the plains of France. This one mission, covering thousands of miles and involving dozens of aircraft and hundreds of men, has the deepest impact upon the relations between the United States and the land to which we rush our assistance. The far-flung operations of the air divisions at Evreux alone represent an effort beyond the capabilities of many nations of this world.

Yet this is but one facet of the operation of the Hercules every day and night of the week, every week of the year. Without fanfare, without even the knowledge of most of our own people, thousands of Americans have been shaping the course of international events. The tool they have used in doing so is this unlovely machine of flight, the brute cherished by its crews and already established throughout the world as a messenger of mercy from that distant land called America.

It is, also, a weapon of startling capabilities that has shaped another course of events. The Hercules, among other things, is first and foremost an assault transport. It is the implementation of a new kind of warfare.

It has, in its tenure of only a half-decade of its operation-in-strength, probably done more than any other single weapon in our arsenal to limit and to prevent the outbreak of wars around this earth.

It has won more good will and friendship for the United States than any elaborate program of our nation involving the distribution of tens of billions of dollars.

It has revolutionized the concept of strategic logistics. It is a machine that thunders across oceans and continents, that carries bulky and ponderous cargo on strategic missions. More wonderful than this capability, however, is the most unique of all the attributes of this machine.

It enjoys freedom from concrete. It can leap an ocean, and descend into a jungle clearing. It can cross a continent into wildernesses barely explored, and alight precisely on a dirt field, or settle to earth on a sandbar. It can, it has performed these missions, and it does so consistently.

It can, it has—it does—operate from airfields so high above sea level that its crews find it advisable to keep a supply of oxygen on hand. It is this capability, as much as any other, that astounds even the most experienced veteran who has spent decades in the air. The Hercules is a machine that on an everyday, operational basis defies experience, sneers at aerodynamic law, and permits the United States to carry out operations around the world that, before the production of this machine, it found impossible to pursue.

This is the inherent and intrinsic value of the Hercules. It is not just another airplane.

It is an instrument of national policy. Its astonishing performance enables this country to function in a manner only a few short years ago considered beyond the reach of aircraft. It opens new possibilities and opportunities. It performs in a manner that our cold-war opponents have attempted to duplicate, and have failed.

There is at least one airfield high in the mountains of India littered with the wreckage of several of the latest transports of the Soviet Union. There, on the upper levels of the world where men live and have fought, the Russians attempted to support the operations of the Indian Army. The attempt was made, and it failed. In that thin, cruel air, operating from crude and unfinished runways impossibly short in length, these Russian transports have crashed.

Their losses struck hard at the Indians, who reeled back from the onslaught of the powerful Chinese forces. Angry with the emptiness of Russian claims and bitter about the repeated loss of the desperately needed transports, the Indians had no choice but to drag the wrecks to the sides of their crude dirt runways.

For many months the Russian wreckage has been ignored. The metal slowly succumbs to rust, beneath successive overlays of fresh dust.

The dust is hurled back from the great propellers of the Hercules assault transports dispatched from Evreux—Hercules that have astounded Indians and Russians alike with a consistent, astonishing operation from this and other, similar fields, and carried out with a no-nonsense, airlines-like schedule. No other airplane in the world, Russian *or* American, could perform these missions selected by our nation to be flown "at the top of the world."

The average altitude above sea level of these Indian strips is 11,000 feet. Hercules have operated in the Asian mountains from strips up to some 14,000 feet.

It is vicious, cruel, unforgiving mountain country. The peaks are sawtoothed. Engines, wings, propellers, and the lungs of men gasp for air. It is *always* cold. It is so high at airstrip level that many airplanes cannot even reach to this height. Pilots who have heard of flying from airstrips as high as 14,000 feet find it almost impossible to believe.

Their incredulous looks become open stares of disbelief when they learn that these crude strips are barely longer than 2,000 feet. At sea level, where the air is thick and heavy, 2,000 feet is a short strip for even a modern light plane.

Here, at the top of the world, is one measure of the success of the C-130 Hercules. An airstrip here is a strip straight from flying hell. A pilot must bring in his huge machine under the most precise control, with his wings slicing too freely for comfort through the thin air. He must fly down an invisible line, an absolutely precise drop, with no margin for error. For the final 1,000 feet, swooping down over jagged ridges, the airplane seems to plunge without control and with terrifying speed toward the ground.

The impact with the surface is brutal. Crews are pounded in their

seats, slammed against their restraining straps. The strips are rough
and strewn with rocks. The airplane hits with all the force of a
controlled crash. It *is* a controlled crash—and with 30,000 pounds
of cargo lashed down in the hold.

Throughout this entire descent, the speed of the Hercules is a
hair-thin line between the lowest possible speed under control and
stalling speed, when the wings lose lift and the pilot loses control.

But it is not the landing so much as the *takeoff* that separates
the men from the boys. . . . Consider the case of one such flight,
a C-130 that landed with a critically needed load of 15 tons of
cargo. Then, the crew *loaded* six jeeps and a water carrier into the
belly of the airplane, lashed them down tightly, and prepared for
takeoff. Imagine, if you can, being in that airplane, on that flight
deck. . . .

The pilot taxis to the last available inch of runway. The jet engines spin at maximum speed, the great propellers whirl as flashing
blurs in the bright sun. Brakes are on full, everything is at maximum
power, and then the pilot commences his demand for the maximum
bite of the propellers. The great blades as they spin change their
pitch—the angle at which they slice into the air. Their speed remains the same as before, but now they are voraciously tearing
huge gulps from the air about them.

The Hercules shakes through every fiber. The airplane responds
to this lash of power with a vibrating, rocking motion that simu-
lates to an amazing degree flight through turbulent air. Then—
maximum energy, flaps down, everything wide open—the pilot re-
leases the brakes.

The airplane does not just move forward suddenly. It bolts; with
unbelievable force it punches itself away from its standing position.
The Hercules claws frantically for speed. There is nothing like a
go–no-go operation here. You open her up all the way, dump the
brakes, and pray that the airplane will do the impossible. If it
doesn't, you're dead. Simple as that.

The pilot holds the bucking, rocking machine on the ground until the last possible moment. He needs speed; every single ounce
of speed is vital here. Nothing is more precious than the speed to
shape the flow of air over the thin wings, to change the pressure,
to create the magic of lift. There is no chance to turn back, to
reconsider. Either there is lift, or there is the end of everything.

That "last possible moment" arrives with shocking suddenness.
It is not a question of speed. It is dictated by the simple fact that
all the runway is gone, swallowed up in the elephantine rush of
the Hercules down that all-too-short airstrip space. When nothing

is left of the runway, the pilot pulls back on the control yoke.

That's all. No refined rotating upward of the nose. No smooth coordination between speed and angle of climb. Things are simple here. When there's no runway left, pull back. There is now one ultimate goal—clear the mountain ridge directly ahead of the airplane.

It is not a matter of clearing it with a wild and careening rush. The pilot squeezes all distance and speed he can from what is available to him and then, feeling with sensitive hands and body the grasp of lift from his wings, he bids the Hercules heave herself into the cruelly thin air.

The machine rises from the airstrip, clears a hump just beyond, and almost at once the pilot eases forward the wheel and dumps the nose of the Hercules. He has a limited space-and-time factor before he runs into the mountain that blocks his path. He has passed the first hurdle—becoming airborne before the strip turns into boulder-strewn ground. Now he must clear a mountain. To help him in this feat he has a brief distance in which to build up airspeed.

The mountain rushes closer as the airspeed builds—painfully slow in the thin, thin air. There is an overwhelming urge to turn away from the mountain, but it would be suicide. To bank those wings would be to rob them of their precious lift. The great machine would respond with a violent, fatal cartwheeling motion. There cannot—yet—be any turns. The pilot must fly directly at, into, the face of the mountain. The airplane trembles in the currents of air sweeping over the ridges. No one notices this. They are transfixed, their gaze split between the needle on the airspeed dial and the onrushing mountain of very solid, very unyielding rock.

Abruptly the mountain is upon and overwhelming the Hercules, and now the airplane must *prove* its worth. Lack of such proof will be a dirty, red blob of fire boiling up the side of the mountain. Memento will be a greasy smear, and an ache in the hearts of those who built and tended this and other sister craft. . . .

The control yoke comes back, the nose lifts, and in a great soaring rush the huge airplane bursts upward into the sky. It claws greedily for height. The propellers flash in the sun, the blades snatch great chunks of air and spit them back over the wings. . . . It is a good grip on the air. The Hercules booms upward, hurtling toward and over the jagged ridges. But the ridges are irregular, and the maneuver must continue with a changing precision. There are enormous outcroppings of rock. The space for the machine is barely 500 feet wide, but only for a short distance. Then more rock looms straight ahead, and open air is to the right.

The Hercules flashes into the gap, bursts onward toward the second obstacle. But now there is enough speed; the yoke comes over to the right, the rudder pedal goes down. The airplane wheels into a sweeping bank. It swings around. . . .

Metal skims over rock. The ridge looms just below; the mountain slides by to the left, well beyond that wing.

With a long and exquisite sigh the pilot and his crew release breath long held in the lungs. Gratefully the nose of the airplane drops as the barrier is crossed. In the valley, on the other side of the ridge and below the mountain, the Hercules accepts the sudden friendliness of gravity. It howls its freedom with thundering echoes of sound against the flanks of the nearby mountains. Speed comes rapidly and the Hercules rushes into her element . . . riding free on lift and speed, master once again of the mountains on this world.

It is unfortunate that so few Americans have even heard of this marvelous product of our country, and it is sad that even fewer are aware of the work being performed by these giants. Nearly 600 of these great machines maintain round-the-clock operations around the world. Many of the missions entrusted to the men who fly the Hercules are not assigned by particular services to meet individual service needs. Instead, the turboprop transports girdle the globe on missions dictated by national policy and needs.

The Hercules is, first and foremost, that instrument of national policy.

It is, so that it may fulfill its kaleidoscopic roles and assignments, a workhorse. It is the nearest thing to a bulldozer with wings. It is a military assault transport that carries shock troops, paratroopers, artillery, armored vehicles and tanks, and virtually every type of weapon, anywhere in the world. It flies with unbelievable agility from ice and snow at the South Pole and in the Arctic, easing to and departing from the frozen surface on massive skis. It is a tanker for mid-air refueling of thirsty jet fighters. It operates on long search missions in "normal configuration" with two of its four engines shut down and the propellers feathered knife-edge into the wind (a condition that would turn most crews in most airplanes a slight shade of white). It is capable of "standard, maximum gross weight" takeoffs with only three engines running.

It performs an endless variety of missions. It carries livestock—a bewildering list of animals—to places sorely in need of such animals. It is assigned the task of remapping, with long-sought accuracy, most of the surface features of this earth—and already the Hercules "Big Eye" machines have found an uncomfortable number of islands well removed from where we thought they were.

Its capacious interior swallows huge, bulky loads as a matter of course. And yet, it is a "gentle" airplane, its interior fitted with attachments for iron lungs and other lifesaving equipment. Its cavernous interior is completely pressurized and heated.

Hercules has landed on crumbling ice floes to rescue marooned scientists . . . and in Antarctica saved the life of a Russian scientist in need of emergency medical treatment. Quick demonstration of capability: the most advanced Russian transports were grounded in "impossible" flying conditions. The Hercules went in, picked up the scientist, brought him out to safety.

Hercules have flown tons of food and medical supplies to typhoon victims in the New Hebrides, to cyclone survivors in Pakistan, to earthquake-smashed cities in Morocco. Iron lungs have been sped across the Pacific to Japan, food and medical supplies to Cambodia and the Philippines. Equipment and instruments have been flown deep within the Sahara to landings in the midst of "nowhere" . . . all within the huge belly of the Hercules.

Troops, tanks, trucks, guns, ammunition, food, supplies, and other cargo loads have poured as needed into the Congo . . . into Guantánamo . . . into India . . . into Pakistan . . . into Lebanon when war reared its ugly visage.

A Hercules has dropped, in flight, a massive load weighing 41,740 pounds, to be borne gently earthward by huge, billowing parachutes.

Brushfire wars stay limited, and others never reach the point of ignition, because of powerful composite forces of fighters and bombers with their nuclei composed of Hercules transports filled with crack American fighting men—poised to enter any part of the world, at any time.

Whatever the mission—bristling with guns, or laden with medical supplies to save the lives of children—the Hercules is at work, 24 hours a day.

This, then, is our story . . . the long arm of America.

CHAPTER I

Checkmate   The age of the
atom is not yet two decades old. Yet this fledgling era has known
furious international activity, a period in which the printers of maps
have thrown up their hands in despair at the swift-paced change of
political-geographic boundaries.

These two decades have rattled with dozens of wars limited in
scope but savage in their intensity. The stage has been overfilled
with bloody hand-to-hand fighting while great mushroom clouds
lurk in the wings, awaiting their cue to bathe continents in lethal
atomic glow.

We have experienced a growing preponderance of fission and
fusion weapons. Concepts of power have washed away with the
passage of time. Once we regarded with horror the force of a small
fission bomb detonated over a thriving metropolis. Today such a
bomb is regarded as so weak in power that it has come to be regarded among the nuclear community as "acceptable" for future
wars that are limited by agreement in geographical scope.

The strategies of the United States and the Soviet Union run
along parallel lines. Survival, first, is essential at any cost. Russia
seeks domination of the world scene, the United States seeks to
prevent such domination, but in either case the goal is pursued
without resorting, if at all possible, to the nuclear ax. It is a paradox that the very ascendancy of thermonuclear weapons and their
delivery systems has diluted the value of these items for any purpose save that of the ultimate threat.

With so many superbombs available, and with new delivery systems available in the form of giant missiles emplaced beneath the
soil and concealed deep in the oceans, we find it inacceptable to
employ these devices.

But the pursuit of power and sway over the nations of earth
continues undiminished. New weapons are sought to attain these
goals. One such weapon is anachronistic to the nuclear age—the
individual fighting man.

It behooves us to consider this new situation, for the military minds of all nations are coming to consider the period 1960–70 as the "decade of the guerrilla."

Washington and Moscow, more than once on the brink of negotiation by nuclear weapons, have managed to shy away from so disastrous a political failure. This very success in avoiding the nuclear Armageddon prompts both contestants to employ every other possible system of weaponry, especially those which promise the greatest possible results commensurate with the expenditure of matériel and manpower. Thus the lack of hesitation to use men as weapons wherever and whenever such employment suits national needs.

This is by far the preferable choice. The unlimited use of the thermonuclear weapon presupposes not only political, military, and economic failure, but perhaps that of civilization itself. Nuclear arms are exquisitely nonpartisan. They are as likely to wreck national and international foundations as they are to sunder steel and concrete and to be remembered long for their deadly harvest of radioactive fallout.

"Both you and we understand the kind of weapons these are," Nikita Khrushchev has said to the United States, and it is to be hoped that this river of understanding runs deep and true.

The alternative we have readily grasped—managing the arms race in such a fashion that we advance no closer to the brink of nuclear war. The nuclear weapon is inacceptably expensive on the national scale, not in its cost of production or employment, but in the bill tendered as its aftermath.

The balance of terror toward which the United States and the Soviet Union rushed has been attained, and no longer does it evoke its terrible consequences. Terror has been drained dry; the capacity of the human mind to comprehend the predictable results of thermonuclear war was bypassed many years ago. The facts are stupendous but they are reduced to quiet words. Thermonuclear war precludes the existence of the world with which we are familiar. That is it—no more and no less.

There is little need for meticulous descriptions of the effects of these weapons, or of the accuracy inherent in their robot delivery systems. Before this decade is past, the successors to the present thermonuclear weapons—the gigaton bombs—will be available for use. It does not require a slide rule to predict the effects of bombs weighing a hundred tons (and more) sent into orbit about the earth, to be detonated while still in hard vacuum. One such bomb, triggered far above the atmosphere, will result in the momentary creation of a miniature star. From this stellar furnace there will pour heat of such intensity that within seconds it can transform a quarter of the entire United States (or the Soviet Union) into a

phase which we have labeled as "mutual invulnerability" so far as total war is concerned. Neither the United States nor the Soviet Union can attack the other with the full strength at its command, because of the grim consequences that inevitably would attend such moves.

Doctrine changes, however, with capabilities and with need. The current doctrine of the United States and of the Soviet Union, which also is trumpeted loudly by China as she strives for her own nuclear arms, is distressingly clear. Nuclear arms do *not* make war impossible—provided that the contestants religiously observe a set of tacit rules that "limit" the extent of the war.

Indeed, it is now conceived that limited atomic wars are not only possible, but preferable. The latest stratagem of high military circles involves the use of a nuclear slide rule with which one may compute escalating scales of "small" to "medium" to "big" nuclear wars, everything being a matter of degree; confusing the issue is the uncertainty as to the magnitudes in which wars should be characterized as "small," "medium," or "big."

"To rely on conventional weapons in the nuclear age is about as sound as it would have been to stick to the bow and arrow after firearms were introduced," states Dr. Edward Teller. He recommends that we use "nuclear weapons, not to destroy cities, but to defeat enemy forces, or at least to bring about a situation where the enemy cannot successfully [bring] out into the field any massive apparatus, either mechanical or human."

There is a growing murmur of assent for this point of view. The principle of nuclear arms in "limited wars" took root years ago and it has slowly but steadily found new adherents.

Donald A. Quarles, the former Secretary of the Air Force, commented that nuclear weapons actually are more humane than conventional arms. "One hears that the use of our quality weapons in limited war would result in excessive casualties among military and civilian alike. This is not necessarily so. The Korean conflict resulted in millions of casualties. Most of these casualties occurred in the last two years of the war. Had that war been ended quickly, the total casualty lists would probably have been smaller regardless of the weapons used."

Thus we are acquiring a new set of rules to define the limits to which we may travel in prosecuting national goals and desires. Everything short of strategic blows with nuclear arms, or direct attacks against the homeland or major bastions of the great world powers, may now be acceptable. We are coming rapidly through self-applied logic to accept the viewpoint that nuclear strangulation upon many areas of the world is civilized; attempts at nuclear annihilation which involve trespassing on the major powers are "unacceptable."

"History furnishes no specific clues in this matter," wrote J. F. Loosbrock in *Air Force* magazine, "for nuclear weapons have never been used in such a role. But if our possession of nuclear weapons combined with the ability to deliver them now deters a major war, it is difficult to see how this advantage could be erased in a twinkling merely because some of the weapons were used on a local target."

Acceptance or rejection of such a thesis depends upon the country of which you are a native. It is grand to contemplate the swift nuclear strangulation of a "limited war" if you reside in one of the "mutually inviolate" areas. Opinion may be expected to be opposed to this strategy if your little plot of real estate lies within one of the "mutually acceptable" areas within which to wage nuclear war.

The arguments regarding such matters are endless. They are not capable of solution because logic is a strange animal that breeds in different ways, depending upon the national climate that nourishes its growth. Nuclear logic is objective only on a subjective basis, and that is no more of a paradox than "nuclear invulnerability."

One thing is certain. The era of one-sided massive retaliation with thermonuclear weapons has slipped from our grasp. The new era is one of a mutually catastrophic capability. Faced with this reality, the United States and the Soviet Union both are striving for something even more important to each nation, and to the entire world. This is *second-strike capability.*

This new strategy presupposes that no matter how lethal may be any initial strike, the nation attacked will always be capable of launching the second strike of the war. It further postulates that this reaction capability will contain all the ingredients of destruction necessary to transform the enemy nation into a great porridge of radioactive debris. Essentially, this concept eliminates neatly the promise of an overwhelming first strike in which the nation attacked is so battered that it is incapable of effective countermeasures.

This is where we stand today—or will stand within a year or two. Both the United States and the Soviet Union have first- *and* second-strike capabilities. More to the mutual benefit of the two nations is the deterrence to strategic nuclear attacks created by these conditions.

This brings us to a situation which was forecast clearly several years ago.

Other means of waging war, or of effecting major decisions with military forces *short of war,* have increased enormously in their importance.

Such actions spread across a wide spectrum. They may involve small strikes with special forces, such as guerrilla teams that infiltrate enemy territory and conduct harassment of normal life. And they can extend to full-scale warfare which is contained within a specified geographical area. Indo-China is a prime example of escalating guerrilla action into war, with agreements among the major contestants to place an upper limit on that war. Five years of isolated Communist guerrilla action led finally to the involvement of more than 800,000 fighting men for another four years—at the end of which the Communist forces attained a clear-cut victory.

We have long expected that these limited conflicts, in which we have so far mutually excluded nuclear weapons, would constitute a major thorn in our country's international relations—that they would, in fact, increase in number. So long as the major powers retain the means and the desire to forbid the use of nuclear weapons, each country is then free to exploit every other military force at its disposal.

This has led to an interesting situation. The preponderance of strike power, initial and secondary, in the hands of the United States and the Soviet Union, means that this power is beginning to cancel itself out. The great capability to strike catastrophic blows against the enemy remains. But neither side dares to employ this awesome force because of the inescapable consequences.

A stasis has been created. Mutual secondary-strike capability means that the offensive striking power can no longer be employed as a threat—*and secondary, non-nuclear military strength mushrooms in its importance.*

Dr. Harold Brown, Department of Defense Director of Research and Engineering, on March 2, 1963, stated the case aptly when he emphasized that strategic superiority on the part of the U.S. and the U.S.S.R. "may eventually lose much of its meaning no matter what we do. An analogy can be drawn to a mathematical equation in which the first order terms cancel out, and so the second order terms, though smaller than the first order, nevertheless become determining."

We are like two men sealed within a small room, determined to fight to a position of superiority. The arms of each man are equal. Each has a hand grenade and a knife. Either one may use the hand grenade to destroy the other, but in the limited confines of the room, the consequences to both men are the same. With their "first order" weapons canceled out, the men must resort to their "second order" weapons—the knives.

Years ago both the United States and the Soviet Union began to plan for this contingency. If the "determining" factor in the international contest for world leadership came to be forces less than those of thermonuclear war, then those forces must be developed by combining historical methods with modern technology.

We must be able to exert a specific amount of military strength at a certain place within restrictive time limits. There is a saying that the ultimate goal of war is to make the enemy change his mind. That goal is missed when military force must be employed actively, for the process of engendering a new attitude on the part of the enemy is then destructive and wasteful. If the final end of the contest can be made clear *before* the shooting starts, and the enemy desists from his plans, then the ultimate goal of war is achieved. The enemy changes his mind; he decides not to fight at all.

This is the concept of the strike forces created by the United States: hard fire-fight capability within a composite force, able to rush to any part of the world on a moment's notice, so as to keep the opposition off balance. We must be able to counter any move so swiftly that our reaction in force is immediately more conclusive than the enemy's own actions.

Certain elements of this composite strike force were clearly defined: tactical airpower in the form of fighters, fighter-bombers, attack bombers, and reconnaissance aircraft, all to be supported by aerial refueling tankers and on-the-spot logistics. Such a force could move into any trouble spot anywhere in the world, armed, equipped, and ready to fight both with conventional arms and—as a backup—with the nuclear arms carried at all times with the strike force.

But this by itself proved insufficient to meet the need. The use of such weapons automatically spells failure in the goal of *preventing* any major conflict. The purpose of the strike force is, if at all possible, to make the enemy change his mind. Not simply to quit fighting—but not to fight at all.

As we have learned in the past at exorbitant cost—and we are still learning—you do not accomplish this goal with "ultimate weapons."

You cannot threaten a guerrilla in the mountains or a Communist sympathizer in a jungle village with an ICBM buried deep within concrete 5,000 miles away. He is incapable of adjusting his thinking to this scale of force. He cannot comprehend either the missile or its multimegaton thermonuclear warhead. These are terms and concepts entirely alien to his world, to his experience, to his comprehension.

His needs are much more earthy. His world is the gun he holds, the mountains and the jungle, and combat by stealth, infiltration, and any other means at hand.

We have learned that in order to achieve our own goals we must plan our actions to fit within the limits of comprehension of such men. Our goal is not domination by massive military force. And since it is the minds of men we are trying to influence, we must deal with them on compatible terms. We must deal in terms of men.

The fighting man is a common denominator—anywhere in the world. The superbly equipped fighting man with a reputation for combat skills is an uncommonly impressive common denominator.

Splendidly equipped soldiers, in force, backed by tactical air-power and great fire-fight capability at close range, speak a universal language. Such forces are able to contain almost any situation which may be anticipated—or which may exist until a strike force arrives on the local scene.

Waging war with such fighting forces requires more than men traveling on their feet. It demands paratroopers able to drop anywhere in the local spot, at any time. It means fresh troops able to concentrate in any area at any time. It means troops supported with vehicles, powerful recoilless weapons, armor, and extensive supplies—all rolling into an area as a single entity.

But how to meet this particular need? During the Korean War no machine capable of doing so existed. That war, and the bitter conflict in Indo-China, made it painfully clear that a new air assault weapon was needed in the American arsenal—a new air assault transport that could effectively shrink time and distance. It had to do so with heavy and bulky loads carried within its body. It needed high speed over great distance. But since its effectiveness would otherwise be limited by the ground area available in remote areas of the world, it needed independence from concrete as much as any other quality. It must be able to leap continents and oceans, and then utilize as its landing fields grass or dirt strips, roads, beaches, or any other area of "reasonably level" surface.

The official requirements for this new aircraft, as laid down during the early 1950's, seemed impossible of achievement. The Air Force expressed its need for an "advanced, all-purpose, workhorse type, aerial vehicle, that could go anyplace, anytime, without elaborate facility or equipment preparations."

Thus the pattern was shaped. The new assault transport would have to fit the needs of "limited war," of "brushfire" and "guerrilla" wars, while using as its main base the United States itself. This demanded "tactical situation capability married [to] strategic mobility."

In the early discussions between the Air Force and the major aircraft manufacturers of the United States, many engineers dismissed the proposed assault transport as "impossible." One company, the Lockheed Aircraft Corporation, was delighted with the challenge. Corporate heads and engineering brains locked themselves into meeting rooms on a day-and-night basis.

One of their urgent needs was shared by both industry and the military. In order to define specifically the capabilities of the projected assault transport, one had to know just what possible situations might be incurred in its use.

And that meant finding the answer to the question: Just *what* is limited war?

CHAPTER II

How Big Is a War?   WHO—AND WHAT—
defines the limits of the limited war? When does a peripheral
military action cross the boundary into the category of a limited,
local, restricted, guerrilla, or brushfire war? At what point does
a military border clash escalate into "major conflict"?

Any one of these terms, as applied to the military actions which
have plagued the world since 1945, may defy specific definition.
All of them are unfortunately wanting in precision because, above
all, they are relative to a subjective point of view.

The limits of any "war" can be visualized only according to an
individual's experience, imagination, and/or attitude. The only
certain definition is that the conflict at least is "hot," as compared
to the "cold" war. And the transition from cold to hot takes place
when people start dying in numbers from direct action of dissidents or invaders.

The American public endures considerable confusion on this
matter of wars short of major war. The cold war can be understood
readily enough. It entails the use of political, economic, technological, sociological, and military measures—short of *overt armed conflict involving regular military forces*—to achieve national objectives.

This does not, however, preclude military action of one form
or another. Cold war takes in the broadest spectrum of activities,
and as practiced by forces which are supported or led by those
of the major Communist powers, includes any action short of commitment of the major armed forces of nations. As such, it creates
and supports indigenous resistance movements made up of outside
agents and natives of the local country who can be persuaded that
a change in government and power, leaning to the Communist
camp, would be to their benefit. Such indigenous resistance movements have as their specific aim the growth and use of guerrilla
forces, with constant support of these forces through covert supply mediums.

The pattern of resistance to local government has through past
experience become quickly identifiable. There is at first scattered

violence, rising steadily in scale and in breadth throughout the country, and passing from initial persuasion to coercion, reprisals for non-cooperation with the dissidents, terrorism through assassination and sabotage, and finally full-scale guerrilla warfare.

"Guerrilla warfare," explains Admiral Harry D. Felt, Commander-in-Chief of our Pacific military forces,

> is organized subversive military, political and economic operations by poorly armed and equipped terrorists. They operate against established authority and they terrorize populations into withholding support from the legal government. After becoming organized into cadres and then into cohesive bandit groups, their aim is to effect the piecemeal destruction of governmental forces, leaders and citizens in isolated areas. They raid and burn villages, murder officials, kidnap boys of military age. The ambush is a favorite tactic. Guerrillas tolerate no neutrals. They plunder and kill those who do not join them. When the rural populace cannot depend on government protection, the people become victims of Communist intimidation and violence. This is happening to scores of free men and women in South Viet Nam—and it must be stopped.

What compounds the confusion on this matter is that the fighting in Viet Nam does *not* fall within the definition of a "limited war," which more properly would be applied to the conflicts that raged through Indo-China and Korea.

In an attempt to bring a clearer perspective on the subject, Colonel Thomas L. Fisher, II, has studied and discussed the variety of military actions that might be called limited war, and which we should be primarily concerned with deterring. Colonel Fisher explains that

> many possible actions do not present any new or very vital problem to us. Among such actions would be minor border disputes between free states, civil wars incident to political revolution, or small-scale, continuing guerrilla warfare. . . . The measure of our concern should be their cost to us, either material or in terms of our national objectives. Although ideally we would like to deter all war, there is other conventional machinery in existence today to handle most of these problems under international agreements and the United Nations.
>
> So we narrow our area of concern to those wars in which we have a direct treaty commitment to act, as a nation rather than through the United Nations, or in which some important territory is in danger of disappearing behind the Iron Curtain. The two cases are generally synonymous. It is hardly con-

ceivable that there will be a major war between any of our allies under present world conditions. Therefore only a war between a free or would-be free nation on one side and a member of the Soviet bloc or one of its stooges on the other remains for our consideration as a type of limited war vital to our interests. Such a war might include attack by Communist-controlled forces from outside the geographical boundaries of the nation or "volunteer" or pro-Soviet subversive groups already within a free-world, neutral, or even Titoist "independent socialist" nation. In other words the limited wars we are discussing are those in which international Communism controls the opposition.[1]

It is most important that from the outset we establish that our definition of limited war does not necessarily coincide with the viewpoint of the people living in the nation of contest. "The same war would be limited, local, or peripheral," explains Colonel Fisher, "from the point of view of one nation, usually the larger, more powerful, or distant, while it might be total from the point of view of a smaller nation in which it was centered and whose more restricted resources were wholly involved."

No better example is provided than in the war that raged up and down the Korean peninsula. To the United States the conflict was not legally a war, and in search of a better description we tagged the name of "police action" to that bloody struggle. To participate in strength in Korea, the United States mobilized many of its Reserve and National Guard units, as well as many individuals serving in the Reserve. These men and groups were brought to combat-ready status and shipped to Korea.

The mobilization of these forces was for the express purpose of keeping free from commitment as many as possible of the regular —or first-line—combat organizations of the Air Force and the Army. These organizations were to remain available in the event that the fighting in Korea should burst the boundaries of that peninsula, or erupt elsewhere, involving the United States in total war.

Thus *our* commitment to Korea was specifically and definitely related to a limited war.

But for the hapless Koreans, how could any war have been more total than the fighting that raged back and forth across their land? What industry existed in Korea was devastated by hordes of fighters and heavy bombers, including mass attacks by B-29s. Roads, bridges, rails, towns, cities, villages, and farmlands suffered brutal punishment. The destruction of Korean property, goods, and real

[1] *Air University Quarterly Review*, Vol. IX, No. 4 (Winter 1957-58), pp. 128-29.

estate was anything but limited, nor were "acceptable" limits of casualties declared by the Koreans.

Yet Korea, despite the intensity and the scale of the fighting, was from every international standpoint a limited war. The contestants among themselves reached agreement to confine the combat to the geographical limits of the Korean peninsula, and also agreed mutually to respect the sanctuaries of each other's supply bases.

The Air Force in an official evaluation distinguishes carefully between "limited" and "restricted" war by defining "limited war" as: "A war looked upon by one or the other of the contestants as not involving its own sovereignty, and as being limited in one respect or another, as, for example, to a particular geographical area, to the employment of only certain resources, or to a number of contestants. 2. A war considered by a detached observer as relatively limited in some respect, especially with regard to political objectives."

Defining "restricted war," the Air Force regards this as a war "in which the contestants impose upon themselves certain restraints in the choice and use of weapons." Another authority cuts more quickly to the core of the matter by stating: "Between the two extremes of cold war and total war there is only one other kind of war: employment of premeditated firepower under conditions which are manageable and which permit negotiation, retreat, termination, or armistice. Perhaps the terms *limited* or *restricted* are as appropriate as any."

Whatever their semantics, it appears certain that the Communists will not hesitate to ignite these conflicts whenever and wherever they feel that such provocations best suit their needs. It is an unhappy fact of life with which we shall be forced to live for many years to come. The nature of these wars, whatever their title, may best be understood by examining three major military contests that have raged since 1945.

These "Examples of Limited War," provided in the form of brief critical analyses by the Air University of the Air Force, include discussions of, first, the *involvement* in the war, and then, of the *methods* employed by the contestants. The first of these conflicts was that in Greece.

Greece: Involvement

After World War II, Greek Communists, aided with arms and supplies from Albania, Bulgaria, and Yugoslavia, attempted a coup with guerrilla bands operating out of mountain fastnesses in northern Greece. Greece began to combat the menace with British help. On 24 February 1947 the British announced that they could no longer afford the large-scale aid necessary to ensure the victory of Athens. On 12 March the Truman Doctrine went into effect whereby the U.S. assumed responsibility for preventing Communist domination of the eastern Mediterranean. In addition to $350,000,000 in economic military aid, an American Military Mission under General James Van Fleet lent command assistance to the Greek Army. Despite open intervention by Washington and covert intervention by Moscow, *the actual fighters were Greeks* [emphasis added]. The Greek political situation stabilized in 1947, and the Communists found increasing difficulty in supporting the guerrillas. Once it became apparent that the U.S. would stay to the finish, they ceased this support and abandoned the guerrillas to their fate.

Greece: Methods of Combat

The war was fought by the Communists along classical guerrilla lines. Mountainous terrain offered numerous strongholds; raiding and terrorizing whole communities provided subsistence; adjacent Communist satellites furnished arms and munitions. Under U.S. General Van Fleet the Greek Army waged unrelenting war. Said he: "In 1948 the Communists lost 33,000 men by death, capture, desertion. . . . It is a first-class war of international Communism . . . a war of annihilation with no respect for the rules." The struggle had two military objectives for the United States: to rout completely the Communist Greeks and to bring about the economic rehabilitation of Greece. Against 21,000 guerrillas the Greek Army pitted 250,000 men, trained and supplied by the U.S. This large Greek army was made necessary by the virtually impregnable strongholds of the rebels in the Pindus Mountains. Communist nations gradually lessened their support as hope for a coup diminished. The Communists lost Yugoslavia's support in mid-1949 when Tito defected. By October 1949 the guerrillas were completely routed.

Korea: Involvement

In 1945 the Potsdam Conference had temporarily designated the 38th parallel as a dividing line between Soviet and American occupation troops until Korea could be united by free elections. The Communists soon showed that elections would not be allowed. By 1949 both sides had withdrawn their troops. On 25 June 1950 the Soviet-trained-and-equipped

North Korean Army attacked South Korea. U.S. troops and planes moved in from Japan, the U.S. mobilized a force against the aggression. The Communist objective was the taking of Korea, *principally as a springboard against Japan* [emphasis added]. U.S. objectives were to halt aggression, protect Japan. Both sides had sanctuaries, the Communists in Manchuria and the U.S. in Japan, through which the war was supplied. After the Communist Chinese entered the war in November 1950 the only prospect for clear-cut victory for either side was massive air attack on the opponent's sanctuary. Both considered this an unacceptable risk of spreading the war. Truce negotiations dragged on for two years, finally compromising on status quo conditions.

Korea: Methods of Combat

The Korean War was not a case of Communist guerrillas against Allied troops but army against army, tanks against tanks, air forces against air forces. After initial success by surprise invasion, the North Korean army was cut up by U.N. air attack and the Allied offensive sent it reeling back to the Yalu. Intervention by Chinese Communist armies was also temporarily successful, but U.N. forces rallied and for the two last years stabilized the battle line near the prewar demarcation zone. In the air war Communist supply bases and air forces were protected by their sanctuary in Manchuria. Hoarding their newly acquired jet air force, they committed it only for training and probing of U.N. air readiness. With SAC [Strategic Air Command] poised in the U.S. to prevent extension of the war, U.N. air savagely interdicted Communist reinforcements and supplies, so persistently and successfully that the Communists could never stockpile the necessary reserves for an all-out offensive. This slow strangulation was a major factor in their eventual acceptance of United Nations peace terms.

Indo-China: Involvement

A loose agglomeration of three native states with varying cultural and racial backgrounds, Indo-China had been a French colony since 1885. Isolated Communist guerrilla bands had terrorized small sections since 1945, trying to prevent the resumption of French authority. In 1950 the fighting became a war. Action shifted to northern Vietnam, with Communist China training, supplying, and advising Vietminh forces. Communists sought more territory, a gateway to the

riches of Southeast Asia, and a huge morale victory over
Europeans and colonialism. The U.S. supported the French
with money and arms, mostly to oppose Communist expansion. In 1954 the U.S. seriously considered armed intervention. This never occurred, partly because of the political
situation in Indo-China, partly because conventional surface
or air operations would have had to be on a considerable
scale to succeed. *The only alternative, air-atomic operations
against Communist bases in southern China, was deemed an
unacceptable broadening of the war* [emphasis added].

Indo-China: Methods of Combat

Ho Chi Minh's 300,000 Communist Vietminh forces waged
guerrilla warfare, flashing countless hit-and-run attacks from
the cover of the jungles. French-Vietnamese forces, number-
ing 500,000, based their operations on a series of strongpoints
and forts. Their efforts to chase down the raiders became a
backbreaking job of clearing the same areas over and over
again, frustrated by mountains and rain forests and by lack
of support—even opposition—from the inhabitants. French
intelligence networks dwindled and the guerrillas merged
with the populace and lived off the land. Dense jungle cover
and lack of concentrated targets meant that French air forces
could not be effective for close support or reconnaissance;
they were used for bombing of highways and small supply
dumps. U.S. C-119's furnished airlift. Having drained the
French by seven and a half years of this phantom warfare,
the Communists on 13 March 1954 mounted a mass offensive
against the key fort at Dienbienphu. The French held until
8 May, then with the loss of this fort gave up control of northern Vietnam.[2]

From the experience of Greece, Korea, and Indo-China, as well
as numerous other "limited military actions" of history, we are
able to draw certain conclusions that help us to define more clearly
the nature of limited or local wars. The definition emerging from
the mass of international political-military actions, with the greatest
significance for the United States, is that we shall continue to consider any war to be "limited" or "local" when that war does not
directly involve the regular armed forces of the United States with
those of Soviet Russia. This in the same breath precludes any mili-

[2] *Air University Quarterly Review*, Vol. IX, No. 4 (Winter 1957-58), pp.
138-39.

tary action against the overseas bastions or home territory of either of the two nations by the other.

We can expect the area under military (armed) contest to be limited geographically, either by natural terrain (as in the Korean peninsula) or by tacit agreement. The contestants involved will not commit their total military reserves (as in the cases of participating foreign nations in Spain and China prior to World War II, and in Korea), but will throw into the fight just as much strength as they believe necessary to achieve their goals, or to effect any situation which may commonly be considered to be "acceptable."

Most clearly, the sovereignty of the nations involved in either direct support or direct involvement in the fighting will not be an issue to be decided one way or the other by the war. And looming high over the battlefront will be the political considerations—a mixture of political objectives limited to the area under contest, but still of sufficient importance to override any decisions effected in the fighting area.

One of the factors that cloud the issue of limited war is that both nations providing the primary support to the contest, for example, the Soviet Union and the United States in Korea, are willing to accept what Colonel Fisher defines as "mutually acceptable psychological restraints to keep the conflict within cost limits commensurate with the value of the objectives," and each nation hopes "that the war might be terminated favorably to [it] by negotiation."

Nothing so contributes to frustration on the part of Americans as these factors of "psychological restraints" and "negotiation." Our historical participation in armed conflict has invariably been cut-and-dried. If we must fight, then the purpose and the ultimate goal of that fight must be overwhelming victory. The enemy must be either destroyed, or brought to a position where there are no further "psychological restraints." He is then not only willing, but quite anxious, to bring an immediate cessation to further destruction of his forces and homeland by accepting surrender terms.

Such is *not* the case with limited or contained wars, and it has been a difficult (and continuing) process for Americans to appreciate these new facts of life. Black-and-white, clearly defined conclusions, complete acceptance by the enemy of our surrender terms—these are all values inapplicable to the current concept and practice of limited war.

Their validity in the past may be questioned, but that they were put into practice may not.

Mutual second-strike capability with thermonuclear warheads has dictated the change. Our purpose no longer is to press the fighting to a conclusion acceptable *only* to us, for such determination might well be attainable *only* at the price of escalating the limited war into total nuclear war.

Neither our national purposes, nor our national policies, can afford any longer not to consider all the alternatives that might arise from any limited war.

The full-scale involvement to which we considered committing ourselves in Indo-China fell victim to the terrain and to the magnitude of the effort necessary to effect military decisions favorable to us and to our French allies. Indo-China is made up of 285,000 square miles of hellish mountainous terrain, broken only by river gorges. The mountains range from 3,000 feet to two miles in elevation, and they abound in vertical development that compounds greatly any offensive action. The rivers and streams course through valleys that tower skyward with sheer walls, vastly complicating access to the surrounding country.

Eighty-six percent of the entire land abounds in thick rain forest and monsoon forest, lush and unbelievably dense growth that snarls the country and constricts the movement of any mechanized military force. "From mid-January through March," reads a military report of the monsoons in Indo-China, "they produce ten or more inches of rain in the northeastern section . . . around Hanoi and along the coastal strip to a point some 100 miles below Tourane. Another product of the winter monsoon is the *crachin*, a local phenomenon in the northeast that produces two-to-five-day periods of intense fog, drizzle, and low clouds." The report notes that in Indo-China "thunderstorms are frequent and intense. The southwest slopes of the Annam range are particularly wet, receiving up to 45 inches of rain from June through August. . . ."

Mixed in between the monsoons are the fierce thunderstorm periods. From July through September Indo-China is lashed with an average of five typhoons that inundate the land. Above all, the terrain and the weather contributed to a situation in which, according to the *Air University Quarterly Review*, the

> combination of the sharp-sloped mountains, the heavy, extensive foresting, and the heavy rainfall makes Indo-China peculiarly unsuited to modern ground warfare. These natural barriers have restricted the modern transportation system to an even more primitive network of railroads and all-weather roads than existed in Korea. Most of the other roads and trails are streams of mud during the rainy months. Mountain passes are narrow and steep, easily defended by a few men. Few of the roads will support modern vehicles. The roads in the interior are narrow ribbons flanked by almost impenetra-

ble jungle, so that convoys are easily and constantly subject to ambush by relatively small forces.

In the delta and coastal flatlands, most of the land is converted into rice paddies. Soggy with repeated flooding, laced with small streams, dikes, and ditches, and many inches deep in water or mud during the rainy season, they are practically impassable to wheeled vehicles. In the uncultivated flatlands, grass standing six to eight feet tall is excellent camouflage for guerrilla troops.

Little of the coastline offers landing places for profitable amphibious assaults. Except for the ports which the French [controlled], the coast line is protected by fringe islands, shallow water, mud flats, and swamps. An exception to this is the area of broad sandy beaches along the central east coast, but here the coastal strip goes inland only fifteen to thirty miles. Then the mountains rise up in an unbroken mass, with no river valleys to afford ready access to the interior. . . .

The debacle of Indo-China is a naked case history of abject failure. It was a long, bloody, cruel, tragically expensive conflict and an example of the Western world being whipped at almost every turn.

It is not particularly pleasant to face the loss of Indo-China in terms so blunt. But candor in regard to Indo-China has, fortunately, served us well in preparing realistically for the future, and in helping us to refrain from committing the gross errors which drowned the French in a rising flood of defeat.

The terrain, weather, and other conditions peculiar to Indo-China dramatically emphasize the extraordinary difficulties of military operations in that land. But that is not all of it. They stress the difficulties of military operations *based upon our concepts and carried out on our terms of combat.* Indo-China is a classic of Communistic victory achieved, among other means, through brilliant exploitation of our weaknesses. In this case, the "our" refers to the Allied, or Western, camp.

The French outnumbered the Vietminh guerrillas by almost two to one. The French forces were, in comparison to the ill-clad and poorly armed guerrillas, overwhelmingly superior in firepower and facilities. The French covered their operations with some 600 combat aircraft, including swarms of fighters, fighter-bombers, and attack bombers, as well as many transport aircraft.

The United States carried the burden of paying for nearly 80 percent of the cost of the war in Indo-China.

The French in Indo-China fought with raw and naked courage. They also fought their war from an intellectual and emotional ivory tower, and they played beautifully into the hands of the Communists. The French were myopic to the emotions and the needs of the local populace; the Communists were acutely aware and sensitive in their response to such emotions and needs.

Above all, the Communist effort included shrewdly planned and executed psychological warfare. Communist propaganda exploited every opportunity to stress the interrelationship of the army and the people. The Chinese contribution to the Vietminh forces was never displayed as a Chinese contribution, but rather as an Asiatic contribution to Asiatics.

The guerrilla was not the wild savage represented in the American press, an unkempt and ignorant individual who spread terror wherever he went. Nothing could have been further from the truth in Indo-China, and of all the lessons we have learned from this debacle, *this one is far and away the most important.* It is the one lesson, above all others, that led to the creation of the counterinsurgency and special forces military groups in the United States today, as we shall see.

The Vietminh guerrilla functioned, in the most realistic sense of the word, as *the* link between the Vietminh army and the people. And there was never any doubt left as to the fact that the fighting was to free the land from the white oppressors.

For years the guerrilla lived an interchangeable life, functioning one day as a farmer, and the next as a skilled jungle fighter. Nothing was left undone to identify the *people* with the struggle against the outsiders. And, above all, the Vietminh soldiers were impressed by their superiors with the need to respect civilian property and civilian rights.

Among the natives, accustomed to the heavy hand of the Westerner, this attitude and this conduct created a deep impression. Not a move was missed in swaying the people toward the Communist credo. The inability of the Vietnamese government to protect the people, military and civilian, even in their own areas, became a point endlessly repeated by the guerrillas. The fighting stretched on for years, the feeling grew that the Bao Dai government existed solely as puppets for the French, and the Vietminh guerrilla came to be closely identified as a man who (1) respected the rights of the civilians, and (2) was on the scene to liberate the Indo-Chinese from the burdens of colonial exploitation.

Let there be no mistake about it—the Communist guerrilla forces in Indo-China fought with infinite patience and with consummate skill. They never conducted major attacks without superiority in the immediate fighting area. They refused to be pinned down, and brilliantly utilized the vicious terrain to their advantage.

The guerrillas did not fight widespread, unrelated, and unco-ordinated battles. Intelligence from the Communist high commands was superb, benefiting as it did from the willing assistance of the natives. The guerrillas struck at opportune moments, never quite coming to grips with the heavy firepower of the French. They struck hard, and melted into the jungle and within the local popu-lation. The cumulative effect of their raids became devastating. It bled the French white, sapped their strength, undermined their fighting abilities.

And finally the end came in the savage, bloody, ill-fated defense of Dienbienphu. With the surrender of that jungle strongpoint, the fighting ended.

The conclusions of that war lead to grim realizations. The French, despite massive American support, could not employ their over-whelming military strength. The terrain and rain forests clutched them helplessly and denied their military forces the mobility so well exploited by the Vietminh. The French not only lost the active support of the local population, but gained its enmity and suffered from the support it gave to the guerrillas.

A powerful air force went for naught. French forces held isolated islands in a sea of jungle, bereft of adequate intelligence. Airpower without such intelligence is close to being blind.

Finally, the inevitable had to be faced. The Western camp had taken a severe beating. Victory could still be salvaged from this defeat, but at what price?

Intervention by massive, conventional forces of the United States? More billions of dollars poured into the quagmire of the jungles, in a land where the white-skinned man was regarded with hostil-ity? High casualties and tremendous material losses on our part to regain an area which could be defended only at continuing, ex-tremely high cost?

This was the price of direct intervention by conventional arms. It was a price the United States deemed unacceptable.

The alternative possibility of snatching victory from the sorry defeat of Indo-China was by extending the war. What was clearly a limited or contained war had turned to the advantage of the Com-munists, but from a strategic point of view the Communists were winning on a precarious foundation. The Vietminh forces received sustenance, training, supplies, and leadership from China. But in South China transportation and communications were an outmoded, makeshift affair. The transportation system which constituted the arterial lifeline to the Vietminh was made of flabby tissue, and lay invitingly naked to quick and devastating severance by heavy strikes from the air. Interdiction of these supply lines in South China meant

overwhelming strikes against the supply dumps and the transportation system. The efficiency of the Vietminh was in direct proportion
to the functioning of the lifeline from South China. Destroy the
latter, and the Vietminh jungle fighters would become rapidly
snarled in the undergrowth they utilized so well against the enemy.

Extend the war. . . . With conventional arms, this meant air strikes
on a scale to parallel that of Korea. It meant hundreds of fighters
and bombers. It meant a massive supply line from the distant
United States, supported at enormous cost. It meant, also, great
military forces poised to counter any thrusts made by the Chinese
and quite possibly by the Soviet Union.

An uncommon number of our strategists proposed swift precision
attacks with nuclear weapons against the weakest points of the
enemy supply lines. And no one could argue that such attacks
would not be effective in their purpose. The Vietminh forces would
wither on the vine, their weapons nourishment snuffed out along its
vital arteries.

But the *price* . . . How far would such a move take us? Was the
possibility of rapid escalation of this local jungle war worth the risk
of retrieving defeat from conclusive Communist victory in Indo-
China?

It was not. Communism gained its victory through unquestioned
military ascendancy in Indo-China, and through the specter of a
rapidly expanding, bloody conflict of major proportions if we applied our military strength beyond the "mutually accepted" geographical limits of the conflict.

We lost—Communism won.

In that loss lay the seeds of our actions in the future—actions that
could prevent a repetition of the sorry affair of Indo-China.

CHAPTER III

The Flexible Blueprint   ONLY THE BLIND
could fail to see the warning signals inherent in the succession of
military involvements of the United States. After suffering staggering cost and no small number of casualties, we were in dire need
of a blueprint that would permit us greater success in containing
or defeating outbreaks of Communist-inspired violence. The hard
truth of the matter was that the Communists were calling the shots,
and we were reacting, albeit clumsily, to this carefully selected
pattern. Our reaction to incidents of insurrection and outright war
built up momentum slowly. And we could not ignore the fact that
insurgency, guerrilla attacks, and military operations were costing
the Communists only a small fraction of the bill paid by the United
States.

Full comprehension of this problem came slowly. So long as our
reaction continued in ponderous and sluggish fashion, waiting for
dissension to grow to potential disaster *before* we made our coun-
termoves, we would continue to face the same problems of partial
success and/or failure that had attended our participation in brushfire and limited wars.

The record left much to be desired. In Korea we gained nothing
more than a restoration of the irritating status quo, a sorry return
for the overwhelming effort we had poured into that limited area.
The failure of the United States to achieve a goal which our people
(and much of the world) expected of us—a free Korea constituted
of the territories below *and above* the 38th parallel—remains a
thorn in our national pride. To fight a war for so many years with
so great a force and to end up right where we started was a sharp
departure from our military history.

Korea was a costly, bitter stalemate. It was also an object lesson
which took time to sink in. Our national objectives in the future no
longer would be identified with the idealistic but unrealistic concept
of "total victory."

The thermonuclear world bloomed full, and new values came
into being as part and parcel of our international affairs. The Greeks,
with massive American help, outnumbering the guerrillas by more

than ten to one, finally rid their land of insurgency. In Korea we settled for stalemate. In Indo-China the Western world took a hell of a beating.

We could not suffer the pattern to continue. If our goal was equally to prevent brushfire wars from achieving immediate Communist goals, as well as to prevent such wars from blazing into full-scale and possibly nuclear conflicts, then the United States urgently needed new objectives and purposes. Otherwise our future course could only continue in the same erratic and myopic fashion.

The task made veteran strategists shudder. "Planning for limited war," one officer commented wryly, "is like looking at yourself in a roomful of crazy mirrors in a carnival fun house. In this one you're fat and happy. In that one you're stretched mighty thin. In the one over there you're just a shapeless blob."

How, chorused the military planners, is it possible to plan a war when nothing—the location, the bases, the weapons, the tactics, the objectives, even the specific enemy—is known at the time of planning?

At the Air War College of the United States, Colonel Thomas L. Fisher, II, studied what parameters might be used to provide for the United States a pattern of practical and valid responses to outbreaks of limited war. "There are many ways by which possible objectives in limited war are expressed," stated the colonel.

> They may be spelled out positively in terms of advances in our own national interests or negatively in terms of enemy gains. They are often expressed as actions to be taken or goals to be accomplished because of changes in the situation. It is very rare, however, that one finds a complete blueprint laying out in advance the end position that is desired. This is particularly true for the contestant under aggression. Hence our objectives in the past have sometimes been vaguely understood as "victory," further delineation of this term being obscured by the goal of reduction or cessation of physical violence, as was partially true of the Korean War.
>
> But can we not do better than that in the future? We must if we are to determine how to act within desirable war limitations. One of the chief sources of confusion is the great variety and lack of agreement in the expression of objectives—if, indeed, they are expressed at all. What both the statesman and the military leader or planner need is a clear idea of the situation that it is desired to establish as a result of war action. That is, what is the minimum demand that can be imposed upon the enemy to produce an acceptable situation in terms of degree of conflict, residual capabilities, and adequate deter-

rents or safeguards for the future? We also need to know how much beyond the minimum it might be desirable to go at any given time if opportunity arises. This calls for expression of objectives as a spectrum, from minimum to maximum. Objectives should encompass the form of enemy government, its actions, capabilities, and promises; and the control, inspection, or police arrangements needed by us to safeguard our objectives. . . .

It is peculiarly characteristic of limited war that if it is to be terminated short of unconditional surrender the objectives for which we are willing to settle must at some point be clearly formulated and presented as terms to the enemy. Spencer Wilkinson, a leading British military historian, states the object of such wars as "not victory necessarily, or conquest, or unconditional surrender—the usual maxims—but peace upon acceptable terms." This requirement raises a whole series of problems. First, determining objectives sufficient to achieve our minimum aims, including a future deterrence factor. Second, obtaining agreement and support for the objectives among the interested parties of our side, especially in an allied effort. Third, determining the best timing for presenting our terms to the enemy, usually the sooner the better and sometimes even before taking any action—difficult in the case of surprise attack. And fourth, negotiating face-saving procedures, deciding on "asking" and minimum terms, and providing flexibility in our position as the situation develops.[1]

The problem, as concluded succinctly by William W. Kaufman, "is to define the minimum political objectives that we would find acceptable, and the enemy tolerable, *and create the military and other conditions that will make them acceptable to him as well.*"

Summarizing the problem was not enough to discover the best possible solution for dealing with limited wars. Once again we were forced logically to consider the *basis* of the functioning of any military force—to make the enemy change his mind, or, in the words of Air Chief Marshal Sir Charles Portal, "to bring about a change in temper" of the enemy.

And once again we were drawn to the conclusion that the most effective means of winning any brushfire or limited war was to extinguish the flames just as rapidly as they ignited. Even better would be a situation in which our intelligence could pinpoint *in advance* an area ripe for bursting with violence. If this could be done, *and if we had the means to move with great speed and tre-*

[1] *Air University Quarterly Review*, Vol. IX, No. 4 (Winter 1957-58), pp. 131-32.

*mendous military power directly to the source of the potential fight-
ing, we could immediately smother the danger and prevent the
outbreak of the war.*

But in carrying out such plans as would permit us to reach this
idealistic goal, we were right back to the limited-war planning
problems of "looking at yourself in a roomful of crazy mirrors in a
carnival fun house." How could a military force capable of sup-
pressing or rapidly ending an outbreak of fighting operate efficiently
when we could never know just where, and when, trouble might
arise?

We could to some extent narrow down the probable problem
areas, for these essentially would be peripheral to the main Communist heartlands of the Soviet Union and Red China. Despite
strategic Soviet power, this would *not* be a problem in dampening
limited or brushfire wars. The capacity of the Communist world for
taking over small countries, directly or through covert intervention,
was proportional to its avenues of transportation and communications. Without the capability of carrying out mass overwater moves
(which would be in danger of direct interference by the powerful
U.S. Navy and which posed huge logistical problems and conse-
quent great expense) and denied the ability to resort to infiltration,
the Communists were almost certain to continue their practice of
subverting legal authority in nations on the Eurasian continent or
within contiguous areas.

In the mid-fifties Communist pressure was heaviest in the gray
areas of Southeast Asia and the Middle East. Henry A. Kissinger
insisted (also in the mid-fifties) that we would have to keep the
sharpest eye out for explosive conditions in Burma, Afghanistan,
Iran, Thailand, Indo-China, and perhaps Indonesia. To these countries experienced strategists and students of the Communist world
added Syria, Yemen, Egypt, Nepal, Malaya, and Taiwan, and they
returned Korea to the list. On giving careful thought to the matter,
it became evident that as the years passed and power changed
hands, there were few parts of the world that we could be certain
would never enter the arena of possible subversion and overt conflict.

Communist objectives and political considerations, in the light of
the situation existing at any given time, would determine the locale
and the methods of confronting the United States. This being the
case, it became increasingly obvious that the Red pattern was one
of extreme elasticity. Communist aims and wants could be modified
as much as was necessary to adapt to prevailing conditions. Propaganda notwithstanding, the doctrine of the Communist world has
shown itself to be shrewdly calculating and flexible. They are past

masters in the art of covert relations with dissidents anywhere in the world. Their ingrained habits include cautiousness in their activities, and they have long been willing readily to accept tactical retreat if this move best serves their cause. Patience has helped them in attaining their objectives.

For the United States successfully to counter these Communist methods, it would be necessary for us to depart from our own restrictive practices of the past. We sorely needed new concepts and the means of implementing them to eliminate the built-in elements of weakness that plagued our limited-war resistance to Communist-inspired violence.

Colonel Fisher cut neatly to the heart of the problem confronting the United States when he stressed that

> there is no clearly defined set of limitations that constitutes the parameters of limited war. Instead there appears to be a whole range, or spectrum, of possible degrees of limitation. Indeed it may logically be doubted if there could ever be a truly unlimited war. The purpose of a nation in limited war is to change to its advantage the elements of limitation . . . That is, we may bring about a desired change in the enemy's objectives (or modify our own); we may cause a shift in his methods to ones more acceptable to us; or we may reduce the area or vigor of conflict. Conflict is a continuum, from minimal friction to total violence. Limited war is not a "problem" susceptible of "solution," but a complex, continuing situation in which everything done or left undone produces a new situation and in which the means employed affect the end achieved. . . .

Slowly but surely we evolved a plan that would give the United States the "means" to deal successfully with what Colonel Fisher so clearly underscored as the intrinsic problem faced in limited war—"a complex, continuing situation."

One obvious solution, of course, was to station military forces-in-being at every potential trouble spot around the world, with firepower sufficient to contain and to defeat any move that might be initiated by the Communists. In practice, the cost of this would be staggering. It would also disperse the military strength of the nation to an intolerable degree; we could achieve ideal tactical displacement only by leaving ourselves strategically naked.

By following a step-by-step evaluation of the strength and relative positions of the United States and the Soviet Union in the first decade after World War II, the Air Force began to work out its answers to the vexations of limited wars. From all the possible solutions, one thought predominated. Since it was not feasible for the nation to blanket potential trouble areas, another means of striking to the heart of violence must be found. Could the Air Force create such forces—a composite of its strength, made up of those elements of airpower that could be brought to bear swiftly and decisively in the danger zone?

No doubt existed as to the efficiency of airpower to accomplish the purpose of neutralizing any outbreaks, provided we could apply our strength *in time*. And there was the rub. The success or failure of any such venture depended upon the clock.

Small, mobile forces, highly trained and carefully equipped to grasp superiority in a given area and situation, had long been effective in American military history. But never in the past had the time factor been so critical. Now, suddenly, because of the strategic distances involved, time became an enemy.

A further complication arose in selecting the airpower instrument to be applied to the limited-war situation. The aircraft in question had to be of tactical configuration, designed specifically to operate under conditions of any possible terrain—to get down close and slug it out at point-blank range. Tactical aircraft historically have always been short-legged. Now, almost overnight, we faced the need of applying seven-league boots to these battlefield killers.

Equally as important as the need for great range was the size of the force. It had to be truly composite in nature—fighters, fighter-bombers, attack bombers, reconnaissance aircraft, and a new type of strategic-range, tactical-assault-capability logistics and troop transport. The logistics of keeping a composite strike force sufficient unto itself for as many days or weeks as possible demanded performance unavailable in any existing transport. And to add to these requirements, the composite air strike force must also be able to carry shock troops to the scene in order to (1) provide ground perimeter defense, and (2) act if necessary as a deadly infantry-light armor force with great fire-fight capability.

As the war in Indo-China blazed to its ignominious end, the Tactical Air Command began the task of assembling from all known data the answer to the question of whether we could in fact create a meaningful composite striking force.

As important as any other element was the evolutionary process of the power play of the Soviet Union and the United States, and the manner in which airpower to date had affected the course of events involving the world's two giants. There was more to the question of limited war than met the eye, for the brushfire war tactics of the Communist camp had arisen from necessity more than by original design.

The first of the factors that would lead to the composite air strike force was the emergence in the years after World War II of the "massive retaliation" policy of the United States. Strategic airpower for many years remained a weapon of overwhelming dominance in the hands of the United States, while at the same time its capabilities were denied to the Soviet Union. The imbalance of power—and this is exactly what it was—kept the U.S.S.R. not only at bay, but greatly off balance. Up until this moment the ponderous military strength of the Soviet Union had lain in its reliance on defense in depth. A vast army of many millions of soldiers, and massed artillery, constituted the bedrock of Russian military power.

It did not take overly long for the Soviets to appreciate that their overwhelming strength on the European mainland would avail them little in a clash with the United States. The capabilities of the United States through the Strategic Air Command spelled out the destruction of Russian cities, factories, supply and communications centers—the very fiber of the nation. Any decision for war by the Russians would simultaneously signal the commitment of the United States to the destruction of the U.S.S.R.

Determined to continue the influential spread of Communism, the Soviet leaders nonetheless shied hastily away from any direct test of American nuclear steel. "Their next moves toward world domination were more subtle," explains Major General Henry Viccellio, Commander, 19th Air Force, Tactical Air Command, "both as to means and as to choice of area, so that the United States reaction would fall short of an attack against the homeland of Communism."

This was the second factor, and out of hard respect for the strength of SAC "was born the peripheral, or limited, war, supported by the U.S.S.R., but not involving actual employment of organized Soviet forces."

General Viccellio stresses that "Korea is the number one example of a limited war. The conditions were ideal. It had been fairly well established by United States actions and words that a military vacuum existed in South Korea. . . ." And, as the general noted astutely, "a series of military vacuums existed around the world, many of them snug up against the Iron or Bamboo Curtain." [2]

In this fashion Communism made its attempt not to contest, but to circumvent, the nuclear power of SAC; without incurring the perils of total war commitment, the Communists could now prosecute to the full the advantages inherent in subversion and limited war. Korea and Indo-China were the result.

The third factor was our reaction to Communist-inspired limited

[2] *Air University Quarterly Review*, Vol. IX, No. 1 (Winter 1956-57), p. 27.

war, just as the limited-war policy had been the Communist reaction to the brutal devastation inherent in the capabilities of SAC.

"The Korean War," states the Air Force in candor, "demonstrated our inability to combat aggression in a swift and decisive manner. That constituted a fact. We had to do something about this inability, and we had to do it fast."

That "something" began in 1953. It involved revolutionary concepts in airpower which, if their validity could be conclusively established, would endow the United States with a unique capacity to counter aggressive moves anywhere in the world.

The new concepts centered about the fighter-bomber. The jet-powered fighter-bomber was a lethal weapon in the hands of skilled pilots. But it suffered from two serious deficiencies. Its armament necessarily had to be restricted to the weight-carrying capabilities of the airplane. And though the fighter-bombers could carry several tons of bombs, these weapons were of conventional explosives. Their application in any brushfire war hinged upon several disturbing factors.

If a composite air strike force was *known* by the Communists to be limited to conventional weapons, then it was obvious that the strike force could be effective only upon the movement of a great number of aircraft. This would violate our own concept of a miniature tactical air force, armed with a full range of weapons, including atomic bombs. Knowing the limitations of the American force, the Communists could counter our airpower moves easily enough with nothing more than opposing fighters. Once again we were on the horns of a dilemma.

But only briefly. During this period the Tactical Air Command was deftly removing the last obstacles to strategic deployment of tactical warplanes.

In fact, TAC had been burning the midnight oil for several years in attempts to stretch one-man fighters into strategic-range killers. The TAC fighters simply lacked the range to cover any great distance, and if they couldn't overcome this failing, they wouldn't be much good in emergencies many thousands of miles away, when their very success depended upon speed of arrival. In January of 1952 the Fifth Air Force in Korea decided that the best test of extending fighter range could be made under conditions not of simulated combat, but during the actual fighting.

High over Japan, F-84E fighters of the 116th Fighter Bomber Wing practiced for several months to perfect aerial refueling techniques with KB-29 tankers. Seventy pilots went the route in individual experiments, and then grouped together in squadron and wing formations for additional refueling. If the planes could refuel as part of a powerful airborne force, then the proposed composite strike forces could unquestionably become a reality. The initial experiments weren't without their "hairy moments," and mechanical complications mixed with pilot inexperience to produce a success rate of only slightly better than 50 percent.

Several group combat missions were flown over Korea, but these proved to be less signal successes than glaring revelations of needed improvements. The research program was known as the Far East Air Forces Probe and Drogue Inflight Refueling Project, and heading this program with the weighty title was a pilot of great skill and even greater determination. Lieutenant Colonel Harry W. Doris, Jr., had demonstrated personally the enormous possibilities of refueling airborne fighters.

Shortly after five A.M. on September 28, 1951, Doris staggered off the Yokota runway in Japan. His Lockheed F-80 Shooting Star was saddled with a huge load for the small single-engine jet fighter—two 265-gallon wingtip tanks, two 500-pound bombs, a maximum load of ammunition for his six .50-caliber machine guns, and four five-inch rockets. Before he came back to earth, Colonel Doris refueled six times in flight, in good and miserable weather, in daylight and in darkness, without ever once breaking radio silence! He was aloft for 14 hours and 15 minutes.

Oh yes—*he also flew five combat missions during the same period.* First he dumped his bombs into an enemy supply dump at Kilchu. He strafed troops, slammed his rockets into buildings, flew weather reconnaissance up and down the Korean coasts, did a combat surveillance flight, refueled in storms, and landed finally, his body aching but his airplane heavy on fuel.

In the ensuing months the Tactical Air Command withered on the financial vine, while funds and massive supplies and equipment for inflight refueling went to the Strategic Air Command. But fighters flew tremendous distances across the Pacific and the Atlantic. In August of 1952 Operation Longstride convinced even the doubting Thomases, when the 508th Fighter Escort Wing leaped 4,485 miles nonstop from the southern United States to Lakenheath, England. In the greatest nonstop mass movement of fighters, the aircraft refueled three times. Later the same month another powerful force of fighters flew 4,470 miles nonstop, from the United States to bases in French Morocco. Two refuelings during a flight completed in ten hours 21 minutes, did the trick.

In general, however, TAC officers fumed in helpless anger at the results of long-range TAC movements. In December of 1954, with little equipment and even less reliability in the hand-me-down TAC tankers, it required 72 *days* to get the 388th and 31st Fighter Bomber Wings fully deployed to Europe.

In the summer of 1954 the Tactical Air Command received its first squadron of KB-29 tankers. The planes were old; TAC would have preferred faster and better tankers, but it was all they could get at the time. The heavy bombers were drastically modified into airborne fueling stations, with perfected hookup equipment to facilitate slaking the thirst of the fuel-gulping fighter-bombers. TAC lost no time in ordering tests with these planes to be carried out at every possible opportunity.

During the same year the Air Force, through TAC, ordered a major exercise to define additional parameters of flexibility and performance of tactical airpower units. Operation Boxkite had a profound impact on what tactical air commanders considered their "normal" operations, without air refueling. The orders required the movement of a powerful force of tactical air fighters and support equipment over long distances—their destination a "raw airfield" with minimum and deliberately crude facilities. Fighters thundered from California to an auxiliary air base in South Carolina. Moving immediately behind them came transport planes carrying mechanics, maintenance equipment, weapons, and the other paraphernalia necessary to keep the fighters "primed and cocked." Upon their arrival in South Carolina, the fighters were unquestionably capable of immediately beginning any combat mission. The support groups were designed to keep them in this condition.

Boxkite didn't solve all problems, but it did lay to rest many of them, and it clarified those trouble spots that needed, and now would receive, added attention. One result was that the 405th Fighter Bomber Wing, operating with Republic F-84F Thunderstreaks out of Langley Air Force Base, Virginia, perfected to a fine art its techniques in air-to-air refueling.

The pattern was being established in definitive fashion. But there yet remained several critical factors—and Tactical Air Command worked overtime to move from concept to reality.

"The art of delivering the atomic bomb by fighter aircraft was being perfected," states General Viccellio. "At the time few saw the impact this capability would have on the future. Realization was not long in coming. If a force of nuclear-armed fighter-bombers could be moved to the trouble spots of the world quickly enough, it could effectively counteract the obvious Soviet policy of quick jabs at the soft spots of the Free World. . . ."

With the new "art of delivering" perfected, the Tactical Air Command created the Mobile Tactical Strike Force, comprised of units

High over the Pacific, a KB-29 tanker prepares to refuel an F-84G Thunderjet. Note the rigid fueling boom extending below and behind the KB-29; this system has been replaced for fighters with the more flexible "probe and drogue" equipment in KB-50J tankers. (*Air Force*)

from the 405th Fighter Bomber Wing with nuclear-armed, air-refueling F-84F fighter-bombers.

The move proved to be premature, for the Mobile Tactical Strike Force suffered serious limitations. Able to utilize only one type of combat aircraft, it was proportionally limited to the type of mission that it could fulfill. Its logistics support was a nightmare of inadequate planning and inadequate transport aircraft. It was a far cry from the kind of powerful strike force that had been envisioned.

By the summer of 1955, Tactical Air Command resolved its need "to possess a specialized air strike force capable of conducting *all* phases of the tactical air mission on a limited scale."

The Composite Air Strike Force (CASF) was now a reality. To plan for the deployment and the employment of these forces, to train their units, and, finally, to command them, the Tactical Air Command in July 1955 activated the 19th Air Force.

The 19th Air Force, however, was a unique organization without weapons, aircraft, or any hardware implements. It was literally a headquarters staff armed with a paper air force that existed only in the form of extensive and exhaustive plans. When the need for an overseas operation became clear, the 19th Air Force would be commanded by TAC headquarters to pull out the appropriate paper plans, and simultaneously would be given authority to create a CASF of the desired configuration directly from the functioning and operational units of TAC. Thus the CASF existed as a shadow organization within the over-all structure of TAC itself, and by nothing more than this assignment of official authority to the 19th Air Force it could be created in a matter of minutes. And at the same moment that the CASF came into being, the Commander, 19th Air Force, automatically became the Commander, CASF. He continued to function in this capacity until the CASF was separated from the emergency situation and all aircraft and men were returned to the normal TAC structure.

General Viccellio became the initial commander of the 19th, and he recalls that at that time many nations were "newly independent and weak, perfect targets for conquest by the Communists. Governments were generally shaky, and in almost every case a strong Communist underground movement was present. Against this background, then, the Composite Air Strike Force was born. The United States could not afford to station forces-in-being on a permanent peacetime basis in every locale, sufficient for any eventuality. But a small, lethal force, only hours away from any area of the world, would be a deterrent limited only by the effectiveness of the force and the time required to move it to a troubled area. . . ."

The general detailed the composition of the fighters and bombers, explained the development to "commonplace status" of air refueling, and stressed particularly that a CASF "with its heavy transport airlift" could "supply this force with the myriad impedimenta of modern combat units."

We had gained in the development and logistics support of the CASF, explained General Viccellio, an extraordinary new type of force. "With this capability to move strike units thousands of miles in a matter of hours, the United States could, for a relatively minor investment, hold a small force in readiness at a central location and cover the trouble spots of the world, rather than attempt to station and support expensive forces throughout the various areas. The centralized force has one other obvious advantage. It could be deployed to any area of the world and employed in that area without disturbing the posture of existing defensive or counteroffensive forces. Theater forces could then concentrate on and train for their primary task. They would not have to shift to other areas to meet emergencies, thereby opening gaping holes in a barely adequate defense establishment. Also the SAC 'massive retaliation' potential would not be affected. Uncommitted and poised for action, it would act as a valuable restraint on any thoughts of expanding the local conflict into a general war. . . ."

The promise of the mission capabilities of the Composite Air Strike Force grew steadily brighter. As experiments continued and weak points were eliminated, it became evident that, upon call, the Tactical Air Command could indeed provide precisely configured forces capable of rapid deployment and sustained operations in any area of the world. Through 1956 and 1957 CASF units went through the development mill of realistic operations and exercises, intended to place CASF operations under great stress so as to reveal areas needing still greater improvement.

In the summer of 1956 CASF Operation Mobile Baker was executed. Fighter-bomber and other tactical units deployed nonstop from the United States to various stations in Europe and North Africa, working on tight schedules with tanker aircraft in over-ocean rendezvous.

Still the rough spots persisted. Despite many overseas deployments, the CASF concept jolted operational patterns and practices. Nothing of the magnitude and speed of deployment of the Composite Air Strike Force had ever existed before. The lack of knowledge became painfully evident, as did the urgent requirements for more careful planning, more detailed coordination, and more intensive training. In November of 1957 Operation Mobile Zebra put the CASF system once again to the acid test. A composite force roared out to different bases in the Far East; when the operation ended the Tactical Air Command at long last considered its strategic deployment of tactical airpower an operational success.

Despite such promising developments and attainment of operational capability, "something" was still missing from the national point of view. The specific objectives and purposes in limited war, absent in previous entanglements of our country, still defied acceptable understanding. We were still groping for the answer to a clear-cut mode of conduct in limited-war situations, and the cries for freedom to employ nuclear weapons in tactical situations were overshadowing the intrinsic purpose of the Composite Air Strike Force—to *prevent* the expansion of any armed conflict into one of nuclear proportions.

In the arguments advanced as to the "logic" of employing nuclear weapons lurked a critical danger. The concept that had gained many adherents was one of measured punishment—tailoring the punishment to fit the crime, as it were. The advocates of liberal use of nuclear arms claimed that "punishment" was to be used in the sense of atomic weapons to destroy infantry and other combat forces in the immediate battle zone, to permit "hot pursuit to destroy on their bases any opposing air forces involved," and destroy nuclear stockpiles at the first instance of their use. Colonel Fisher noted that the nuclear-punishment concept prohibited the bombing of "cities or population centers unless the enemy started to do so, and it would not blockade or attempt to capture any area. And, most important, it would announce all these restrictions in advance."

Unfortunately, this is one-sided logic, and there is absolutely no guarantee that such logic would be appreciated or recognized by the enemy. The proponents of nuclear punishment insisted, as did Air Force chaplain W. E. Ferguson, that we are "morally bound to do what we can to preserve freedom and to create a climate in which freedom can prosper. . . . Rather than let the enemy draw unacceptable limits, we must use airpower, equipped with the most advantageous weapons, to strike those targets that would prove costly to him. . . . Full application of airpower with its best weapons is less brutal than alternative ways of fighting modern wars because it is decisive, sure, and swift. Prolonged torture is immoral when swift victory is possible."

It is also possible to extend this logic. Since a small nuclear bomb might score only a partial hit on an enemy target, its effectiveness would then be compromised. To be certain that we shall be "decisive, sure, and swift," why not, then, use the most decisive weapons of all? Why not sling thermonuclear bombs, one after the other, into the supply dumps, the air bases, and even the jungle fortresses of the enemy? They will *guarantee* through the total release of tens of millions of tons of explosive force that there will be no prolonged torture of the enemy in the target zones.

And quite likely we shall then be embroiled in the kind of thermonuclear war we have struggled desperately to avoid.

Donald A. Quarles, at the time Secretary of the Air Force, insisted in the mid-fifties that "the best way to prevent a local war from expanding into a total war is to end the local war quickly and decisively."

Once again logic suggests the commitment of the weapons best guaranteed to end that war quickly and decisively. Why take any chances? Use whatever weapons are available to be absolutely certain the job is done; and once again we face the specter of a clash with nuclear arms.

What the logicians seemed to avoid in their arguments was the fact that we were proposing the use of nuclear arms on the soil of somebody else's country. And such arguments were received with mixtures of outright hostility, suspicion, no small disgust, and a deep fear that the United States might actually employ the nuclear weapon. It was all very well and good to theorize in war games, but it engendered dangerous emotions on the part of the middlemen—the people of the small country that would receive the nuclear blows and suffer the psychological trauma and radioactive aftermath.

The tactical situation might be won and the strategic balance shifted slightly, but local peace could be attained only over the radioactive corpse of the small nation involved. Despite our military logic, these thoughts were certain to prevail, and they did, whenever the matter of nuclear strikes came up.

The United States on the international scene proclaimed itself as striving mightily for the banning of nuclear weapons. Tactical situations and nuclear advantages notwithstanding, any use of nuclear weapons as instituted by the United States would make a mockery of our words. Either we were committed to a long-term policy of trying to rid the world of the nuclear weapon, or we were not. The black-and-white of the argument dominated the thinking of the small nations of the world, and they were little interested in American logic that imperiled them more than it did the United States.

That our military forces should retain, at all times, the *capacity* to employ nuclear arms was not a point at issue. Without that capacity we would leave ourselves naked to actions initiated by Communist forces, which might strike decisive blows at our capability to defend ourselves. But a capacity to employ a weapon is a far cry from the actual employment, and the distinction could mean the difference between conventional arms in limited wars or an explosive spread of that conflict to thermonuclear contest on an international scale.

Above all else, the execution of tactics as arising from the manipulation of weapons in war games failed to consider that the struggle accepted by the United States was as much for the minds of men as it was to contain the spread of Communist-inspired anarchy in nations around the world. Precipitous moves with nuclear weapons by our country would create an abyss of distrust we might never overcome.

If the United States proved incapable of meeting the Soviet challenge *without resort to the nuclear weapon*, then the United States also was providing clear evidence of its incapability in handling international relations in their broadest sense. Tactical advantages notwithstanding, use of the nuclear weapon would lose us the most important struggle of all. We would win the contest on the battlefield, and the price would be that "abyss of distrust."

The United States deemed such a price to be uncompromisingly prohibitive. We would have to meet the enemy on his own terms, at the places he set, and at whatever time he decided. The odds were greater, the problems unquestionably knotty, and the challenge much more meaningful to the United States and the world.

The decision was made. Nuclear combat capability would always be kept "at the ready." But our policy would hew closely to the summation of the problem presented by Sir John Slessor in *Strategy for the West:* "Any action must always be subjected to two acid tests—will it pay us tactically and will it achieve the strategic result we want from it? . . . One cannot draw a blueprint for these hypothetical future campaigns, cannot say definitely in advance, this or that should be or should not be done; it will depend entirely upon the circumstances at the time and whether it will help to achieve our objective or not."

Our blueprint, then, would remain one of the greatest possible flexibility. Every attempt would be made to keep the nuclear sword well within its scabbard.

We would employ the great striking power of the Composite Air Strike Force, and we would take every advantage of its unique capability to don seven-league boots to meet any situation, at any point in the world this side of the Iron and Bamboo Curtains.

Only one ingredient now was missing. In the formation of such a strike force we still lacked the "common denominator" of weapons. We needed a means of mixing the combat aircraft of a strike force with a hard core of crack fighting men, so as to create a single element of fighting power that ran from the man on the ground to the man piloting a razor-winged killer in the air.

In 1953, with the echoes of jungle warfare from Indo-China ringing through the halls of the Pentagon, the Department of Defense made it clear that the nation needed a swift, mobile troop and logistics carrier that could rush from this country to any part of the world—and with complete freedom from concrete at whatever point might be its destination.

In California, a man named Willis M. Hawkins had already been working with a select group of engineers to fulfill that requirement. The chief preliminary design engineer for the Lockheed Aircraft Corporation, Hawkins in 1951 had "started from scratch" to create this new machine. Tactical Air Command strategists had spent long hours in thrashing out with Lockheed what the new aircraft would have to do. It would, of necessity, be revolutionary in design and even more revolutionary in performance.

Hawkins exclaimed wryly that all he needed to do was to create a "modern combination of the jeep, the truck, and the transport airplane."

A TAC officer grinned at the Lockheed engineer. "That's right." Then he added, "And whatever ideas you come up with—make them better. We'll need it. . . ."

CHAPTER IV

Squat, Square, and Rugged THE BIRTH OF A
new airplane is an occasion for expressions of wonder and laudatory
comments to paste in company scrapbooks. In the jet age the
debuts of machines with razor wings and sleek shapes produce
bonanzas of such superlatives. To the Lockheed Aircraft Corporation, producer of the nation's first combat jets and some of the
sleekest shapes ever to take wing, such plaudits had come to be
expected.

In 1952 the top corporate officials of Lockheed assembled in the
office of Vice President Hall L. Hibbard for their first look at a
large-scale model of the new assault transport even then taking
shape in the huge factory buildings. Excitement ran high among
the Lockheed officials, for the production prospects of the new airplane promised years of full-scale manufacturing work. Finally an
engineer removed the covering from the model of the Hercules.

Stony silence met the new airplane. The high-wing transport was
so radically different that no one would venture any comments. The
model wasn't sleek, the wings weren't swept back, and the un-
aesthetic lines jarred the onlookers. Finally, to break the heavy
silence in the room, Hibbard commented:

"Beautiful paint job, don't you think?"

Two years later, when the first YC-130 prototype rolled out of
the factory in Burbank, California, the commentary on the appearance of the new Hercules hadn't improved.

The airplane simply didn't "fit" into the concepts of jet power.
It was squat and square; observers readily admitted that it certainly *looked* rugged. The wing sat high atop the fuselage in sharp
contrast to almost every new airplane being produced. The only
streamlining that could be seen was in the bullet nacelles that
housed the four Allison jet engines. And almost as if to rob the
nacelles of their graceful lines, four great propellers were clamped
onto the needlelike spinners. This alone represented a radical departure from current thinking in the industry. Jet engines meant
fabulous speed and the most graceful of lines. The Hercules seemed
a step backward, since it used the jet engine but persisted in re-

taining the propeller. It was the first airplane in the country to enter production with the new system—the first of the turboprops.

The nose of the Hercules beggared aerodynamic law and challenged the senses. No rounded or streamlined shape there, but a huge, fat housing where the forward part of the cavernous fuselage ended abruptly. Later in the life of the airplane the nose was to evoke even more comment, when it would be extended along the plane's lower half with a great, black, and bulbous shape into which would go complex radar equipment.

The belly of the Hercules seemed almost to scrape the concrete of the flight line. No gear legs could be seen. From each side of the fuselage, about midway between the fat nose and the towering tail, there extended two huge bulges. These were landing gear pods. The black tires weren't even fully revealed, and it seemed that the airplane rested more on caterpillar treads than it did on wheels. The Hercules didn't really rest on the ground; it hugged the concrete and glowered.

The more one looked at the first of the Hercules, the more difficult it became to accept the fact that this airplane was just *starting* its life. The fuselage seemed designed to produce the maximum possible resistance to the air. It wasn't just large; it seemed to bulge, from the beginning of the airplane almost all the way back to the tail. From the top to the bottom of the huge body the Hercules measured more than 13 feet, and from side to side the distance went to more than 14 feet. The airplane itself stopped just short of 100 feet in length, most of it made up of the hulking body. Then, almost as an afterthought, came the huge tail, slanting up from the airplane and towering more than 38 feet above the concrete.

Observers looked at the ponderous fuselage, then stared again at the wing, tapering to unexpected sweeping and graceful lines near the tips. They kept looking from huge body to slim wing and back again, as if wondering what strange fortune had brought the two together. For certainly it didn't seem possible that the wing, stretching just a little more than 132 feet from tip to tip, was going to drag this monster through the air.

Those were the initial impressions of the Hercules, and the critical problems of limited wars in remote parts of the world seemed far removed from the flight line that day at the Lockheed Air Terminal. Hundreds of people gathered at the field on August 23, 1954, to witness the first flight of the prototype Hercules, and they were in for a treat. For none of them had ever heard the unmistakable thundering growl of the new giant on the ground. Hercules was definitive in her appearance, and equally so in her sound.

Engines with propellers on them emit particularly familiar noises in gaining life. The initial sound is a wheezing, groaning complaint of metal, of gears turning as the heavy propeller is dragged around and around. Finally the wheeze builds into a complaining low-pitched, growling scrape; abruptly this changes as compression takes place and the engine roars with familiar thunder, belching forth a great cloud of white smoke. It's a process so familiar at airports that even the peculiarities of the sound rarely evoke a turned glance.

Everybody listened when Stanley Beltz, the Lockheed test pilot, started to fire up the new Hercules. They listened because there wasn't anything else to do. In the bulging left wheel housing there was hidden a powerful gas turbine compressor. It was one of the items built into the Hercules which was designed to—and would—endear the machine to its users. The ground crew fired up the compressor, and sound that cracked like a whip smote the ears of the onlookers. The compressor builds up almost immediately to full power, and it emits one of the most fearsome shrieks ever heard around an airplane. The sound is an intermingled thunder and hoarse complaint that makes the strongest of men wince.

It also gives the Hercules the cherished freedom from the elaborate ground equipment that for years had plagued large airplanes. From the compressor air howled within ducts to start the engines. It also provided air conditioning for the entire airplane on the ground, or preheated the engine nacelles before firing up the Allisons, and fed life to an air turbine motor which in turn drove an electrical generator. Inside that housing, packaged with the left landing gear, was the answer to a pilot's or an airport operator's dream.

The Hercules wasn't designed to operate quietly. It was an item of military hardware intended to move about on its own, and to disdain the expensive, complicated ground equipment with thick umbilical cords usually required to bring airplanes to life.

But what puzzled everyone at the Lockheed terminal was the fact that while that hulking airplane gave vent to furious sound, nothing seemed to be happening. The four great propellers moved not at all. There was, to the observer, only that ear-bruising avalanche of sound.

In the cockpit, Stan Beltz, Roy Wimmer (copilot), and flight engineers Jack Real and R. E. Stanton methodically went about their ritual of preparing the Hercules for the initial test flight. The checklist carried more than 160 items, each of which required religious attention. The ritual attends each and every starting of the big airplane. On a test flight things are just a bit more sensitive. On the *first* test flight they are acutely so.

The first indication the observers received that the airplane would gain life came with the slow turning of a propeller. There was no grinding complaint of metal being dragged through resisting gears. The jet engine began to turn with almost imperceptible motion. Its sound began low and built up steadily, but with the ground compressor turbine giving vent to its voice the engine's own moan was hidden. One of the big propellers began to turn, with a smoothness that defied its motion. Faster and faster it spun until the blades disappeared within a great shining blur. Then another propeller began its rotary swing, and another, and finally all four jets whined with full power, and the flight engineer closed down the compressor.

Now the real sound of the Hercules could be heard. The people listening to the deep booming thrum of the airplane, unmistakable then and now, assumed they could hear the change of engine power as the sound varied. They were wrong, for the turboprop is a contradiction of the familiar in propeller-driven airplanes. The powerful jets whirled at maximum speed and delivered maximum power, while the pilot shifted the angle at which the propeller blades bit into the air. Few people realize that it is the propeller that creates most of the noise of an airplane, and with the Hercules the sound is particularly distinctive. There is no thrashing of pistons and internal flailing of parts, no process of explosive combustion or clanking of gears, all producing the angry roar of the internal combustion engine. The jets whirl at nearly 14,000 revolutions per minute, the propellers spin at just over 1,000 revolutions per minute, and it is all a functioning of power of marvelous smoothness.

It is the bite of the propeller blades into the air, hurling back unseen but vast quantities of air, that creates the sound. Without the clattering roar of the piston engines, the Hercules sounds like a vast bass fiddle played at some extraordinary volume, the pitch of sound changing with the pitch of the propellers.

Stan Beltz released the brakes. His left hand turned a small wheel near the wall of the flight deck. Each movement of that little wheel forced power to flow through lines and the power brought a response from the heavy dual nose gear of the airplane. Beltz turned the wheel gently, and the nose gear turned with the same movement. It was all very simple, and the power remained invisible within its lines. But the airplane responded to the whims of the pilot with all the gentleness of a baby carriage.

Near the end of the runway, in the runup area, the crew of

Hercules Number 1001, the first of two prototype aircraft, ran their machine through its final preflight check. All the dials and gauges read as they were supposed to read. Finally nothing remained on the checklist. Hercules 1001 was as ready as she would ever be for her baptism of flight.

Beltz rolled the airplane out to the end of the runway and turned into the wind. He locked the brakes as the Hercules pointed her great broad nose into the distance. Then his hand moved the power levers forward. Converters within the big spinners shifted the tremendous energy of the Allison engines into the propellers; the long blades changed their pitch quickly to take deeper bites into the air. The aircraft trembled violently from nose to tail, "dancing the jig" of full power and maximum brakes holding her back. Then Beltz "cut her loose."

The big airplane shot forward. Somewhere about ten seconds after the first movement, the onlooking crowd gasped. The airplane was no more than 850 feet from the point where Beltz chopped the brakes free. And at that point, thousands of feet sooner than anyone

Moment of life . . . The first Hercules eases the dual-wheel nose gear off the Burbank runway in its maiden flight. (*Air Force*)

expected, Beltz eased back on the control yoke. The first Hercules wasted no time in showing her disdain for the ground. It was as fine a rejection of the earth as any test pilot could ever hope for, and Beltz was *not* trying for a spectacular takeoff. The rate of acceleration was almost unbelievable to those on the flight deck, and the control yoke came back only after safe flying speed—and then some—had been reached. Still, it took only that 850 feet to separate airplane and runway.

The maiden flight of the Hercules was also her delivery run to the sprawling flight test center at Edwards Air Force Base, 60 miles from Burbank. Here in the clear air of the Mojave desert, where pilots and engineers alike bless the weather that permits nearly all-year flying, the Hercules would begin the long endurance regime to which she would be subjected by the flight test and engineering teams of Lockheed.

When Hercules 1001 eased to the concrete surface of the Edwards runway, a small but vitally interested group of spectators was at hand to provide the welcoming committee. These were the men who would attend the exhaustive technicalities of engineering test flights. Despite their slavishness to the slide rule and the gauge, each and every one of them had the same question to ask of Stan Beltz. It had nothing to do with measurements that could be made with a slide rule or a meter. A man flies an airplane; a man uses all his vast experience and his skill as a test pilot to make his judgment, on that basis, of any new machine.

A first flight is never intended to be an exciting or harrowing mission. The purpose is to get the airplane from the factory to the flight test area. But it is enough to tell a pilot what he wants to know, and what everyone else clamors to hear.

With the Hercules parked on the ramp and the engines shut down, a small mob pushed its way into the new machine. The lead group clambered up the ladder onto the flight deck, where one man shouted the question for all the rest.

"*Well?*"

Addressed to a pilot of a new machine, coming from an engineer, the one word represents a host of questions.

Beltz released his seat and shoulder straps, leaned back in the seat. "You know," he said quietly, resting his hand on the control yoke, "this . . . is a *real* flying machine."

Hercules had passed her first test—with the most critical, the most demanding, and the least compromising of all the people who would ever take her through the skies.

But the story of the Hercules doesn't begin with this first flight, or the design competition in which Lockheed beat out every manufacturer in the country, or even in the midst of the small wars raging around the world when military planners looked to the future. Behind every airplane of the complexity, the reliability, and the performance of the Hercules lies a deep and meaningful heritage.

It is from this lengthy and proven soil that great airplanes are nourished to life.

CHAPTER V

Genetics of a Giant   No one ever
makes a great airplane. It doesn't spring full-grown from the
drawing board, or from the most elaborate of production lines. It
isn't rushed from the factory flight line into successful service, in
this country or anywhere else in the world. And there aren't any
single heroes in this process of development, no one man or small
group of men who can be separated from a much larger group of
dedicated people, all of whom infused their talents and efforts into
the final product.

The creation of a great airplane is an evolutionary process, one
of building and changing, of discovering and adapting, of penetrating into areas unknown before this particular airplane, and
accepting the challenges inherent in any such penetration. The
creation of a great airplane today is an extraordinary blend of
science and engineering, of technology and skill, of men and of two
other indispensable factors—faith and courage. With all our computers and slide rules, the moment of truth in testing any great
machine in the air comes from a man. And then, from this first
spark of life, its further development flows outward from many
men.

This is not a departure from the hard facts of life. It happens
with every great airplane. There is a process of evolution, a step-by-
step genetic growth, of the machine. It traces back to the men who
conceive the idea, who base their conception on a kaleidoscopic
background of experience, of technical knowledge, and even on
intuition. The man who believes it is all slide rule and drill press
and lathe is either uninformed or a fool.

Some airplanes are destined for greatness; others are doomed
from the first stroke of the designer's pencil to obscurity or years
of oaths and curses from men who strive to take from the machine
what it does not have to give. Some airplanes seem to become
imbued with a life of their own that is recognized and cherished
by their crews. It is infused into every rivet and line of metal; it
is indefinable but it is real.

This is true of airplanes like the Douglas DC-3, equally famed as the Air Force's C-47, and more fondly known as the Gooney Bird. It is an airplane that has been flying now for nearly three decades, an airplane that carried mail and passengers and fought storms and blizzards even before many of its pilots were *born*. It is an airplane that today could never pass the requirements of the government for a new commercial airliner—and it will fly just about forever. The death knell of the Gooney has been sounded so many times that no one wants to try any more.

And why? It was never the fastest, the largest, the longest ranging, the most powerful, the highest flying airplane of its type. It was none of these chararcteristics that set it so far ahead of its competitors. But it had, and it has, a greatness all its own, and there are old and tough pilots who become misty-eyed when they recall to mind the things they have done, and that have been done for them, in the fabulous Gooney.

Or the B-17 that Boeing built, the queen of them all, the most beloved and respected of all the bombers ever built or that ever will be built. The Flying Fortress offered beauty and grace in every one of her lines, a song of power from her engines that no other bomber could ever reach, a note that played from thrashing pistons and flailing propellers that to every man who flew her was sweet and pure. What was it the B-17 had . . . and that every now and then, when she comes to life in a special flight, she has never lost?

No one can define it, but it is there in her every line; it surges through the wings and the body, an indefinable trembling through the machine, a "something" that men feel but can never measure. Two years ago, the writer sat behind the controls of an old B-17, weary from a war long past and the weight of the years in between. We patched her up from her sorry state after lying in the desert for 14 years. Mechanics did impossible things with her and breathed life anew into the body and the wings. With two of her sisters we flew her back across the Atlantic, by day and by night, through clear skies and through storms. And every man who ever flew her will understand what I mean when I say that all through that flight we could hear the voices of a thousand ghosts, flying with us. . . .

Some airplanes come to life with great traditions behind them, with decades of skill and promise that has time and again borne its special fruit. Some airplanes stand at the head of a lineage of machines that have carved history and endeared themselves to the men the sweat from whose hands finally stained the controls. Some airplanes become great because there is greatness in the planning and the creation behind the latest in the line.

In this respect the Hercules' ancestry rings down through some of the most cherished entries in aviation's hall of fame. This machine's

The world-famed *Winnie Mae*

lineage reaches back more than five decades, a span of years to the beginning of the industry, a period of time during which more than 500,000 people have labored on the different machines stamped with the distinctive lines of her designers and makers.

Those designers *are* the history of aviation . . . Lloyd Stearman, Allan Lockheed, John Northrop, Hall Hibbard, Gerald Vultee, C. L. Johnson, and many, many others. The airplanes wrote and made the history of aviation, and the men who flew them were once known to Americans everywhere, and many of them still are writing history. Men and planes like Wiley Post and Harold Gatty in the famed *Winnie Mae* . . . Jimmy Mattern and Bennett Griffin in their Vega . . . Amelia Earhart, racing her Vega in triumphant solo flight across the Atlantic, to coast-to-coast records, to world's distance records for women fliers . . . Laura Ingalls in her all-white Air Express in a solo flight from New York south across the Andes, up the east coast of South America, and 17,000 miles later back to her starting point. The Lockheed Altair flown by Sir Charles Kingsford-Smith and P. G. Taylor was the first airplane to cross the Pacific west-to-east. George Hubert Wilkins and Ben Eielson in 1928 hurdled the Arctic wastes from Alaska to Spitzbergen in just over 20 hours, and brought world acclaim to their feat. Their airplane—the renowned Vega. Later that same year they became the first men in history to fly over the Antarctic. To honor their two Vega airplanes, in which they discovered South Graham Land Island, they named the eastern tip Cape Northrop in honor of the Vega's codesigner, and the rugged range beyond, the Lockheed Mountains.

Some of the greatest names in speed and exploration flying won their historical niches in Lockheeds—Art Goebel, Bob Cantwell, Frank Hawks, Herb Fahy, C.B.D. Collyer, Roscoe Turner, Jimmy Doolittle, Ruth Nichols. . . . Charles and Anne Lindbergh did some of their most memorable flying in Lockheeds, in the Sirius (built to meet Lindbergh's requirements). In 1931 their Lockheed took them from Washington, D.C. across the Bering Sea to Tokyo. In 1933 they flew a 29,000-mile survey flight from New York to Labrador, Greenland, Iceland, Europe, the Azores, Africa, Brazil, and back to New York. Their airplane today hangs in the American Museum of Natural History, only one of many Lockheeds that hold a place in our permanent history.

The list grew steadily—airplane "greats" included the Vega, Altair, Sirius, Orion, and the Air Express, all single-engine record-breakers. In 1934 the company produced the first of its multi-engine transports, the Model 10 Electra, which may be considered the beginning of the ancestry that leads directly to the Hercules. For the twin-engine, all-metal Electra also was a radical departure from the norm of its day, and with performance that produced headaches among its competitors. It wrote its own chapter of history in the air—flying with airlines such as Northwest, Mid-Continent, Pan American, Braniff, and Delta, and serving with the airlines of Poland, Romania, Yugoslavia, Greece, Hungary, Czechoslovakia, France, Holland, Venezuela, Chile, and Argentina.

And there were dozens of private buyers—among them Amelia Earhart, who had already fattened the record books with her flights in different Lockheeds.

Lockheed produced the Model 12, the Electra Jr., as a smaller and faster business and airlines transport. Before production phased out because of World War II, several hundred of the rugged twin-engine planes were in service around the world—and some of them are *still flying* in charter airlines with passengers.

At the request of the Army Air Corps, Lockheed modified one of the Electras into the XC-35—which represented one of aviation's most significant advances, the world's first successful pressurized substratosphere airplane. To the Air Corps in 1937 went the coveted Collier Trophy for the most valuable contribution to aircraft development for that year—in Lockheed's high-flying Electra.

1937 was also the year that Lockheed began to move in a big way into the business of military airplanes. Within the five years from 1937 until the United States entered World War II, this company experienced one of the most phenomenal rates of growth ever recorded in American industrial history. Lockheed burst its bounds to expand from fifth-ranking airframe manufacturer to the

World-traveling Lockheed Sirius, choice of Charles and Anne Lindbergh

First of the Electras, milestone in aviation history

largest of all. Its work force multipled *40 times* to more than 50,000 people. And the one airplane that started the ball rolling was a twin-tailed transport with an appearance that belied its performance.

It was squat, chunky, and incredibly rugged—a forerunner in these characteristics of the Hercules. This was the Model 14, a midwing monoplane that outraced by 30 miles per hour any other transport flying in the country. The Model 14's wing pioneered the use of integral fuel tanks (retained to this day). It also featured revolutionary new flaps which gave the Model 14 superb short-field performance—a characteristic for which the Hercules is better known than any other.

Rugged and chunky—the durable Hudson bomber

Never in their wildest dreams did the Lockheed staff, who had fought up from the black despair of the depression of the early thirties, anticipate that they would build more than 3,000 of their Model 14. Airlines in the United States and in foreign lands, including Japan, placed substantial orders for the plane. But "the change that changed Lockheed" came from England, with British orders for the airplane modified as a powerfully armed bomber.

In its new role the Model 14 became one of the most famous airplanes ever built—the Hudson. It fought throughout the entire world.

The year 1937 represented another turning point for Lockheed—the beginning of a new airplane that became the most famous fighter in the world, and that performed in a manner that earned it a permanent place among the "greatest achievements" of aviation. This was the immortal P-38 Lightning, the first twin-engine, single-seat fighter to fly; the first fighter to exceed 400 miles per hour in level flight; the first fighter to run into the effects of compressibility (shock waves moving at the speed of sound that can tear a fighter to pieces); the first fighter over Berlin in World War II; the first fighter over Japan in 1945 . . . the record is seemingly endless. Space does not permit even a sketchy review of the Lightning's spectacular role during that war, but perhaps this item will suffice.

Tremendous confidence of pilots in Lockheed P-38J Lightning came from incidents such as that involving this fighter, flown in a strike against Iwo Jima by Lieutenant F. C. Erbels, Jr. With his left engine shattered by ground fire, the right wing ripped open and burning, and other heavy damage, the pilot flew back to Saipan in a four-hour and 40-minute flight. (*Air Force*)

Of America's ten leading fighter aces of World War II, four flew the Lockheed Lightning. And two of them were our greatest aces ever: Richard Ira Bong, who with 40 kills became our all-time Ace of Aces, and Major Thomas B. McGuire, Jr., who followed right behind Bong with 38 confirmed kills.

During the final years preceding that war, more and more outstanding aircraft with the Lockheed imprint appeared, especially in the transport line. Howard Hughes in 1938 set a pageful of records in his Model 14, including a round-the-world flight in three days, 17 hours, 14 minutes, and ten seconds. Of more specific interest to engineers and pilots: Hughes took off from Yakutsk, Russia, with a fuel load that came to 226 percent of the empty weight of the airplane, a feat considered "impossible" in engineering circles. Trace back the load-carrying ability of the Hercules today to this twin-engined ancestor. . . .

To top off the record-breaking Model 14, Lockheed in 1939 produced its famed successor—the Model 18 Lodestar. It served many countries as the fastest transport in the world, and once again the exigencies of war resulted in mass military production orders. More than 3,000 Venturas—military version of the civilian Lodestar

—rolled out of the factories for service with the United States and Allied countries.

Establish one more linkage through the years to the Hercules: the Lodestar was the first American plane adapted for the training of paratroopers.

In 1939 another design moved off the drawing boards and into the wind tunnels in the form of models. Only 15 were produced during the war in the military version known as the C-69.

The entire world came to know it by a different name after the war—the most famous of all the Lockheed airplanes ever built. The Constellation . . .

Statistics in passing provide but a scanty reflection of the incredible production effort of World War II. The United States from December 7, 1941, to the end of the war in August 1945 produced more than a quarter of a million airplanes. Of these, one out of every 11 rolled out of the Lockheed production lines in Burbank, California. Nearly 20,000 airplanes were built—including nearly 10,000 big P-38 fighters, 6,000 patrol bombers, and, as part of the Boeing-Douglas-Lockheed pool to produce the B-17, a total of 2,750 of the four-engined heavy bombers.

And After the War . . .

The genetics of an airplane aren't always visible to the eye, but they can be traced down by a careful study of evolutionary processes through the years. One of the men responsible for the success of the Model 10 Electra was C. L. Kelly Johnson. In 1939, when the P-38 raced through the air as the fastest military fighter in the world, Johnson and Hall Hibbard in secretive meetings did some long-range forecasting. They tried to convince the Lockheed management that the piston engine's ultimate development was already on the horizon, and that Lockheed would be wise to turn to a new power plant called the turbojet. None of the men at that time knew of the secret work in Germany and England on jets, but in 1940 engineer Nathan Price received the green light to design the first Lockheed turbojet engine. Two years later the revolutionary turbojet was patented, and the excited team of Johnson and Hibbard whipped out a design for a jet fighter.

Excitement notwithstanding, the Army Air Forces ordered Lockheed to concentrate on the P-38 and its other aerial weapons, and to drop its jet project. But as so often happens in wartime, a year later the Army was back, pounding on the Lockheed door. In 1943 the first American jet flew. The Bell P-59 Airacomet was a revolution in design and construction, but even with its jets it could barely outspeed our top piston-engined fighters.

Could Kelly Johnson wrap a new fighter airframe around the British Goblin jet engine? In his excitement Kelly Johnson swore he could have the airplane flying in just 180 days. He didn't make that figure—he beat it by 37 days. It was the kind of "impossible" feat that builds tremendous capability throughout an industrial organization. For this is the same Kelly Johnson who led a Lockheed team in producing the spectacular F-104 Starfighter and— much more in the public eye—to meet a critical government request, in a "phenomenally short time" designed the famous U-2.

Lockheed went into World War II with the fastest fighter in the world, and they ended up the same way. In January of 1944 the first experimental XP-80 Shooting Star jet was beating up the California desert with speed runs of more than 500 miles per hour. Test pilot Tony LeVier recalled the first flight: "Pretty soon we saw a tiny speck at the horizon. Before we had time for another thought, that speck was a full-sized airplane that roared over us with a swish that became a green blur and disappeared. We were jumping up and down. Kelly Johnson and some of the others were crying unashamedly. He knew we'd done it. . . ."

In January of 1946 Colonel Bill Councill eased a new Shooting Star off the runway at Long Beach, California, and headed east. Four hours and 13 minutes later he howled into a landing at New York's La Guardia Field, in the first of a series of sensational jet records that ushered in the new age of jet speed. In 1947 the Shooting Star brought particular satisfaction to the entire aviation industry. Colonel Albert Boyd streaked at an average speed of 623.8 miles per hour over the California desert—and brought the world's speed record back to the United States *for the first time in 23 years.*

Before the Shooting Star finally left the production lines, after five years of steady output, more than 1,700 of the small, sleek fighters went to the Air Force. They were our first jets in combat in Korea, performing the major role in the brutal low-altitude fighter-bomber strikes of that conflict. They flew 26,000 missions— 40 percent of *all* the Korean air fighting.

Once again, the lineage endured, and the Shooting Star proved to be one of the "great" airplanes. The rugged little jet mothered a great family of other airplanes that remained on the production lines for more than 13 years—an industrial miracle in the jet age.

Diversity continued to mark the Lockheed line, with increasing emphasis on the big airplane. Prior to World War II, Lockheed had received its first U.S. Navy orders for the P2V Neptune. Emphasis on proven designs delayed the Neptune's first flight until shortly after Germany surrendered, when the need for long-range hunter-killer patrol bombers had vanished. But there's a saying that if a design is *really* good . . .

Lockheed produced more than a thousand of the Neptunes through a series of successive improvements—for a total of more than three-quarters of a billion dollars. In 1946 the third Neptune to come off the production line carved its special place in history. With four men and a kangaroo mascot aboard, the airplane lifted off a runway at Perth, Australia, at a gross weight of 43 tons, an incredible figure for a twin-engine aircraft. It came back to earth after a record-shattering nonstop flight of 11,236 miles.

The "biggest name" in Lockheed history unquestionably belongs to the Constellation, famed throughout the word for its graceful lines and the unmistakable sign of its "triple tail," with three huge rudders. Even in 1944 the airplane demanded attention. Howard Hughes raced one across the country in less than seven hours for a coast-to-coast record flight. Three days after the end of the war Lockheed had firm orders for more than 100 commercial Constellations from eight major airlines, the beginning of an extraordinary demand that would result in hundreds of the large airplanes rolling off the production lines.

In all versions, the Constellation represented more than one and a half *billion* dollars in orders, the kind of testimonial to an airplane that speaks the loudest in the competitive commercial market. Before its production lines ended, and the Constellation gave way to the swift and powerful new Electra, it had far outgrown the original models. The latest commercial Constellations spanned 150 feet across the wings and flew nonstop commercial routes of 6,000 miles. Military versions with big turboprop engines cruised at more than 400 miles per hour—an unbelievable figure for a four-engined propeller transport designed *before* World War II. And hundreds of the Constellations are still, and will be for some time to come, in service around the world.

There were many other notable airplanes in the ancestry of the Hercules, but the largest of them all was the great Constitution, an enormous transport that began its development in 1942. Built to Navy specifications, the Constitution weighed 184,000 pounds and in its huge double-deck fuselage carried a payload of nearly 35 tons—or 180 passengers. The Constitution, which first flew in 1946, never escaped the penalty of inadequate power. It proved to be too big for its day when long-expected engines failed to materialize. Four engines of 3,000 horsepower each gave the Constitution a long-range cruising speed of about 269 miles per hour, not enough to make anybody happy, least of all the Lockheed engineers.

One of the all-time "greats" of aviation is Lockheed's internationally famed Constellation (*above*), which has carried the flags of dozens of nations and flown for many military air services around the world. Lockheed Neptune (*below*) is boosted from Antarctic icecap at the South Pole by rocket bottles. U.S. Navy purchased more than 1,000 Neptunes from Lockheed. (*Upper photo: Lockheed; lower photo: U.S. Navy*)

With present-day turboprops, the Constitution would have been a smashing success. Without them, it couldn't keep pace with the smaller but much faster commercial airliners. And so it went out of service after performing Korean airlift operations and cargo runs until 1955.

The Constitution is linked closely, in one respect, to the present-day Hercules. The project engineer on the Constitution was named W. A. Pulver. When the first production Hercules were delivered from Lockheed's sprawling factory at Marietta, Georgia, in 1956, the assistant chief engineer for the entire division was the same W. A. Pulver. For several years now Pulver has been President of Lockheed-Georgia, establishing the closest relationship between the past and the present in big transports.

Other aircraft by the thousands have flowed from the Lockheed production lines . . . 6,000 T-33 jet trainers among them. *Nine out of every ten* jet pilots flying in the United States today received their training in this Lockheed airplane, as well as many thousands of foreign pilots. Thousands of planes of other models developed from the T-33 (itself descended from the original F-80), such as the F-94 Starfire and the T2V SeaStar, added to the Lockheed roster.

The U-2 has written its own story and needs no further attention here. . . .

For the first three years of its flying life the spectacular F-104 Starfighter remained cloaked beneath the strictest veil of secrecy. And for three years a frustrated company kept its silence as the F-104 broke every international speed and altitude record—almost every time it flew. Today in service around the world, limited in its top speed only by the heat of friction it generates in its passage through the air, the Starfighter is also in production from Japan to Germany, as the leading fighter to counter the best produced by the U.S.S.R.

There were projects that saw the light of day only briefly, and then disappeared forever from view; projects that received the ax because engine developments failed to keep pace with engineering products. The Constitution, although it saw service for nearly a decade, suffered such a blow. So did the Saturn twin-engined airliner, and the vertical-rising XFV fighter plane.

Lockheed is much more today than the familiar aircraft corporation which wrote its brilliant history for many decades. From its great industrial plants roll new products of the current age, such as the long-range Navy sub-killer, the P3A, successor to the Neptune and latest to bear the proud name of Orion. There is the JetStar, a small bullet-shaped four-jet transport that is the ultimate in modern

Sleek F-94C Starfire interceptor was outgrowth from T-33 trainer, which itself evolved from famed Lockheed P-80 Shooting Star. Lockheed built 1,700 Shooting Stars (first U.S. production jet fighter), more than 6,000 T-33 trainers, many hundreds of Starfires. (*Lockheed*)

transportation—and which transport pilots insist upon flying as though it were a fighter.

Robots have catapulted to importance among Lockheed products. Some of them are relatively unknown to the public, like the ramjet-powered X-7, and the now obsolete X-17 hypersonic research rocket. But others are not at all strange to Americans.

Like the Polaris missile . . . Or the workhorse of the age of space, the Agena upper-stage rocket that Lockheed designed for Thor and Atlas boosters. The Thor-Agena combination has chalked up a fantastic space reliability and capability record; you might recognize it more quickly as the Discoverer series. . . .

The same Agena has sent Ranger spaceships to the moon, and beyond, into perpetual orbit around the sun.

Who has not heard of Mariner II? Who does not know the mission of this fantastic robot that sailed the seas of space to fall past the planet Venus, and send back to Earth the results of the first robot exploration of another world?

But who knows that close behind Mariner II, also falling past the sister world of Earth, was the Lockheed-built Agena rocket that whipped the scientific wonder into its extraordinarily precise path through the solar system?

A Home for Hercules

Distant and unrelated events sometimes seem predestined to reach a common meeting ground. In 1951, Lockheed engineers were conducting their first preliminary design proposals for the revolutionary new assault transport that was to become the Hercules.

At this same time, other Lockheed personnel were pulling the wraps off a building at Marietta, Georgia, that sprawled over more than 76 acres. This was the government plant that since the end of World War II (when a massive production line turned out the last of 667 B-29 bombers) had been shut down. The government wanted the factory reactivated under Lockheed management, with an initial assignment to whip back into shape a major force of B-29s stored in mothballs.

Lockheed flight crews went to Pyote, Texas, and spent many harrowing months refurbishing the heavy bombers for flight—while fighting off thousands of rattlesnakes that infested the field and the stored airplanes. The crews flew them back to Marietta, where skilled technicians worked day and night to whip them into shape for bombing missions in Korea.

But this proved to be only a warmup. Would Lockheed repeat a World War II performance, and institute production at Marietta on the Boeing B-47 Stratojet? The six-engine jet bomber represented the peak of American strategic airpower, and immediate mass production was imperative.

In January of 1951 the Lockheed offices in California sent a task force of 150 employees to Marietta to pave the way for the Lockheed army that would follow, and that would be recruited from the local area. Within one year 10,000 people were at work within the factory that boasted, beneath a single roof, more than four and a half million square feet of working space.

Today that work force has increased to 17,000 people. The production line for the Boeing jet bomber has long been closed down. The six-engine raiders, no longer the swift killers of yesteryear, are passing into obsolescence.

But the production lines still hum, for Marietta, Georgia, since late 1954, has been "home" for the Hercules. It is from this gigantic plant that some 600 of the great assault transports have rolled off the production lines, and that many more are scheduled to be created by the Lockheed industrial force.

The first two experimental Hercules, YC-130 Nos. 1001 and 1002, grew their wings in Burbank. For the first three weeks of test flying at Edwards Air Force Base, California, the original test crew remained with Stan Beltz. Later testing of the Hercules prototypes was conducted at Palmdale, 25 miles from Edwards.

Leo Sullivan—who today is the chief engineering test pilot for the Lockheed-Georgia Company, and who has literally lived with the Hercules throughout its growth from an experimental first airplane—eventually flew No. 1001 back to Marietta.

When they returned to Marietta, it was almost as if some major events in Lockheed history had run full circle. W. A. Pulver, who had watched the Constitution languish for the powerful engines it never received, was to hold a critical place in the new program to develop further an airplane smaller than the Constitution, but capable of performance that Pulver never dreamed of in his former days.

There were also men who had worked on the Neptune, and the long-lived Constellation program. There were engineers who many years before had labored to create the Hudson and the Lodestar. Active in the engineering development of the C-130 at this time was the late R. W. Middlewood. There were even a few men who remembered the original Model 10 Electra coming to life. And some of this elite group went back even farther in their experience, to the time when Lockheed built airplanes of wood: great airplanes like the Vega and Altair and Sirius and the others.

Now they were ready to imbue the latest in the line with what they hoped would be that "something special" that enables an airplane to live "forever."

There's a Marine pilot who has (since those early days in Marietta) flown the Hercules many hundreds of hours through some of the most dangerous situations that any man or airplane could be subjected to—and has emerged virtually without a scratch. From violent thunderstorms to grass-choked jungle strips in Asia, from the savage cold of Antarctica to refueling rendezvous over the Pacific with jet fighters, he has made the rounds as the pilot of a Marine Hercules.

His experience led him to comment that the Hercules had already become "the Gooney Bird of the jet age."

And that's about the nicest compliment that *any* airplane could ever receive.

CHAPTER VI

Slide-Rule Philosophy   EVERY ENGINEERING TEAM
has a philosophy of design around which they attempt to wrap a
new airplane. If their endeavors meet with great success, then they
find it uncomfortably difficult to categorize their new product.
Adjectives are limited, and often fail to convey the thoughts of the
engineers, the design philosophy of their effort, or even the characteristics of the final product. The team finds quickly that their slide
rules avail them not at all in this problem, and so they rub skulls
in the hope of collectively producing a meaningful and brief description of *versatility*. This quality defies description because it is
multi-faceted, and thereby elusive. In the case of a powerful, new,
unique, *and* versatile airplane, the task is almost impossible.

This was the problem that Lockheed labored to solve. As the
design of the Hercules progressed, it became possible to define the
parameters of performance from the revolutionary airframe and
the new Allison turboprop engines. Through the organization that
produced the Hercules there grew slowly a sense of excitement.
It is felt in every new project when the results of the vast coordinated effort, from that of the chief designer to that of the unknown
electrician who completes wiring jobs on the production line,
promise revolutionary performance.

No one man could truly foresee the complexity of roles and
missions that lay ahead of the Hercules. The airplane of great
longevity is created with a flexibility in its design that permits
it to adapt to needs and situations, and this is particularly true of
the Hercules. In the beginning, however, confidence in the future
of the new airplane rested only on past experience, the physical
hardware of the new machine, and extrapolation of the machine
into its future roles. Before they could become reality, the aircraft
would have to run the gauntlet of brutal punishment, deliberately
inflicted and almost malicious in its severity.

This is an aspect of aircraft creation not too well known beyond
the industry itself. Punishment is the cultivation of reliability and
success. Deliberate punishment, calculated to exceed if at all
possible the forces to which the airplane would be subjected in

every extreme of its operational life, was the lash under which the Hercules would come to full stature. The building of prototype airplanes and the huzzahs that attend the rollout from the factory of the initial production models do *not* an operational airplane make. . . .

It is impossible to create a huge new airplane, a departure from conventional design and a harbinger of unique and successful performance in the future, without incurring the penalty of certain undesirable characteristics. Every engineer would give his right arm up to his shoulder if by some sorcery he could ferret out these traits and characteristics before the airplane went into production and shuttled rapidly out to the field for full operational service. Unfortunately, there simply does not exist any crystal ball through which one can study every future contingency. Into every machine which comprises several hundred thousand interrelated parts, and which must be subjected to the enormous forces of high-speed flight, there are built anomalies popularly referred to as *bugs.*

The faster and more successfully these invisible creatures are removed from the aircraft, the sooner one may hasten to a product accepted without reservation by the people who will entrust their lives to that product. Pilots, crewmen, and even passengers can become downright violent in their denunciations of a machine that conceals unpleasant flight characteristics, or that embodies certain structural deficiencies that manifest themselves in the form of lethal failure. Nothing can or will condemn any new machine so swiftly as the pilot's grapevine—the "kiss of death" of those who, since their lives are on the line, must sit in final judgment.

Sometimes it is not a matter of error, but the result of probing into flight regimes where there is only a vacuum, rather than experience or precedence, to guide the engineers. No better example may be provided than in the history of Britain's De Havilland Comet, one of the most beautiful machines ever to grace the skies. The poetry of line in the Comet remains unmatched by any jet machine that has ever flown; it is a sight to warm the hearts of pilots everywhere. And in its early months of passenger-carrying service the Comet vindicated its promise of heralding the new era of jet-age flight.

And then, with shocking suddenness, a Comet vanished from its scheduled, carefully monitored path of flight. Without warning, without a single sign to point to danger, the beautiful craft became a mass of shredded metal and tumbling bodies that spilled tragically down from the skies. Then it happened a second time, again without warning. Fear and mystery stalked the Comet, and engineers went sleepless and searched their souls for a clue to the cause of failure.

The answer did not lie in the aerodynamic complications of flight. The Comet sailed the upper atmosphere, and to do so with safety and comfort for its passengers, the long and slender fuselage became a package of the lower air. The round metal fuselage was sealed and then pressurized so that all within could breathe the denser atmosphere and relax in circulating heated air. That the pressurization system would impose severe loads and strain on the body of the Comet was wisely anticipated, and multiple protection against these forces was integrated in the Comet structure.

But no one could foretell that under sustained strain the metal of the airplane, much like the human body, would become fatigued, and that when this came to pass, and the forces of high-altitude pressurization persisted, fatigue would in turn lead to failure. The end result was that suddenly, without warning, a minor failure led to a great ripping tear in the body of the Comet and . . . the disasters that shook the entire aviation world.

From the tragic experience with the Comet there emerged a new standard of precaution throughout the aviation industry of the world. Into every new airplane built that would fly under the strain of pressurization went greater structural strength. And then, in response to the harsh dictum of Murphy's First Law of Physics—"What can go wrong *will* go wrong"—they added the fail-safe feature. If the structure or the skin *did* yield, and failed, the resulting tear would travel only a very short distance. The airplane would be so constructed that it would have rip-stop characteristics. A pressure failure would mean a minor tear in the skin, loss of the pressurization, and that was all.

The lessons of every airplane ever built were infused into the design philosophy of the Hercules. Which is why, during its engineering test development, the airplane also "went to sea." One aspect of the Hercules' evolution closely paralleled the development of a submarine.

The hydrostatic test program of the Hercules was intended to inflict brutal punishment on the airplane, which in the normal course of its operational life would endure great forces every time it flew. The entire cavernous fuselage of the Hercules is pressurized. Indeed, this is one of the brightest aspects of the plane's versatility. The cargo compartment—not including the spacious flight deck—is huge. Its clear width is ten feet, height nine feet, and length 41 feet. In addition, the ten-foot movable ramp also is utilized for cargo.

Thus there is a total area of 4,300 cubic feet of cargo-passenger space aboard the airplane, excluding the areas for flight crew. The very roominess of the fuselage complicates the problems of imbuing it with fail-safe strength, for there are no supporting beams or cross-beams to bear the load. And this entire area *must* be pressurized—for the Hercules in its normal everyday working role was designed to carry large numbers of people. When the airplane was used as a troop transport, 92 fully equipped fighting men would walk into it, plus the flight crew. Or the Hercules would swallow 64 paratroopers, completely equipped with their weapons, chutes, and assorted paraphernalia. An even more important reason why the entire plane must be pressurized for its flights six and seven miles above the earth would be its function as a medical-evacuation or hospital airplane. Seventy-four men, ill or wounded and flat on their backs, could be loaded comfortably into the Hercules with ample room between each and attendants aboard to meet their needs. (These were "normal" personnel loads; in practice the Hercules has carried many more people than this.)

Moreover the Hercules, which would fly in the cruelly thin air far above the earth, demanded air conditioning as well as pressurization. It must be comfortably heated when the outside temperature plunged to 100 degrees and more below zero; it required a massive flow of cooling air when the needle soared to 120 and above. Both temperature extremes, perhaps even greater ones, could be expected under normal operational conditions for the airplane.

There were other factors to consider. . . . Hercules is the first airplane of its kind ever designed with *built-in*, integral systems to accommodate iron lungs and other emergency lifesaving equipment. The airplane's interior almost teems with special facilities invisible to the eye, and these were to pay dividends beyond calculation in the years to come, when the Hercules would carry newborn infants, the very aged, the critically ill, the displaced and the fleeing . . . the full spectrum of humanity. No one could forecast, either, that Hercules planes would become winged Noah's Arks for geese, cattle, monkeys, dogs, cats, goats, pigs, and a seemingly endless variety of animals.

The engineers enclosed the capacious volume of the Hercules within a shell of tremendous strength. At 35,000 feet above the earth the airplane would cocoon its occupants with a pressure altitude equivalent to that of 8,000 feet. This could, in an emergency, be bettered. Lockheed designed the fuselage with such inherent strength that, despite its rim of walls and lack of cross-members, the airplane while flying at a height of several miles could duplicate sea-level pressure conditions.

As they labored to create an airplane that would make all this possible, the engineers could not for an instant forget that the Hercules would never enjoy a "normal" flying career. Its operational life would consist of batterings not only from the elements, but also from the unique missions which the versatility of the airplane would allow. That meant the wicked punishment of operating from surfaces so crude and rough they couldn't even be called airfields. It meant crash-stop landing impacts, rolling over crazy-quilt surfaces, all with loads of 40,000 pounds or considerably more. It meant all this punishment in addition to the loads imposed by flight at speeds of from 300 to 385 miles per hour in everyday operations, with all the complicating factors of temperature extremes extending over a range of more than 200 degrees.

Flight testing would validate the soundness—or reveal the lack of soundness—of the engineering that produced the Hercules. But flight testing would not be enough. Metal fatigue, of the sort that ripped those two Comet jetliners to shreds in flight, did not come suddenly, nor was there any adequate warning of its onset. It was produced by a factor of time as well as anything else, and the Lockheed engineers therefore found themselves faced with the need to compress years into days or weeks.

Hydrostatic fatigue tests were the answer, in which a complete Hercules, submerged within a huge tank, could be made to endure the equivalent of thousands of flights over a period of many years. So an aircraft company went into the business of building swimming pools for airplanes . . . one pool in which to torture large sections of the Hercules, and an even larger pool in which to immerse the entire airplane.

The tragedy of the Comets taught engineers that stress from internal pressurization is cyclic in nature. They had always believed that internal pressure imposed additional stress little different from that created by other stress forces. Cyclic stress, however, repeatedly creates a series of wavy motions in the airframe structure. Its repetition and character lead to fatigue damage which, in turn, weakens the airplane's ability to withstand the loads imposed by turbulence in flight or by the battering encountered in rough-field operations.

The Hercules that enters the liquid atmosphere of the torture tank is surrounded with mean-looking jigs, hydraulic jacks, straps, "whiffletree linkages," and other paraphernalia with which the punishment is inflicted. This equipment subjects the entire airframe to forces equivalent to those of flight, including climbs and descents, turbulence, takeoff and landing loads, vibration and buffeting, and the cyclic forces of pressurizing and depressurizing. Each "flight" lasts the equivalent of three to five hours in the air, with water pressure imposing brutal and changing loads on the structure, skin, braces, fittings, doors, and other critical areas.

Not content with the readings of gauges and the conclusions

of electronic computers, D. S. Morcock, the senior research engineer of the Engineering Test Laboratory Division, asked several skin divers to lay aside their spear guns and carry out some scientific studies of Lockheed's "submersible airplane." The divers made periodic and meticulous underwater examinations of the entire plane, adding their visual observations to the findings of the thousands of instruments fitted to the Hercules structure.

At long last the punishment ran its course. The Hercules had suffered the equal of many years of intensive and rugged operations, of high-altitude flight, violent maneuvers, crash-stop landings . . . the spectrum of flight most calculated to bend and twist and weaken an airframe.

The question was then asked: had these hydrostatic pressure fatigue tests not been made now, and the airplane sent into operations—would there have been pressurization failure at some point?

The answer was gratifying. Under no conditions, including physical damage to the airplane, would any pressure forces or effects have compromised the structural integrity of the Hercules airframe, or in any way affected the intrinsic safety which had been designed into the craft. The end result of the long tests was a significant reward for each engineer. One man called it "the pleasure of a deep and untroubled sleep. . . ."

That Man Murphy

No one book could ever do more than to pass lightly over the requirements, safety checks, inspections, crosscheck reviews, and other procedures involved in the creation of a new machine such as the Hercules. It would be impossible because of the sheer weight and volume of these interrelated activities. The lists of items to be checked with microscopic care are astonishing to behold. At the writer's request, an attempt was made to assemble the reports on them into a single pile. Alas, it proved impossible to achieve the effect desired, because the thick volumes seemed to have no end as they arrived from dozens of departments and offices. The first pile soon rocked precariously, and we were forced to begin another, and then another. Common sense dictated a halt to the proceedings, for in front of us was a total of many tens of thousands of pages, the piles still growing, and representing no-nonsense, no-frills guides for production, development, test, and other elements of creating the winged craft.

They have a saying in that vast and sprawling structure where the Hercules production lines are laid out that the worst inspector, the most dogged, persistent, and uncompromising man to work with, is that man named Murphy. Contemporary legend has it that

Murphy is around simply to gum up the works, to create trouble, to set the stage for failures and disasters, and that the cross the engineer must bear is the need to wage eternal struggle to keep Murphy from success in his trouble-making. Murphy, of course, laid down that inescapable law that "What can go wrong *will* go wrong. . . ."

One buiding . . . and within it millions of square feet of production, assembly, supply, checkout, test, and other activities, all conducted at one time, all interrelated and woven into a fabric of coordinated activity. It is an astonishing sight to behold and an even more amazing sound to hear. For such a structure, where Hercules are born, one after the other, is a source-bed of sound the like of which is produced by no other facility of its kind in the world.

There is a physical undercurrent of sound, the blended noises of machine tools, the rumble of heavy vehicles, the staccato bark of rivet guns, the hiss of welders' torches . . . the voices of men and women, the clank of steel against steel, the jackhammer roar of construction gangs within the building, alongside the production lines, gouging deep trenches for power lines and other equipment. The sound comes from everywhere . . . it drifts through the structure from huge doors rolling on steel rails at the edge of the building. It comes in deep, crying groans from the overhead cranes that lift with eggshell daintiness immense subsections of airplanes, groans that shudder in bass tremors, that die out slowly, like ripples of sound washing themselves out of existence, mixing finally into an inaudible sonic froth.

Small-wheeled trains rumble through the corridors. Voices call to one another. There are shouts to guide men handling heavy machinery, cries of laughter as a group of men share a joke, the heavy crackling tones of loud-speakers providing information to other men somewhere in the vast recesses of the structure . . . horns and bells, raucous buzzing, racing motors, the whine of massive machinery.

Every day, when the sky is light and when it is dark, every day the giant lives and hums and vibrates with the life productive of the great winged machines.

And throughout the fiber of the whole vast effort, unseen by the casual visitor, there runs always the effort to imbue the work with the lifeblood of truly great engineering—with quality and reliability unquestioned when the machine trundles slowly from beneath the roof toward the sky it is destined to master.

"A chain is as strong as its weakest link" is a cliché worn by time but as true today as it ever was. In terms of large aircraft the violation of this concept is, inevitably, failure and perhaps disaster. As related to aircraft, such as the Hercules, the links of the chain embrace every one of the tens of thousands of separate parts and fittings that are integrated in the single, final product. Those links include the basic materials from which the structure is formed—aluminum, magnesium, steel, titanium, exotic mixtures of alloys, and plastics of a variety largely unknown to the general public.

Not so obvious as these basic building blocks are the protective finishes applied to the aircraft by such processes as alodizing, anodizing, dichromatizing, electroplating with cadmium, chromium, zinc, and many other metals, and then painting with primer coats, lacquers, enamels, and other finishes. Buried within the structure and integrated into its shell are the hundreds of functional units—the control motors, generators, meters, gauges, and related equipment. Then there are the major systems of great complexity: hydraulic, electrical, landing gear, and still others.

C-130E Hercules production line of Lockheed-Georgia industrial complex at Marietta, Georgia. (*Lockheed-Georgia*)

They form not so much a chain as an exquisitely intricate fabric massing many tons, and all functioning with the precision of a fine watch and enjoying the durability of a bulldozer.

That is, *if* the quality of each of the tens of thousands of parts can be assured.

In the science of employing raw rocket power to hurl intricate robots of science beyond the earth and outward to other worlds, nothing has ever been so maddening to engineers as their search for reliability in small, seemingly insignificant parts. The law of reliability with these howling giants is that before success may be achieved in reaching out to the moon, one must first assure the success of an intricate mountain of valves, nuts, gaskets, wires, hoses, connections, et al.

Much the same problem exists with a large aircraft such as the Hercules. But in one sense the problem is compounded by the anticipated life of many years, and by the continued pounding and battering the aircraft will undergo. The towering rocket lives a dazzling but painfully brief existence. Its time span from the first spark of fiery life to ultimate destruction is measured only in brief minutes; perfection is required for the barest tick of the clock by which the Hercules must be measured in reliability of performance.

Thus the assembling of the thousands of parts involves an activity in the aircraft industry which might be called "the great detective game." The rules are black suspicion and an unyielding conviction that everything can and will go wrong. The tools employed by the "detectives" include the latest devices produced by a science equally convinced that dedicated suspicion is the only acceptable way of life.

The materials that arrive at the great plant in Marietta for integration with the Hercules aircraft taking shape on the production lines are regarded as suspect until their qualities can be unquestionably proven. Not even their conformity to size and form is considered at first. A select engineering group maliciously attacks every last ounce of the material, beginning by checking the specific properties of the metal or other object under scrutiny. Once the specific properties are ascertained, the engineers employ greater stealth in probing the *methods* by which those properties are obtained.

The goal is to ferret out weaknesses and inferior values. This information is packaged neatly and shipped to the organization within Lockheed which then seeks to determine the cause of failure, and most important, to determine the corrective action necessary to prevent repetition. The ultimate objective, of course, is to stop unacceptable materials from ever reaching the production line.

For example, the metal alloys employed in aircraft production are blended with extraordinary care. Their constituents must be present in exacting proportions so that the alloys that result have the strength and toughness demanded by the engineers. *Their* criteria is knowledge of the various forces, stresses, and loads that will be imposed upon the airplane during its operational life.

When a single aircraft part, meticulously produced from one of hundreds of alloys, fails either in tests or in service, the metallurgist must suffer a torrent of abuse from those who are responsible for the production of the airplane, and especially those who will entrust their lives to the Hercules and will expect others to do the same. But as any metallurgist in the Lockheed laboratories will tell you—as they indeed have told me—invective *before* an accident is far preferable to reading accident reports.

The metallurgist must answer the question that he asks of himself: "*Why* did the part fail?" And almost in the same breath comes the query: "Was the material up to specifications?"

The answers can be determined only by scientific sleuthing. First the metallurgist cuts a small piece of metal from the affected area. This is mounted carefully in plastic to form a mold about the diameter of a quarter and about one inch high. The final steps in preparation are to grind the top of the test specimen to a smooth surface and then to polish the specimen with a paste containing diamond dust. The result is a surface with a gleaming mirrorlike finish.

To the metallurgist that surface means exactly what a fingerprint does to a detective. The metallurgist produces his metal "fingerprint" by etching the gleaming metal surface in a special chemical bath. This mixture dissolves (or attacks) different ingredients in the metal at different rates. When the chemical bath simmers down, the metallurgist sees before him a shallow pattern— literally a fingerprint of hills and valleys.

Now it is time to call on the optical and electronic sciences. Elaborate microscopes with built-in cameras view, and record in the smallest of detail, the pattern of the metal. To pursue his suspicions the metallurgist may magnify the pattern to 100,000 times its normal size. Magnification of this order can expand a pinpoint to the size of a barn door.

The results of this investigation, and many other tests, are sufficient for the tiny piece of metal to yield its secrets. Not only can the metallurgist identify the material beyond any question, but he will also chart the method and procedures that were employed in its manufacture.

Within his laboratory the metallurgist-detective uses a series of special furnaces so as to simulate exactly the temperatures of production heat treatments. His operation is a Lilliputian version of the actual industrial process, but it reproduces faithfully the working conditions. He uses standard and microhardness testers to check the surface and cross-sectional conditions of metals of all kinds. One of the most versatile of his laboratory tools is the modified X-ray machine. The metallurgist is armed with a variety of these instruments. His standard X-ray machines will detect subsurface voids, cracks, shrinkage, porosity, inclusions, and other defects in metal parts and components. X-ray diffraction equipment, on the other hand, determines the rays reflected from the crystal faces of the metal. Different types of metal crystals have their reflecting faces tilted at different angles, and these angles, patterns, or frequencies have been exhaustively catalogued for cross reference so as to identify numerous metallic chemical elements, compounds, and metallic phases. The metallurgist uses this particular information to determine with great accuracy the effects of stress and the extent of fatigue damage in different metals. By means of an intricate series of studies, the metallurgists in the great Marietta factory quickly track down any weak points in small parts, subassemblies, and major assemblies. A failure, or a visible weakening of any part of the aircraft, can be identified, and its *cause* ascertained, with minimum loss of time.

No manufacturer produces all the components of his product within his own facilities. Major contracts involve a vast subcontracting throughout every spectrum of the industrial community, from the largest of firms down to the one-man metal workshop in a small town. It is not possible to achieve perfection in the quality of all the parts and assemblies that arrive at Lockheed; nevertheless, it is Lockheed's responsibility to assure the soundness of the final assembled product. The metallurgist and his equipment serve as one element of what production managers fondly call "quality control." It is by no means entirely sufficient to the task at hand, however, and the "eternally suspicious" industrial staff turn continually to other devices and instruments.

The Matériel Inspection division of the Hercules production complex, for example, in order to hunt down the slightest deviation from factory standards, uses an ultrasonic test tank that "drowns metal in sound." The sonic shower provides a searching look into the molecular composition of forgings and extrusions. These are immersed in the tank and then subjected to the bombardment of ultrasonic waves which radiate from an electrically pulsed crystal. Echoes from the sound waves rebound from the front or back surfaces of the object or from any *internal* defect in the forging.

All this is brought to the attention of the "Immerscope," a versatile device which performs electronic sorcery by first registering the sound waves as they echo from the target, and then analyzing the composition of the metal being tested. At the same time it points the accusing finger (electronically speaking) at any hidden defects. The echoes (or *pips*) are amplified and reflected as a trace pattern on a cathode-ray tube. Just as a radar operator can read the size, speed, altitude, and course of aircraft from the glowing pips on his scope, so the suspicious inspector can obtain a detailed picture of the internal composition of the suspect metal.

Precaution is the byword of production, and extra precaution pervades these electronic detectives. The Immerscope is equipped with a flaw alarm system. When any deviation from preset values appears before its electronic nostrils, it sniffs out the flaws and then "acts in a hysterical fashion" by flashing lights and sounding a raucous buzzer. While the pips representing the back and front surfaces of the metal object will be of equal size on the tube, anything unusual such as a defective seam weld stands out like a broken tooth on a crosscut saw, and causes the Immerscope to clamor for attention.

Since sound travels through metal at what is virtually a constant speed, the spacing of the pips represents indications of the thickness of the metal. The operator can vary the relative proportions of spacing to elapsed time; he can let one inch of sweep on the cathode tube represent two inches or several feet of aluminum. The operator who is skilled in the principles of reflection and refraction of light rays can quickly interpret the information relayed by these echoes, and translate the data into an accurate flow analysis of the part being inspected. As he reads the information from the tube, a second inspector marks the deficient areas on the part and is able to trace out a pattern of discontinuities as revealed by the Immerscope.

There are, of course, many other "detective agencies" within the huge industrial team that labors to produce a line of Hercules transports free of defects that, except for this constant suspicion, would inevitably compromise the quality of the large, intricate machine.

All this represents but one aspect, no matter how intricate in itself, of the "slide-rule philosophy" that dictated the methods and procedures by which the Hercules would grow from blueprints to airborne reality. The ceaseless vigilance which we have just seen assures the highest possible levels of reliability from the standpoint of materials, but it is another matter entirely to insure that those materials are employed in a manner to enhance the versatility of an airplane that will be subjected to the worst of operational conditions.

Here, too, there is a philosophy of design, but one which must encompass a spectrum entirely removed from the factory. There, reliability and quality remain within the control of the manufacturer. Once the airplane departs its production line and is passed on to the user—the military—it enters an environment of drastic demands and, often, severe abuse to meet operational requirements. How, then, to have the factory product live up to the hopes of the engineers when it is no longer under their control? The answer lies, largely, in the concept of "repetition."

To increase the reliability of all the various systems—and thus the aircraft as a single entity—the engineers designed the Hercules on the basis of redundancy. Duplicate systems integrated into the aircraft are the cause for huzzahs from crews and airfield personnel the world over when they have a machine that can sustain a major failure of a system, and continue right on with its mission because a backup system automatically kicks into operation.

The hydraulic system of the Hercules, for example, derives extraordinary reliability from multiple pressure sources. Within the aircraft there are four hydraulic pumps, each driven by the powerful main engines. These pumps supply pressure for the utility and booster systems. An electric motor-driven pump supplies pressure for the auxiliary system. If either source fails, the other system is already in operation to prevent interruption of the functioning of the aircraft as an entity.

This is one aspect of creating reliability, but it was not, in the opinion of the Air Force or the Lockheed engineers, sufficient unto itself. Additional precautions were necessary if the Hercules was to live up to requirements as a machine that could operate in remote areas of the world without elaborate ground equipment. And then, the wear of parts and the inevitable failures of equipment were certain to inflict their problems upon the Hercules, as upon any mechanical device ever built. With devoted attention to the principles established by the omnipresent Murphy, the engineers bent to the work of easing the tasks of parts replacement and repairs when necessary.

This meant attention to detail of design in a manner unique to large aircraft. Thus the hydraulic equipment of the Hercules, such as reservoirs, accumulators, valves, etc., has been compactly grouped in a single location to assure simplicity and ease of maintenance of each system. Engineers traveled to military bases and spent, collectively, many thousands of hours studying past and existing prob-

lems. Lockheed technical and maintenance personnel who operate
in the field were called upon for their advice and opinions.

The end result of this vast effort was maximum possible convenience in maintenance and replacement of parts and subsystems.
The Air Force mechanic can stand on his feet on the flight line (no
high rigs or ladders necessary), and have before him *all* the connections necessary to test, check out, and maintain the heart of the
Hercules hydraulic system.

But this is only the hydraulic system. What about the constant
need for electrical power in a machine of this size and complexity
—and with such complex mission requirements? The hydraulics are
bad enough, but it is the electrical systems of large aircraft that
make flight engineers and mechanics weep in frustration. There never
seems to be *enough* electrical power, or enough power in different
forms for all the many needs that constantly arise—often seemingly
without precedent—under operational conditions in the field.

Never has there been an airplane produced with such versatility
in electrical power systems as the Hercules. Over and over again
the writer has listened to flight and maintenance crews around the
world joyfully sing the praises of the forethought which has given
them freedom from balky, inadequate, and insufficient electrical
systems.

The Hercules is virtually a flying powerhouse. It receives its
electrical power from four 40-KVA three-phase AC generators, and
one 20-KVA three-phase AC generator. One generator is mounted
on each engine (and is an independent system with that engine),
and one is driven (also independently) by the air turbine motor of
the auxiliary power supply; this is employed essentially for standby
or ground operations.

The necessary direct current power for the airplane is provided
by four 200-ampere transformer-rectifiers which convert the AC
power to DC, and by a 24-volt, 36-ampere-hour battery. To facilitate the task of the crew in operating this electrical power system,
there are elaborate but extremely clear schematic diagrams integrated with the instruments and the control units of the airplane.

It is admittedly difficult to wax eloquent over such basic hardware as electrical and hydraulic systems, and to apply glowing
language to what is publicly considered as the prosaic in aviation.
But there is nothing prosaic about being forced to work with balky
equipment in the scorching heat of the desert or the equatorial
regions, or to struggle with ill-designed and ill-performing lines,
connections, and subsystems when the temperature is down to 80
degrees below zero—*on the ground*—where the Hercules was de-

signed to, and does, operate as a matter of course. And there is nothing more enraging to a flight crew or to operations dispatch personnel than to know that an airplane costing two million dollars, its services in critical need, is chained to the ground because a simple part of that airplane has failed and there is neither a backup system at hand, nor a convenient hangar filled with spare parts and staffed with expert mechanics. Such facilities do not exist on dirt strips 14,000 feet high in the Asian mountains, or in the Sahara Desert, or in jungles. Neither is it possible for an airplane to repair itself, or to carry the volume or weight of anything more than the most basic and critical of spare or emergency parts. The one solution that satisfies requirements of economy, efficiency, and practicability is to produce the airplane so that it can endure a failure *and continue to function.*

A task of the engineering staff that demands one of the rarest of attributes—20-20 foresight—is to anticipate the normal needs of an airplane, and then determine how to fulfill those normal needs in minimum time and with minimum cost and effort. At first glance this seems almost obvious, and one assumes that this is a design philosophy reflected in all major airplanes.

Such an assumption is sadly mistaken, as a visit to any major airport in the United States will reveal quickly. For many years we have been flying the most advanced piston-engine airliners in the world, machines that represent the peak of accomplishment in aeronautical engineering. But have you ever witnessed the exhibition that is displayed every time one of these aircraft is fueled at the airport? And most especially when it is raining or snowing? The pinnacle of aerodynamic science then requires several large gas trucks to drive to the airplane, hopefully squeezed close to the wing. At this point the flight-line mechanics must climb ladders and then clamber out onto the wing—which is a neat trick when the wind blows fiercely and the metal wing surface is wickedly slippery from snow and/or ice. It is not enough that the man (or men) must perform spectacular feats of balance; he must do so while dragging the heavy fueling hose with him to a little hole in the wing. Here he squats down, frees a locking receptacle, inserts the hose nozzle into the tank opening, and fills that tank with all the science of any pump jockey in your local gasoline station. Only there are several tank openings to be dealt with for each aircraft fueling. From practices such as these, it is not difficult to understand why one of the hazards of airplane servicing has been scraped skin, bruised backs, and broken bones—sustained in the abrupt end of a fall from a wing onto a concrete surface.

This is the sort of nonsense that prevailed for years, and no one could in objectivity argue the case for its persistence. Lockheed took clear steps to avoid such pitfalls with a machine that would one day become synonymous with the word "versatility."

The result of avoiding the errors of the past is clearly evident in the Hercules. Refueling the airplane is accomplished at a single-point receptacle and refueling panel located in the right wheel well fairing—which means *ground level*. It also means saving time and reducing the personnel necessary to perform this task.

One man can refuel the huge airplane. The control panel, easily operated at ground level, contains a full display of quantity gauges and facilities for checking the fuel-system valve operation.

The Hercules has four large fuel tanks which are integral with the wing—and all four are fueled from this one point at ground level. The tanks supply separate direct-fuel feed for each engine, or if necessary they can feed into a common crossfeed manifold. Two center wing tanks also supply fuel to the crossfeed system. In a design arrangement to warm the heart of the most unforgiving flight engineer, the Hercules' crossfeed system will furnish fuel to any of the engines from any combination of tanks. What if it's necessary in flight to jettison fuel quickly? This need does arise, and the engineers have anticipated it with a system that allows *all* tanks to be emptied simultaneously to the level desired. To prevent dangerous errors of miscontrol, the flight engineer is presented with color-coded fuel-system schematic diagrams in conjunction with instruments and controls. And he doesn't have to look for these schematics—they're an integral part of the engineer control panel presentation.

Looking ahead, the engineers knew that it would be impossible under all conditions for large fuel trucks to be available to utilize the single-point refueling capability. The airplane might be in a remote dirt field where the only fuel available would be in the form of small gasoline drums. Atop the wings, then, are additional fuel-tank filler caps to meet any conceivable situation.

There's an "extra gimmick" built into the fuel system of the airplane. It might prove necessary to "rescue" a Hercules, or any other type of turboprop or jet airplane, kept on the ground at some location without fuel. Could this airplane be supplied with emergency fuel in a hurry? Could the supply effort take place without large, movable fuel tanks?

With the Hercules, it can. The airplane can roll up to the machine with the empty tanks. One man at the fuel control panel of the Hercules can dump (through hoses, into barrels, into tanks, etc.) 40,000 pounds of excess fuel from the wing tanks, or any desired quantity up to that amount.

So goes the pattern of slide-rule philosophy. . . .

Throughout the entire effort to prepare the Hercules not only for flight, but for the full regime of punishment it would be expected to endure without failure in the air, Lockheed engineers carried out deliberate abuse of the airplane with an intensity that pilots have called "diabolical." This one group of engineers is dedicated to the principle that "if we can break it, operational flying also will break it."

The idea is to hammer, beat, twist, bludgeon, and otherwise smash at the airplane in special tests to reveal any inherent weaknesses overlooked in the design or machine shops, and to correct those weaknesses before flight takes place. One part of this torture program involves the hydrostatic fatigue tests already described. Paralleling this effort were the air pressure tests, in which engineers sealed the fuselage and pumped it full of high-pressure air, seeking weak points. In this kind of test the engineers' success is explosively announced, with a "blowout" of the section that yields before the steel fingers of pressure. Apparently the hydrostatic work had indeed been extensive—for the anticipated failures under air pressure never materialized.

In the remaining tests the engineers show no mercy, and people with a fondness for airplanes must leave the area, finding the sights before them rather unacceptable. Static testing is a bruising, wicked affair, with the engineers seeking the "breaking limits" of the airplane under specified gust and load conditions. The method of ascertaining this information is simple—it involves loading tons of iron bars onto the wings until the wing structure creaks and groans through every inch and bends downward for many feet.

Simulating "extreme" flight conditions in this manner, the engineers then study the screens of closed-circuit television, with the transmitters placed within the wings. This reveals to them—through a permanent film record as well—every detail of yielding, bending, and the inevitable minor failures. Design modifications are made accordingly, a particularly satisfactory process when the tests have proved that the wing has not only met, but far exceeded, all Air Force strength requirements. The modifications are *not* necessary, nor are they required, but they do add an extra margin of strength with a minimum of cost and effort.

To establish the strength of the Hercules' cargo floor, which would be forced to withstand heavy loads in actual use, the engineers amassed a load of iron weighing 6,500 pounds. They hooked it up to a powered cable system, and then trundled it back and forth more than 2,000 times across the floor of the airplane. That sort of massage is guaranteed to reveal defects in *any* structure ever made. . . .

The Hercules' landing gear especially must be able to withstand brutal shocks, since its purpose is to operate on unfinished and crude surfaces. Engineers rigged torture racks that lifted the gear legs high, and then slammed them down with punishing force—again and again. They twisted the gear, introduced sideward effects during impact, froze and broiled the gear, and cheerfully kept up their grueling work. And then, to be sure, they set up an automatic cycling system—and for eight hours, without a break, the landing gear was cycled up and down, up and down. Each cycle demanded perfect operation of pressure systems, the gear itself, and all fairing doors.

Finally the limit to all this deliberate mayhem was reached. Slide rules, engineering extrapolation, thousands of hours in wind tunnels, parts testing, the flights of models, electronic detective work, and the associated tools of the "torture engineers" could do no more.

With this phase of preflight development completed, the Hercules was now ready for its next series of elaborate tests. Other men stepped forward to accept responsibility for the machine.

These were the engineering test pilots and their crews. It was their task to validate—or to disprove—all that had been promised up until this moment. It is the most exciting phase in the creation of an airplane . . . the hundreds of test flights in the element for which the machine has been designed.

It also establishes "moments of truth" for a new creature with wings. Compromise and failure at this stage are inacceptable—and the penalties can be harsh to the point of being lethal.

CHAPTER VII

The Proving Ground   THE SECRETARY LIFTED
her hands from her typewriter and winced. The high glass
windows to her right vibrated with a visible movement that
threatened a shower of splinters. Then the entire building seemed
almost to tremble as a deep thunderclap of sound washed over
the structure. The woman at the typewriter shook her head to
dispel the howl that now had eased down to a comfortable, pounding roar. This she not only could withstand and resume her work,
but she no longer consciously heard the cry of energy.

Not all secretaries must endure sonic invasions of this nature.
But not all secretaries work in the flight-test offices of the Lockheed-Georgia Company in Marietta. And the cry of Hercules turboprop engines, intermingled with the hoarse blast of Jetstar transports, is an occupational penalty of working in an office that is part
of the same building where engineers expertly drag every ounce
of power from the airplanes they study. To prove to their humor-
less satisfaction that everything functions perfectly—because pilots
do not evince humor at anything less than that—they spend hours
at engine checks, hurling thunderclaps of sound at everything
nearby.

After a while the people working in the building learn to interrupt their conversations smoothly, and without break in their
thoughts and words, whenever the roar reaches a level where it
pervades the building and drowns out attempts at speech.

At Marietta the writer came to appreciate the problems of the
secretaries, and in the process learned the game of sandwiching
conversation between the thunder. I spent several weeks working
with the men who shaped the Hercules assault transport into exactly
that—an assault transport instead of an experimental airplane.

The task required extraordinary measures of work, skill, experience, coordination among people—a deep-flowing river of engineering test flight and development that would "make or break" the
machine into which so much effort had already been put. For it
is the pilots, blending flying skill with scientific knowledge, who

shape the airplane into the realization of its promise. In their hands rests success or failure.

The modern test pilot is a very special breed of person. He bears no resemblance to the test pilot of yesteryear. Flight testing in aviation's fledgling days was every bit of the dash and adventure that Hollywood in its celluloid presentations claimed it to be. Leather jackets, goggles, helmets, and white scarves were the vogue. The pilot kicked the tire, climbed in, fired up the engine, and went into the blue to "wring out" his machine. It wasn't a bit scientific—if the airframe didn't come unglued and the wings didn't separate from the fuselage, everyone cheered, a contract was signed, and the office gang broke out the beer.

Maybe a wistful sigh can be heard every now and then from a weary test pilot who has flown with meticulous, slide-rule precision, whose back aches from holding *exactly* the speed, heading, and altitude demanded by the engineers . . . but that's the only audible longing for the past.

It's not *all* science today, not by any stretch of the imagination. But it is a superb blending of science and personal skill and courage, and this is the combination from which great airplanes receive their assurance of long and reputable life.

Leo Sullivan is Chief Engineering Test Pilot of Lockheed-Georgia, and to him, like others who work so closely with him, the Hercules represents not so much an airplane as a major part of his entire career. In 1955 Sullivan and a select team of pilots and flight engineers spent several months in California flying the two prototype Hercules airplanes. Then the experimental machines were flown to Georgia, which Lockheed had selected as the permanent home of the Hercules. From almost the beginning of the Hercules program, Sullivan has been an integral element of the long development cycle.

It is not possible to discern the intimate habits and characteristics of a machine so huge and complex as the Hercules through any one man. It is necessary, instead, to paint the picture through the eyes, the attitudes, the feelings of the group of men who have verified beyond all question the promise of the aircraft. But no one was better suited than Leo Sullivan to determine the behavior and long-sought capabilities of the Hercules in flight.

The flight-test crews comprise the last step in the transition of the Hercules from its creators to its users—the military agencies of the United States. But it is a long and intricate step indeed. . . .

The earliest test flights of this airplane were hours of painstaking precision. Excitement and the more hazardous phases of "bending metal" would come later. In the beginning, Sullivan and his men were required to determine the inherent stability of the YC-130 prototypes. In March 1955 the first production C-130 rolled off the production line, and this airplane and the others that followed immediately after it all moved to the flight-test division where the test program accelerated to full speed. Thus the exhaustive investigations into the Hercules in its original form were not limited to the prototypes, as is often the case, but included production models as well. Hercules 3001 was the first to be spawned from the world's biggest factory, and this airplane particularly was destined for deliberate batterings by its crews—before it would embark on a long career, which continues today, of specialized military service.

Leo Sullivan has been in this business long enough to recognize the "shadow areas" of development, and his test flying is carried on with a keen insight into the side of this story that is rarely known beyond the "inner circle" of the industry.

"I think an airplane is a combination of a fantastic chain of circumstances," he explained. "In the case of a military airplane, a government order, there is, first of all, the preliminary design effort to get the best possible power-plant combination—engine to airplane. After that, you must face the problem of the manufacturing and production of the machine to acceptable standards, and then you go through the flight testing to prove that the original design meets its required standards."

He paused as thunder assailed the windows of his office, then continued: "On many occasions, as the aircraft grows and develops, the scheduling and the timing, in relation to budgetary limitations, determine many of the things that you do with the airplane. This is one of those invisible but terribly important factors. You do the best you can with what you have, but in a great many cases you must do it over several times. You're not always right and luck has something to do with your progress. Even today, although we talk of the aircraft industry or aeronautical engineering as an advanced science—which it certainly is—there's still room for a lot of breaks, for everything to come out just right, with so many demands, requirements, and standards being integrated into that single final package. . . ."

In the original flight-test regime, the Lockheed pilots flew with Allison engines that, at this time, were still going through the growing pains of development. There were the ordinary, prosaic, everyday problems that were to be expected, and they were compounded by others that arose with the first propeller designs. Some of the pilots explain their woes at the time by recalling that "we flew through a succession of propellers. . . ."

The YC-130 on a flight test cruises past Stone Mountain near Atlanta, Georgia, during formative years of the Hercules. (*Lockheed-Georgia*)

In the first test airplane, unfortunately, not all the equipment desired for flight testing was available for the engine-propeller combinations. Lockheed was something less than happy about this; the test pilots made it clear that the situation left room for improvement, but nothing could be done to alleviate the situation. The "chain of circumstances" had imposed the most stringent time requirements for pushing the Hercules to operational status, and if Lockheed waited for the planned and desired equipment, the entire program would suffer accordingly. It became a matter of accepting the lack of certain equipment just to get the airplanes into the air in order to pursue as rapidly as possible the entire flight-test program.

"It's impossible to predict these things beforehand," explains Sullivan, "and, when you get down to it, this is exactly what we get paid for. As a matter of fact—" he grinned—"if you really study this situation, we wouldn't have jobs as test pilots if everything in engineering *did* come out right."

But Sullivan—and the other pilots and engineers—took special pains to emphasize that this was the kind of "nitpicking observation" they were required to make.

Most test flying, especially with the big airplanes, rather quickly falls into the routine familiar to all pilots, rather than being a period of sustained high emotion because of the novelty of the new airplane. Much of the flying is done "on the gauges" with unflagging howls of protest from the engineers and technicians if the pilot so much as shifts his butt in the seat, when he is supposed to fly hairline accuracy through the sky. This is not excitement, or the romance of flying. It is plain, old-fashioned hard work.

And the test pilots let you know this, and very quickly. They are not an excitable breed of people; it is a rare occasion and a rare airplane that brings them to shed much of their inhibitions and to wax enthusiastic about the machine they drive around the sky, day after day, month after month, year after year.

The Hercules as an engineering achievement is a "rare occasion"; and as dozens of pilots, one after the other, without contradiction, have emphasized, it is one of those "*very* rare airplanes." These pilots, the majority of whom have absolutely no relationship to the Lockheed-Georgia Company, are the greatest of the drumbeaters in praise of the Hercules.

In the early days of its flight testing, this was yet to be discovered. Under these conditions, each new factor learned about the airplane became a source of growing delight to the test crews.

"The '130 was about as nice a flying bird as I'd been associated with up until that time," Leo Sullivan recalled. "It certainly handled better for a big airplane than anything I'd flown to date. . . . You get this kind of feeling not from any deliberate abuse of the airplane, but from its quieter, more gentle flight regimes. This is when the small things become very important, when you can determine the intrinsic sensitivities and characteristics of the design."

The Hercules was the first American airplane ever to enter production with turboprop power, and the Allison jet engines represented a complete departure from the past for the test crews. This proved to be Sullivan's first opportunity to fly any airplane with turboprop power, and the Hercules measured up as a brute with energy to spare.

"My first reactions were most pronounced," Sullivan said with emphasis. "Immediately we had plunged into a completely new regime of flight. That was so obvious that it excited us. We had, compared to what we had been flying to date, fantastic advantages in thrust capability, in acceleration on takeoffs and control of the aircraft under all emergency situations, because of the throttle power-level arrangement.

"It was a wonderful thing to know what lay beneath your hand. All you have to do to get power is move that throttle, and you get an instantaneous prop response. There just isn't any lag.

"You move your hand and *bang!* the airplane kicks itself through the air. The original design of this machine specified capabilities for short fields, where instant power response is *everything* . . . and the people sure did their job."

From the very onset of the testing program the over-all response of the flight-test crews brought broad grins to the faces of Lockheed officials and Air Force observers. Words such as "tremendous" and "fabulous" or "unbelievable" crept into the engineering reports, which were usually as excitable as a technical report on baking bricks. To the veterans of the industry, this was a barometer of growing success with more meaning to it than anything else to come out of the program.

"In the handling, and the short-field characteristics which were built into this airplane," Sullivan added, "we were real lucky. In fact, the test pilots were astounded at the job the Hercules did beneath our hands. For a while the postflight debriefing sessions sounded like a bunch of excited fighter pilots talking about a real hot machine that was being used for mixing it up in dogfights. It certainly did *not* sound as though a big, four-engine transport was behind all the excitement."

But there are different kinds of excitement in a flight-test program, and the Hercules didn't disappoint anyone who claimed that every new airplane was going to have its "moments and its thrills."

On the third flight of the first production Hercules, Sullivan ran the airplane through airspeed calibration tests in order to determine with accuracy the entire speed regime of the transport. He began with high-speed runs, the engines pulling the Hercules through the air with all their power, throbbing like a great fluttering rumble of thunder.

Then he progressed down to the other end of the spectrum, finally rumbling along at low altitude over the Lockheed runway at 95 knots. A member of the crew tapped him on the shoulder. Leo Sullivan heard an unnatural groan and turned to look into a pasty white face.

"Leo—I'm sick. Man, I don't know what's the matter but I just *got* to get on the ground." Sullivan said the man had begun to turn a shade of green and this was unusual, because he'd never known him to become ill while in flight before. Assuming the worst, the pilot decided to land at once. At this moment he was flying west, directly over the field. He banked into a steep left turn, dumped the gear and flaps, and slid the big airplane earthward to the runway.

Shortly before they touched down, a quick-disconnect fuel hose in the number-two engine snapped free. Sullivan and his crew were unaware that fuel was spraying in a torrent to the rear. It was, in fact, spraying a highway with a great shower of kerosene. An amateur photographer driving by jammed on his brakes, jumped out, and shot sensational pictures of the Hercules blowing a long stream of perfect smoke rings out of the engine.

The runway loomed beneath the airplane when the sick crew member glanced out the side windows. With icy calm he said: "Leo, number two is on fire."

If that crew member had not become ill and made it clear that he was desperate to get on the ground, Sullivan would have made at least another one or two speed passes over the field. "And it is entirely conceivable," he said quietly, "that we would have caught fire in the air. With our slow speed the fuel would have sprayed all about the engine. . . . Well, as it was, the engine exploded after we were on the ground.

"Man, I ought to buy that guy a gold-lined burp cup."

Everyone left the airplane quickly as the flames roared up and around the wing. Sullivan walked around to the site of the fire. Eager to note every detail, he didn't realize that he was standing *beneath* the blazing wing. Suddenly the flames cut through metal and the wing snapped with a *Crack!*

"It was pretty stupid to be standing there," Sullivan said candidly, "but I was fascinated by the whole thing. It was my test airplane, after all . . . and it just about smacked me square on the head."

Apparently the man who became ill was convinced that this episode was a portent, and he never flew again in that airplane.

Hercules 3001, however, did considerably better. The fire, which had cut as cleanly as a torch through the wing, was extinguished almost immediately afterward. Lockheed repaired the airplane, installed a new wing, and painted the new number on the high tail.

That airplane is in service today with the Air Force Missile Test Center, bristling with advanced electronics equipment and operating along the Atlantic Missile Range where, among other tasks, it tracks space vehicles as they plunge back to earth at five miles per second.

The Integrity of Structure

Big airplanes are designed to be flown through a comparatively gentle spectrum of flight. Essentially the wings are to be kept level with the horizon, except when the airplane is placed in a turn and it is necessary to bank the machine through it. The maneuver, however, is one usually executed with precision and with the least abuse of the wings.

Because of the demands that would be placed upon the Hercules, Lockheed designed this airplane with a normal structural integrity of 3g. This means that under maximum gross weight conditions, the airplane may be abused to the point where its wings will have exerted upon them a force three times that of normal gravity. It is a wicked force to withstand, and it may be better appreciated when we think of a 200-pound man being exposed to a force of 3g. Under this tremendous pull the man suddenly weighs 600 pounds, and his feeling is that his limbs have turned to lead, his head is a massive bucket of cement, and his muscles have become inexplicably incapable of allowing him to move. The 3g force distends his muscles and limbs, creates a pounding in his ears, bends his bones, alarms his heart, and pulls body fluids into his lower extremities in what is known medically as the "fluid shift." In less gentle terms, it turns his body into a distorted bag of blood.

It also plays hell with airplane wings. But the Hercules was built to withstand a force of 3g under *normal* operating conditions.

We should say that this is positive g. In other words, the force moves downward—in the human body, from the head down to the feet. When an airplane endures a positive-3g force, the wings bend upward, straining against the pressure as though they had flapped upward and then frozen into place.

Even rougher on the airplane is negative g. In this case the direction of the force is reversed. It moves in an upward direction. Airplanes are not intended to withstand negative-g loadings. They are designed to fly against the force of gravity, so that the wings support the load of the airplane. A negative-g force applies pressure in a direction opposite to that intended by the designer.

"We have been out to a factor of minus 1.37g," explains Sullivan with disarming calm. "This is a negative-1.37g factor on the airplane and I'll admit that this is quite a distance 'around the Horn' below zero g. . . ." It means flying in such a manner that the airplane becomes weightless and *then* suffers a reversal of normal forces and pressures. It is, from this writer-pilot's seat, an absolute bitch.

Such a test flight is as though the airplane were performing an enormous roller coaster run through miles of sky. It means entering a long, shallow dive under power, accelerating rapidly, and picking up great speed. Then the pilot eases back on the control yoke until the broad nose of the Hercules comes back up through horizontal, reaching higher and higher and grabbing for sky in a great parabolic curve. At exactly the angle planned, the pilot pushes forward on the control yoke so that the airplane can enter its parabolic arc. If this is done neatly and cleanly (and the engineers scream protests if it is not) the Hercules achieves a beautiful balance between the upward push of centrifugal force and the downward pull of gravity.

At that moment, and so long as the parabola is maintained, the airplane is weightless. The condition within the airplane is just as much zero g as it has been for the astronauts and cosmonauts whirling around the planet.

Leo Sullivan took delight in perfecting the game of the weightless cigar. Under the zero-g arc he would open his mouth and permit his cigar to gently float away from his face. The trick was to let it drift slowly so that, as the airplane came out of the arc, Leo could stretch out his arm, grab the cigar, and return to the world of us earth folk.

A fair number of the Lockheed test pilots have accumulated more zero-gravity time in the Hercules than did Shepard or Grissom in their suborbital space shots!

"We had some development problems in this phase," explains Sullivan, "because we couldn't get the oil pressure in the gear boxes to stay where it was supposed to be. After all, these big birds are intended to fly under normal 1g conditions and not to be tossed around the sky like a shuttlecock . . . so when you got upside down, or in zero g, the oil that was in a gear box no longer was there. The oil in the tank, too, had floated around until it was at the top, or floating somewhere in between, instead of at the bottom of the tank where any sensible engineer assumes it is going to be. The suction to pull oil for the gear boxes and the engines is at the bottom of the tank, and our maneuvers, of course, violated all the 'normal flight expectancies' of the engineers. All this gave the engineering people gray hair, and they quickly had to build special compensatory equipment into the bird."

The Lockheed test pilots discovered that their strenuous maneuvers had compressed their seats as they made punishing, high-g pullouts from dives. The discovery came in an embarrassing manner when they entered the zero-gravity flights. Suddenly everything, including the seats, became weightless "so that all the springs come pushing up against the cushion, and by the time you come down, and the airplane goes on back through its g loadings, man, you *know* you are going to receive a mighty jab where you sit.

"You also find out in cases like these," Sullivan quipped, "just how 'neat and clean' the flight line people keep an airplane. Because suddenly little pieces that you never expected to see in your life come floating up from the floor and behind the control column, and there are nuts and bolts and washers, and pieces of wire and things like that floating around, just as if they were suspended in a big bowl of invisible, quivering jelly."

But Lockheed shouldn't feel bad about that. The Mercury capsules for our astronauts were kept under the most meticulous, surgical, better-than-hospital rules of cleanliness, and the astronauts also found a few odd things floating around them in space.

The zero-g flights are part of the program to prove the structural integrity of the wing while it contains a maximum fuel load —and while suffering adverse loading conditions. The fuel then provides through its increased weight a "bending moment" for the wing. The transition from normal to positive g, into weightlessness, on to negative g, and back down to extreme positive g "beats the hell" out of the wing and flexes it through an extraordinary range. To compensate for the forces battering at the wing, the internal structure and outer skin and all the associated plumbing and wiring must bend and flex like the pinion of a great bird.

The flight program requires maximum punishment all the way around, to as much as three times the force of gravity, so that the instruments aboard the airplane may record every last detail of structural "give" and pinpoint the strength remaining in the wing. In this fashion the engineers establish clearly the operating limits of the airplane, and they obtain an accurate idea of the point at which the wing must ultimately fail.

It is a flight-test series which must be conducted with consummate skill.

"You go through a structural program of maneuvers," Leo Sullivan says in deadly seriousness, "that no one in his right mind would get into, except that in this business you must prove that the aircraft will fly through all its design limitations, and sometimes more. And you don't—you *can't*—do this either sitting on the ground or with daredevils in the air.

"There are no Clark Gables in this business. We work with maximum instrumentation. We string gauges out on those wings, and we telemeter our data to the ground. The best people in this business, anywhere, are on the ground monitoring those instruments. They read off the results of what we're doing in the air. . . . We build up to maximum possible loads on the airplane slowly. We go to 80, then 90, and finally to 100 percent of what we are trying to do to prove the integrity of this machine.

"There's no nonsense about it. This is precision engineering work, and sometimes the requirements are so damned stiff that we go back again and again until we thread the needle in the sky with the airplane to satisfy the engineers, and bless 'em, they don't satisfy *easy.*

"And neither does the airplane. Every airplane built has its breaking point. I don't care if you build it to fly from grass fields or go to the moon, it will take just so much and no more."

The man talking about the limitations of the Hercules has flown the airplane at a weight of 155,000 pounds. He has then pushed the Hercules beyond its "normal" limits, and pulled out from his maneuvers at this weight with a force three times that of gravity.

At that moment Leo Sullivan was flying a propeller transport airplane that weighed more than 465,000 pounds. In a machine of the size and configuration of the Hercules, this is the kind of flying that rapidly separates the men from the boys.

It also establishes in a rather dramatic fashion that the airplane has been built with the ruggedness expected in a bulldozer. . . .

And strangely enough, it would be a bulldozer that brought home with grim impact the strength of the airplane.

Years after Leo Sullivan and the test crews completed their maximum-stress tests, a Hercules was cruising at 25,000 feet over Asia, with a massive bulldozer lashed with chains and cables in the fuselage. "Something" went wrong. No one has ever figured out exactly what happened. But without warning the Hercules suddenly pitched forward in a violent nose-down maneuver.

Before the startled crew could do anything, the airplane was screaming earthward in a vertical dive, and then began to "tuck under" in the dive. It reached vertical and started into an outside loop, which is guaranteed to tear any big airplane into thousands of little pieces.

Working frantically in the flight deck, the crew managed to regain control. At this point the airspeed indicator had swung all the way around and had become entirely meaningless. The plunging Hercules shook wildly from the tremendous forces of air pressure, and a million demons of wind shrieked all about the airplane.

For 20,000 feet the Hercules plummeted from the sky. The crew eased the ship out with less than 5,000 feet between them and the earth.

It took some time to regain their equilibrium in that crew compartment. The airplane didn't behave properly; in fact, it had picked up an unusual vibration that worried the pilots—if anything could have worried them after that howling dive. No one knew what damage had been sustained; they just couldn't believe the airplane was still flying and in one piece. They experimented by slowing down the Hercules to 130 knots, and the vibration disappeared.

The crew wasted little time in getting down at the first major airfield. The pilots climbed down and the excited cries of the flight engineer brought them quickly to the landing gear well on the right side of the airplane.

"Good God," the engineer whispered. "Will you look at *that*. . . ." The fairing cover of the gear and wheel well had been ripped completely off the airplane, all the way up to the wing. The Hercules looked as though an enormous steel claw had gouged out its side.

The pilot said, "Yeah." That was all. Because he had looked up, and he was pointing with his hand. He didn't need any words.

When the fairing tore off the airplane in the dive, it whirled crazily back in the terrific airstream. As it flashed away it ripped off 11 feet of the right horizontal stabilizer *and the complete right elevator.*

The only difficulty encountered after the pullout was that slight vibration at a speed exceeding 130 knots.

Another Hercules inadvertently provided a demonstration of structural integrity during a test flight. The airplane is designed, as we know, with backup systems, but even the specials built into the Hercules didn't avail the crew on this occasion. The landing gear refused to come down. The crew tried everything in the book, but *all* the systems refused to work. This isn't unusual in the early stages of a testing program, but no one relished the idea of dragging the Hercules in on her belly, sans gear.

They had no choice in the matter, of course. The pilot held the airplane off the runway as long as he could, and then sank to the concrete with a terrifying screech of metal. When the Hercules finally ground to a stop, friction against the concrete had torn a big hole right down the center of the belly.

The crew jacked up the ship, lowered the gear, "put a strip of aluminum down the center of the belly to hold the loose pieces in place," and took off. They flew the airplane nonstop from North Carolina back to Marietta for repairs. It was back in the air, good as new, four days later.

Testing an airplane such as the Hercules means much more than maneuvers and precision flight to meet engineering needs. The Hercules is a working airplane, and it was designed to perform a wide variety of utility missions—among them dropping by parachute huge loads and weights, meaning trucks, armored vehicles, supply packages, tanks, and other military items. Before the airplane was turned over to the Air Force, the Lockheed test pilots were required to demonstrate by actual performance the suitability of the airplane for such missions.

In the original air-drop tests with the C-130A model, the heaviest weights hauled out of the rear platform of the Hercules and lowered safely to earth by parachute were road graders that weighed 28,000 pounds. Through this series of tests the Hercules almost every week broke its own world records of air-drop loads. The 14-ton road graders were believed to be the absolute limit even for the Hercules, but as the tests progressed it became obvious that even the most enthusiastic supporters of the airplane had sadly underestimated its capabilities.

Air Force pilots have released in flight, pulled completely free and clear for safe parachute descent to earth, individual test loads *weighing up to 41,740 pounds.*

"The purpose of the tests as conducted by our flight teams," explains Leo Sullivan of Lockheed, "was not to prove the weight or drop ability of the airplane. This is an Air Force job. Our purpose was at the time to determine scientifically the capabilities of the airplane under extreme forces of flight, while the plane was fully instrumented. As a result of the transits of the various loads, we could determine beyond any question what was the structural capability of the craft. . . ."

In this mission the pilot slows his airplane down to a speed between 130 and 150 knots. The trick is to set up the airplane so perfectly with the trim that it will maintain its attitude even if the pilot removes his hands from the controls.

The freeing of the dump package is extremely fast. At the rate the heavy cargo booms out of the big hold of the '130, it requires only two to four seconds before everything is free and clear. The speed of the cargo release is important. The time involved is so brief that the airplane doesn't have the opportunity to react violently to the great changes in weight, and the shifting center of gravity. Thus it avoids the violent pitching maneuvers, the wicked lifting of the nose, which would otherwise result. "That is," Sullivan adds, "just so long as we can shoot the whole works the way it's intended to go.

"We've had occasions during the early programs when things didn't go right. In the drop zone they released the cargo, dumped the chute out, and then, well—the chute broke free. Without the open parachute to pull the load free of the airplane the cargo doesn't accelerate rapidly.

"Instead, it groans its way out. And let me tell you that this is the time when you find out whether or not your airplane *really* can take it, because you are going to go through a *wild* pitch maneuver. The nose wants to climb right out of the sky. It takes all the down-elevator control you can get and every last ounce of power in those engines there is to save the day. . . .

"The stuff just falls out the back end and it tears up every law of aerodynamic engineering ever written. If the Good Lord is with you and those people in the factory have done *their* job right, why, you know you'll come home to eat dinner, after all. And so far, everyone who has ever been caught in this situation has always come home."

CHAPTER VIII

Test Pilot's Roundtable   THE LIFE OF A
modern airplane is an endless cycle of testing. The initial flights
of the experimental prototype models are soon followed by a
swelling number of airplanes that rumble one after the other
through the factory doors. For years after the initial contracts are
signed, the long flight lines remain empty of all but promise. Then
a wondrous change takes place. Emptiness is replaced with row
upon row of flashing silver wings and bodies. Once only the sound
of the wind could be heard; now the flight line shudders to the
thunder of massed engines and flailing propellers. There is an air
of deep excitement about such a scene, for here great airplanes
are born and cast free to roam the skies of an entire planet.

New faces arrive, first only a few, and then a stream. The pilots
come first from the Air Force, and their airplanes are distinctive
in color and markings. One by one, then in twos and threes, the
airplanes shout their cry of energy and reject the earth on gleaming wings. This is the spawning ground of the huge eagles that
recognize no borders and no barriers except space and time. It is
something that one can sense, a realization of the power of the
creative mind. It is the projection of the mind to all lands and
across all seas, knowing that the increasing number of final takeoffs from the runways alongside the factory is creating a vast
force to plumb the depths of an entire world.

The first stab at operational flying—complete acceptance of the
airplane as a working instrument in the national arsenal—is exactly that, a stab into a new realm, and not a breathless plunge.
Testing an airplane as a new and unproven device is only one
part of the story; subjecting it to the unknowns of operations in
the field means exposure to situations, forces, and circumstances
that cannot be predicted or simulated. So even operational flight
is a continuation of the early test program, with the men who
produce the airplanes looking over shoulders, going along for the
ride, but in a manner designed to ferret out every new scrap of
information on the airplane—and, hopefully, to add to the worth
of the machine.

The quest is always to improve the product, and for this reason it is an effort that can never be completed. How to improve reliability, to wring more performance from the craft, to widen the spectrum of versatility . . . these are the steps along the way to full operational acceptance and a vast fleet sailing the seas of air that flow over all lands.

The first YC-130 flew on August 23, 1954. Less than a year later —on April 7, 1955—the first production C-130A burst skyward from the Lockheed runway at Marietta after a run of only 800 feet. Long months of arduous testing followed. More and more airplanes became available for the test pilots, and the Hercules began to drift to different parts of the United States to show her true colors. The airplane no longer was experimental; neither was it operational. This is the shadow zone—the long stretch during which pilots and engineers seek out trouble under all possible conditions of terrain, weather, temperature, and an infinite variety of operating conditions.

On December 9, 1956, the 463rd Wing of the Tactical Air Command's 18th Air Force accepted its first group of C-130A Hercules "multi-purpose turboprop transports." At Ardmore Air Force Base in Oklahoma the military pilots acted like kids with a shining new toy. Their excitement stemmed from the most critical of evaluations of the airplane by military crews who had "beaten up" the Hercules. They had the first turboprop transport in the United States, the fastest transport in the Air Force, and a promise of versatility that sneered at old concepts of the limitations on aircraft operations.

Behind the delivery of Hercules transports to the 463rd Wing stood two and a half years of systematic tests and proving trials. The Air Force and Lockheed in a coordinated effort conducted seven major phases of the official flight testing program. The first six of these tests were functional suitability tests falling into the research and development category, and it was their purpose to discover and eliminate any detrimental aspects of the airplane. "Functional design and systems operation tests" is the official tag for this effort. The seventh test normally constitutes the end of the research program, since it is made with aircraft equipped with every stitch of gear the Air Force will employ in the everyday life of the plane.

The conditions of testing are those of simulated combat. Crewmen dump thousands of tons of field equipment and supplies by parachute from the airplanes. From other Hercules thousands of paratroopers leap into the blue, simulating actual air-drop attack. The aircraft are then loaded in weight configurations from "light" to "overload," and subjected to hammering blows from crude and unfinished fields. This phase settles in bone-jarring fashion the matter of rough-field operation.

When the long and torturous program is ended, the airplane is considered suitable for operations, and is slated for assignment to different groups which will immediately place it in active service. The guesswork is ended; the aircraft is operational. The promise begun so long before has come to fruition.

But the testing cycle has *not* yet run its course. It continues unabated, because the manufacturer feels always that there is room for improvement, for building into the airplane certain features that will enable it continuously to outdo itself.

During the summer of 1956, only one year from the flight of the first production Hercules, Major Joseph P. Tracy of the Flight Safety Division of the Air Force cast a wickedly keen and ex-

"On December 9, 1956, the 463rd Wing of the Tactical Air Command's 18th Air Force accepted its first group of C-130A Hercules 'multipurpose turboprop transports.'" Practicing formation flights with the new "Can Do!" assault transports. (*Lockheed-Georgia*)

perienced eye over the airplane. As an officer whose words would be studied with surgical care by pilots throughout the Air Force, Tracy would naturally be more inclined to be conservative rather than optimistic in predicting the value of a new and still experimental machine. Production status notwithstanding, no military pilot considers an airplane as "accepted" until the machine has withstood the battering of crews who are not likely to exhibit "tender, loving care" in their daily activities. So every word that Tracy had to say carried extraordinary weight.

In the late spring of 1956 the major wrote:

> Ever since the YC-130 first lifted off the runway in California, we've been following the development of the machine with a great deal of interest. It is not particularly a big airplane when compared with such aircraft as the C-124 or the C-133, but it appears now that it can carry a whopping load on relatively short hauls and in all probability beat the tar out of its bigger brothers when it comes to speed. . . .
>
> The C-130 is one of the first turboprop jobs and from our limited flight experience with the plane, we'll make book that such type power is here to stay. . . . You'll be seeing more and more of these high-tailed dudes in the near future. The front of the C-130 resembles a goat but you may rest assured that it's nowhere near as stubborn. . . .

Major Tracy did some crystal ball gazing and said that "if the engineers are right, this gal will gross out at 108,000 pounds, which sort of takes it out of the Cub category. You run the power levers up to maximum . . . release the brakes and rather casually nudge the nosewheel steering as needed, and in nothing flat you're airborne. Eight hundred feet or so ground run and—jump!"

How did the machine *fly?* This is what the pilots who would spend hundreds and even thousands of hours in the airplane during the coming years wanted to know. "The C-130 has no apparent bad habits. . . . This plane gives a lot of honest warning before stalling, power on or power off. . . . The C-130 is a beautiful flying machine."

Major Tracy, like almost everyone else concerned with the Hercules, was inclined to be even more conservative than events would prove. The Hercules in the C-130A model did indeed gross out at 108,000 pounds, but only for a limited time. This was its "fighting weight" as a machine to get into the middle of combat situations and slug its way into crude and remote fields. But the Hercules is also a transport, and very quickly the gross weight climbed to 124,200 pounds for this work.

Almost at the same time that Major Tracy reported on the "beautiful flying machine," the then Lockheed-Georgia Chief of Flight Operations Bud Martin cast himself more definitively in the prophet's role. "The Hercules is establishing a new standard of handling and flying for airplanes," he said. Martin then explained that long experience with airplanes allows any pilot to sniff out the thoroughbred lines in a new steed, and he committed himself with the forecast, "Any airplane that is as far advanced and performs like the C-130 is bound to be the beginning of a *family* of airplanes."

And then Bud Martin also fell victim to conservatism, although at the time it seemed as though a strong feeling for the Hercules had "colored" his remarks. Martin predicted that the Hercules and its offspring would serve as front-line transports for at least a decade.

Test pilot Bud Martin voiced his predictions more than seven years ago. It's less than three years to the end of that decade, but not even the Lockheed test pilot could have anticipated the size of that "family of airplanes" of which he spoke.

There are today *18 different versions* of the Hercules flying a bewildering variety of missions around the world. Leo Sullivan points out that "the A model, as well as the B and E, all look alike except that the E is built here in the factory with long-range tanks beneath the wings. The A still has the three-bladed propeller, while the B and other models have four blades on each propeller. The original A model came out of the factory designed for a maximum gross-weight takeoff of 108,000 pounds. Then we learned we could add another 16,000 pounds under 'normal takeoff' conditions. Along came the B, and we set the standard gross weight of that airplane at more than 130,000 pounds.

"For about a year now the E model has been flying in its operational dress with a takeoff gross weight of 155,000 pounds. The difference in takeoff weight is absolutely tremendous—47,000 pounds. It is difficult to impress on anyone who's not in this business what an extraordinary growth in lifting capability this is. And what really counts is that the heart-and-soul configuration of the airplane hasn't changed at all. Sure, we've refined many of the features, we've made things easier and more comfortable for the crew, but we have not really changed the airplane, while we *have* gained fabulous increases in performance."

Pilots began to drift into the operations room where Sullivan and I were talking. Before long there were two dozen pilots and engineers with us, sprawled loosely around a huge conference table. Smoke from cigars and cigarettes filled the room. It quickly became the kind of situation where the men who have nurtured a machine from embryonic form to brilliant success gather together, and without prompting warm to the subject with which they have been intensely preoccupied for many years. Such occasions are rare but welcome among pilots eager to discuss their airplane, and fill a need quite distinct from cold technical and engineering reports.

"Look at what we did with weight capability, married to speed and range," Sullivan continued. "When we flew a mission of about 2,200 miles with the A model, we carried somewhere between 20,000 and 25,000 pounds. Headwinds were a problem and over any appreciable range cut the payload down in favor of reserve fuel.

"Now we've got the E, and it's normal to fly a coast-to-coast nonstop mission with 35,000 pounds of cargo aboard the airplane— at much greater speed, despite winds, and with a great fuel reserve. This built-in reserve is one reason why MATS [Military Air Transport Service] is so excited about the airplane.

"Their E model in normal operations can fly a 24,000-pound payload over a distance of 4,000 nautical miles. Using land—or statute—miles as the measuring system, this means a nonstop flight with this load for a distance of 4,600 miles. This comes to virtually a *round trip* flight across the United States and back without a stop. And that is a lot of performance for an airplane that looks almost exactly as it did when it first rolled off the production line back in 1955."

That C-130A flew with large three-bladed propellers, and they generated enough noise inside the Hercules to make their sonic assault a major topic of conversation. The noise assailed anyone within the cavernous fuselage. Passengers inside the old A model said it was like flying in the middle of a boiler factory with everything going full blast. The wind streaking past the fuselage at the 360-mile-per-hour cruising speed of the A added to the monumental din. Much of the noise, however, came from the propellers. The blades were unusually long, and their tips rotated at much greater speed than those of the four-bladed propellers that are on the later models. The "propeller chop," air whipped away from the tips, slammed broadside against the fuselage.

The wags in the industry said that with the C-130A, Lockheed surely had solved the problem of noise with the turboprop—they funneled it all *inside* the airplane.

Each Allison engine in the C-130A generated 3,750 horsepower. Even as the early Hercules models toppled records like tenpins before an unerring champion bowler, the Air Force was casting a keen eye on Lockheed's proposals for its successor—the C-130B.

Finally the Air Force signaled its go-ahead, at the same time enunciating a change in the philosophy of design. The A model had performed so superbly in its short-field characteristics that the Air Force felt its capabilities in this respect could be decreased slightly and improved performance achieved in other areas. (As events were to prove, the short-field characteristics would become even more vital than they were when the Hercules first went into operations.)

The Air Force wanted to use the C-130B more for passenger, and combination passenger and heavy-cargo loads, than it had originally specified. Allison had been working steadily to increase the performance of the jet engines, and delivered to Lockheed a new-model engine that turned out 4,050 horsepower—an increase for the airplane of 1,200 horsepower. Lockheed abandoned the three-blade propeller for a four-blade model with less blade diameter, and a blissfully accepted sharp drop in noise characteristics.

The result was profound. The range went up to 3,200 nautical miles with maximum cruise speed of 360 miles per hour, and the airplane grossed out at 135,000 pounds. Then, later, along came the model E with its superb long-range capabilities.

In between, however, the Hercules family consistently spawned model after model to meet an astonishing variety of mission requirements. To the Marines went the GV-1 Hercules (now the KC-130F), which delighted the flying Leathernecks—a single airplane serving as a mid-air refueling tanker, troop transport, medical evacuation aircraft, paratroop-drop carrier, high-speed cargo carrier (38,000 pounds for 2,200 miles), and assault transport, besides performing other missions.

The Marines (as well as the Navy and the Coast Guard) took to the Hercules with what the Corps officially termed "extraordinary application" of the airplane. Lockheed technical representatives came back to Marietta with their reports of Hercules flight operations with the Marines, and then fierce arguments raged in the front offices—because not even Lockheed believed that the airplanes could be kept so constantly in commission as they are flown by the Marines and the Navy.

Their maintenance is described as fabulous. The Marines are chip-on-the-shoulder proud of their Hercules, and they *do* lavish "tender, loving care" on their birds.

One pilot in our self-grown meeting pointed a finger to emphasize his words. "I see no reason why the Hercules won't be used for twenty years and even more," he said. "I'm an ex-Navy man, and

I've run many of the tests for the Marine version of the '130. In a way no one dreamed of, it fulfills virtually every requirement for hauling cargo over long-distance conditions anywhere in the world as we know those requirements today.

"The Marines are still using the old Gooney Bird, and that thing has been beating up the airways since back in 1935. The Marine pilots sound like Lockheed salesmen. They're convinced that there has just never been a cargo airplane that comes anywhere close to the '130. It's not just the performance; they're wild about that huge cargo capacity that allows them an unprecedented variation in mission assignments. . . ."

Preoccupation with flight performance sometimes obscures the features of an airplane that endear it even more to people faced with hard, everyday operational needs, and the efficiency of the Hercules for handling cargo as no other big airplane can is one of those features.

"All our attention has been focused on the '130 in its military role, of course," Leo Sullivan said. "But this is a limited view. Let me make myself very clear on this point. I'm absolutely convinced that we haven't done more than to scratch the surface of what we'll be doing—by we, I mean the resources of the entire country—with the Hercules.

"Our job has been with the military versions, but we've also done some serious studies and run flight tests on this airplane in civilian dress. The airplane has a simply fantastic capability for non-scheduled cargo as well as scheduled operations.

"We brought in the top cargo experts in the country—the people who have revolutionized the entire industry of moving heavy and varied loads by air. We said we could do things with the Hercules that made them lift their eyebrows and, frankly, a lot of them just flat-out didn't believe us. But nothing proves a point so well as actual proof of flight.

"It turned out that we can deliver cargo on a commercial basis with the Hercules at very low ton-mile costs. . . . We've run advanced tests with the airplane. It doesn't matter if the airplane is painted in Air Force colors or if it's a commercial bird. It performs the same, and commercial feasibility is simply another way of saying economy. This sort of thing is just as important for the military as it is for a commercial operator. With all the pressure on the services to function in the most efficient manner, the Hercules is the answer to a lot of prayers.

"This isn't just a company pilot talking, because I fly airplanes— I don't sell 'em. But I know this business, like these other people here with us. And you learn very quickly that the criteria of judgment include economy as well as anything else."

Another pilot interrupted. "This isn't very well understood. If the Hercules could shine only as an assault transport, then it would have long ago ended its production run. For the straight military operation, cost becomes secondary, because the need is to get the job done better than any other airplane can do it. Well, the '130 does that all right. But if it didn't deliver economy-wise, all those people who control the budget would have been on the necks of the Air Force long ago. You realize that the airplane is going to be used for years. There are hundreds of them in operation. If all those airplanes over a period of many years add up to a constantly losing proposition in terms of poor economy or expensive, balky maintenance—which means a high out-of-commission rate—then the production order very quickly comes to a screeching halt.

"The record of the industry is filled with airplanes that suffered from those characteristics—and quickly got the ax. Some of them are flying today. But their numbers—and their life span—are limited. They just couldn't hack it, and—"

"Wait a moment," Sullivan interjected. "I think I can put this better in hard figures. We can fly the Hercules across the continental United States with *half* the fuel consumption of the big jets. We're a little slower, of course, but the speed difference in terms of cargo-economy is nowhere as important as some people make it out to be.

"And what is most important of all is that you can land this machine just about anywhere with a full cargo load, and you can take it out of almost anyplace in the country. This is what has the cargo operators and the industrial people so wild to get their hands on the Hercules. They'd be able to go almost anywhere. They wouldn't need huge airfields and extensive facilities. They wouldn't need large ground crews or ground support equipment. They'd have freedom of the sort they can only dream about—right now.

"Originally the Air Force specified for the old A model that we must be able to take off and land, over a 50-foot obstacle at each end of the field, within a distance of 2,500 feet. That's a strip only a half-mile long, *with* those obstacles. And we had to do this with a full combat weight of 108,000 pounds. We not only met that criterion but we exceeded it."

An Air Force major—assigned to liaison duties at the Marietta plant—joined in. "Sullivan has a real point in what he's saying. Remember the old Berlin Airlift? Remember how we were pushed right to the wall in those days with our cargo operations?

"Well, over there the problem wasn't range at all. We were desperate for load-carrying capacity in terms of both weight and *bulk*. The airplanes always carried maximum loads and overloads, because the fuel requirements were minimum. With minimum fuel aboard the '130, as everyone else flew, we could have flown the same missions with more than 50,000 pounds of cargo, and it could have been bulky and massive, and it wouldn't have mattered a bit.

"In fact, we never knew, a good part of the time, how much cargo we did have in the airplanes we flew. The people on the ground shoved stuff in as if we had barges instead of airplanes. We wound the thing up at the end of the runway with everything we could get from the engines, and then we released the brakes and hoped for the best. We were pulling maximum takeoff power, everything screaming wide open, just to drag ourselves in the next hour up to 2,500 feet.

"Hell, that's no way to fly an airplane! But we had no choice. We've never tested the '130 to anything like that, but we know that under critical conditions in the field the airplane has been overloaded, and extensively. On short hauls it's possible to perform near miracles with high-density cargo in the '130. . . ."

Leo Sullivan and the other pilots believe that the Hercules would give the greatest impetus to establishing new industries in remote areas, where special tax rates prevail, labor is available, and the industrial planners could just about walk into the most favorable conditions possible.

"Look at what people have to do today to haul any major cargo

Huge, bulky loads—take them off from almost anywhere and land them almost anywhere on a dirt or grass strip. Job fulfilled by the Hercules

or freight by air," he exclaimed. "If you've got real bulk, you can't even get it into the planes now flying. If you have high density, you've got to pay through the nose because of the load factor. And then, there aren't more than a handful of airports big enough in the remote areas to take the big cargo planes. The result is that the benefits of air cargo are squeezed into a few major arterial routes, and they don't get down to grass-roots industry—where this is most needed.

"We've talked to people who fly cargo, and to the people who are in need of having heavy and bulky loads moved with speed. The idea of the Hercules operating to and from their plants makes their mouths water—because most towns have small airfields, which is all they need. But the Hercules can land on a strip, almost anywhere. And it's nothing to lay down a strip alongside these plants— this is being done in hundreds of places for small private planes. That's the whole gist of it—the Hercules can land anywhere the small ships go in. In fact, most of the single-engine private planes can't operate where we do.

"The '130 can be dumped into a rough strip, and it can literally *back into* a loading area, if necessary, by reversing the props. . . ."

There was more to this line of thought. But the Hercules isn't a commercial air freighter, despite the urgent need and the demand for the airplane. "Someday," say these pilots, it's bound to happen. The successive generations of Hercules transports, with increased power looming on the horizon, will once again bring about a marked advance in the performance of the airplane. At that time the Air Force might find it expedient to sell its C-130A models to commercial freight carriers—for just about the same amount that it paid for the airplanes. But, as the pilots emphasized, this was "roundtable talk," as far as they were concerned—a natural extrapolation of the airplane's abilities to perform an almost infinite variety of roles.

Vern Peterson folded his hands behind his head, almost as if he were looking back through the years. "It wasn't always this way with the bird," he said. "We've lived now for so many years with the Hercules as the most outstanding machine of its kind that it's difficult to remember that she wasn't always so gentle with us.

"She started out with a bang, as Leo knows so well, when the first production model caught fire. It was really something to stand there, and watch the wing burn and fall off the airplane. Of course, the whole thing was caused by that one lousy hose fitting that came loose, but it still looked like hell, despite the fact that this same machine has turned in years of tremendous service since then. . . ."

Vern Peterson went through a fire in the original YC-130 prototype during a routine test flight. Everything went fine, the crew landed the airplane, and began taxiing back to the flight line. The observer in the rear of the Hercules called in that fire had broken out in the left wheel well.

"When the copilot got the report that flames were shooting up from the wheel well," Peterson recalled, "he . . . well, I remember him jumping up out of his seat and walking all over my hands getting out of that airplane. He was just walking out and he said: 'I don't know about you, buster, but *I'm* leaving.'

"And he did; he surely did. He didn't walk around me—he walked *over* me."

The fire crew extinguished the blaze in minutes. After an exhaustive inspection and replacement of the wheel well assemblies, the work of three weeks, that airplane also returned to the air.

We discussed various incidents that occurred during the years of exhaustive testing. The task of the writer is to find the moments of danger, the times of peak excitement, the occasions when life hangs in the balance. The test pilots with me were embarrassed, because they have had precious little of this kind of situation during the development growth of the Hercules.

Jack G. Gilley, the Aviation Safety Staff Engineer at Lockheed-Georgia, had been with the Hercules longer than any other man in the group. His association with the airplane began when the engineers were making their first preliminary sketches, long before Lockheed walked away with the contract from the competition. As the preliminary work began, Lockheed assigned Gilley as the flight engineer to monitor the initial design of the airplane—to "ride shotgun" in the dual capacity of flight safety observer and flight engineer. At my insistence Gilley tried to explain the scarcity of "hairy incidents" so dear to the writer's heart.

"I think my best recollection of the flight-test program goes back to the original prototypes," he said. "I remember that on my first flight—Stan Beltz was still the pilot— we were doing 80-percent structural integrity demonstrations. This consisted of kicking the rudder back and forth rather violently, doing roller-coaster flight . . . all of this to a point that stopped at 80 percent of maximum stress designed into the airplane.

"I flew as the flight engineer on the bird, and I was greatly impressed—even somewhat amazed—at the *lack* of major problems. It's bad enough to beat up a spanking-new prototype, but we were really looking for trouble because we had a relatively new and unproved power plant in the machine. The turboprop was still an unknown quantity, and we anticipated really serious problems. We had plenty of minor setbacks to keep us busy, but it's the over-all program that I'm talking about. It was, very frankly, a delightful surprise to discover that the thing would fly just as we hoped it would.

"When you've studied the case histories of the great airplanes flying today, the story of the Hercules by comparison becomes even more amazing. It is *not* a normal course of events to follow the procedures we did with the Hercules. Usually one of the two major ingredients of the new airplane—either the airframe or the power source—has already been proven out beyond any question. In other words, you don't want to compound your normal problems, which are bad enough to begin with.

"But in our case everything was new. The airplane, the wing, the structure—all of it. And then we were actually proving out the new turboprop engines. Both the airplane and the engines achieved their success together. All the odds were against this. I think that all of us who were on the flight-test program were convinced that we had picked a winner. You have a feeling about this sort of thing, and it turned out that we were right on the button. We—"

Vern Peterson broke in. "Yeah, but all these years gone by help us to forget some of the frustrations of testing. The program had just started to pick up steam when we flew to El Centro in one of the prototypes to do some structural work, and that machine gave us nothing but fits out there because of the engines.

"The Allisons on that airplane wouldn't start when we wanted them to, they would surge and overspeed in the air, and they drove us nuts. It didn't help matters to explain that these were not the regular Hercules engines. They were a new experimental model that Allison was testing, and they had to be tested *somewhere*. Our own airplane was laid up back in the plant for modification work; we still had to fly for our program, and somebody remembered this particular ship.

"It was intended to be used for nothing else at the time but engine development—experimental work. Unfortunately, *we* were using it for everything else. The engines drove us to distraction. They demanded fixes right on the spot. That didn't bother the engine people —they were delighted to have us beating up the engines. I'll bet we really accelerated the development program on that particular engine design, because they *had* to fix things right then and there.

"I'd be remiss if I didn't point out that ours was the only airplane running into this kind of problem. Everyone else was delighted with the Hercules engine and singing its praises.

"I guess Lockheed can be real thankful that Allison did go all the way with their new design and give us so much power. In fact, the record shows that they gave us somewhere between five and seven percent more power than their specifications called for.

"And this, by the way, is what makes the Hercules so incredibly safe. You always have the power to get out of a jam if things start coming unglued. The main thing we had to work out was a matter of hardware, not design.

"Our program was a constant series of bigger and bigger steps. At first you're not sure what the airplane is going to do, how much of a beating it can take. But the more you work with it the more your confidence grows.

"Right now, in fact, we call the Hercules a boring airplane to fly in test work, because we know its capabilities. We *know* we're within a completely safe flight regime. It's funny about this; the more people respect an airplane and stay around it for a long time, the more they tend to get careless. After a while you say that it can do anything . . . and you start unwinding just a bit on your own requirements. And then you are looking for *trouble*. Overconfidence becomes the greatest danger that you've got to face."

Walt Hensleigh has flown the Hercules more than a thousand hours in flight-test work, and long before he came to Lockheed he was renowned for his skill at handling big airplanes under conditions where trouble is second nature to the work at hand.

"I've flown multi-engine airplanes for most of my career," Hensleigh explained, "and on the basis of my experience with a great many types, the C-130 has been just about the most *unexciting* airplane I ever flew. It just hasn't put us up against the wall the way many other ships are inclined to do. Oh sure, we've lost engines in flight and run into other mechanical difficulties that with other airplanes meant hitting the panic button.

"But this thing is so terrific in its power for its gross weight—especially in the early days when we imposed strict upper limits on weight—that the emergencies never amounted to very much.

"Before I went into the '130 I flew twin-engine transports, mostly C-119 and C-123 types. We flew these things loaded up to their maximum capacity. You lose an engine under this condition and right away you're in trouble—but deep. The difference was that those airplanes were limited in their operations by power. The Hercules is a different story altogether. Our limitations are structural. We can carry just about anything you can cram into the airplane, and if necessary we can carry it just as well with only three engines operating. And once we really get up steam, we can do it on two engines. . . ."

Walt Hensleigh did most of the final stability and control testing on the Hercules. This means determining the stability of the machine under normal and abnormal flight conditions—yaw, pitch, roll; everything that might be encountered from smooth air to the kind of turbulence that pounds the wings and heaves rocks at the fuselage.

Hensleigh emphasized that every airplane built must grow out of a series of compromises, and that it cannot possibly satisfy every single requirement of everybody concerned. His task, among others, was to draw the fine line where the attitudes and actions of the airplane in flight would reach the point of no return—and the pilot could, or would, lose control of his machine. From these tests there came a "few moments of consternation," as Hensleigh described them. But one thing was certain—Hensleigh's flight-test reports caused a storm of controversy within the Lockheed engineering division.

Hensleigh was doing sideslip maneuvers with the Hercules, which is something you do readily enough in small airplanes, but is *not* recommended for giants like the '130. Getting into a sideslip means crossing the controls—deliberately crossing things up. You push hard rudder in one direction and then apply aileron control *opposite* to that normally employed to enter a turn. The airplane then begins to fly in a partially sideways direction. During one maximum sideslip test, Hensleigh flew the Hercules through the air at a side angle of 17 degrees "when suddenly the rudder went through a complete stall."

His hands wove a pattern of flight in the room. "The rudder just flops all the way over," he explained, "and you go into a constant sideslip. You take your feet completely off the rudder and it doesn't matter a bit. You're in what we call rudder lock, or fin stall. There's plenty of warning, because the airplane doesn't like it, and it buffets madly and shakes from nose to tail. This is a built-in warning.

"Normally, when you get your teeth rattled by an airplane that's trying desperately to tell you to quit this sort of nonsense, you just ease off the controls and everything is fine again.

"Except, of course—" he grinned—"we were looking deliberately for some trouble. We didn't find that, but what we ran into was mighty interesting. . . ."

Four times in succession Hensleigh and the crew were able to ram the Hercules into the rudder-lock condition. But no one on the engineering staff would believe them! They insisted that the maneuver with the Hercules was impossible.

Hensleigh set his jaw, brought the nonbelievers aboard the airplane *they* had created, and took them up. And then he put the Hercules into a sideslip and "let her go *all* the way."

The eyes of the engineers seemed ready to pop out of their sockets. The great airplane clawed around in the air, rudder locked hard over, and then the Hercules literally slid sideways through the air. The instruments recorded a sustained sideways flight of more than 46 degrees from normal.

"The first time that happened it shook me," Hensleigh said. "I didn't know whether the airplane could possibly go all the way around in that sideslip, and that is one good way of getting into a flat spin. The airplane remains basically level—its nose to the horizon—but it rotates around its axis with tremendous speed, and you're completely out of control.

"It didn't happen that way. . . . The bird slewed around to 46 degrees and it stopped right there. Everyone in the flight deck stared at everyone else in disbelief. I brought her out of the slip, and then we tried it again. From then on we were able to repeat the test a number of times. It was simply amazing the way that big airplane, without any trouble at all, would go into this flight attitude and without any sweat recover at once. Finally it became just another maneuver in the Hercules.

"It would have torn up a good many big airplanes. . . ."

The subject arose again—as it always does with the pilots who fly the Hercules—of the unprecedented control characteristics of the airplane. The writer has had the occasion to talk to military pilots who fly the C-130 in its different configurations, from all its users—Air Force, Navy, Marines, and Coast Guard—and the cheers for the Hercules in this respect are spontaneous and unanimous. Leo Sullivan summed up the points that carry the greatest meaning to the men who fly the airplane.

"I think the '130 is just about ideal in handling and flying qualities," he said. "I have, in my time, flown some truly great airplanes, and I know what pilots want, and the Hercules gives it. It's as simple as that . . . a pilot wants good, quick response rates. He wants his controls to be light and to be effective. The airplane speaks for itself; just ask the crews. . . ."

We had a thorough bull session on some of the "greats" in the big airplane class, in terms of their control response and handling. The old Boeing B-17 Flying Fortress is still considered one of the "sweetest handling" machines ever to take to the skies. Many of the test pilots had at one time or another flown the Douglas C-118, or its commercial DC-6B version, which stands high on the list as one of the most wonderful airplanes ever produced. One pilot waxed enthusiastic about an airplane that few others in the group had ever flown—Britain's Avro Lancaster bomber—and he called it the "most beautiful big piston-engine airplane I've ever been in."

"This is the whole point," Sullivan continued. "It's from this tremendous background of experience that we make our judgment.

There are certain characteristics every pilot wants, and we've finally got them, in a big airplane, with the Hercules.

"With the four engines and the thrust-power ratio that's available you can do things that are simply impossible in a two-engine airplane, and still be here to talk about it. Most four-engine ships could never hack what we demand of the Hercules. When you consider the situations in which we place this machine, the abuse that it receives, the safety record is nothing less than incredible.

"Look at what we have: the high-wing configuration, the low-pressure tires, the braking system, the instant response and fabulous power from those four engines, the reverse thrust capability with real meaning to it. . . . Well, this gives you the greatest possible degree of latitude, or what we call 'holes to jump through' when anything goes wrong. In this respect the C-130 is the most forgiving big airplane ever built.

"The problem, if there is one, is overconfidence on the part of the crews, who finally come to believe that this airplane will take care of them, no matter *what*. We've come to consider this the greatest source of potential trouble."

Jack Gilley broke in. "Look—I know how sold *we* are on the airplane, and what pilots everywhere who fly the Hercules are going to tell you," he said. "But there's nothing better to prove Sullivan's point than a situation in which, historically, trouble is impossible to avoid. The kind of situation in which there are almost always going to be accidents and losses because of what you're trying to do.

"I'm talking about transition from other airplanes into the Hercules. Whenever you take people who are real sharp with their airplanes, and then shove them into a revolutionary new model—like the Hercules—you're bound to run into all sorts of problems."

As the first production airplanes started rolling out of the Marietta plant, Lockheed prepared to train a select group of Air Force crews in the airplane. Jack Gilley at this time was also the Chief Flight Engineer of the testing program, and responsible to the Chief Test Pilot for "formulating and conducting the test training program." This consisted of an intensive ground-school course, followed by exhaustive checkouts and instruction in the air.

Their first task was to "break in" the Air Force test pilots and flight engineers from Edwards Air Force Base, home of the Air Force Flight Test Center in California. This presented no problem, for these were the best of the professionals in the flight-test business, Air Force crews who had flown everything from the giant B-36 (ten engines and 450,000 pounds in weight) on down to small liaison aircraft. They took to the Hercules as though they'd been flying it for years.

The problem, as Gilley and the other Lockheed flight crews saw it, "was the requirement to train the operational personnel from Tactical Air Command. We convinced the Air Training Command that TAC must send a large contingent of their people to be trained by Lockheed instructors. The complexity of the Hercules and the extreme range of its missions required an intensive transitioning and break-in period."

"This was the first time," a pilot explained, "that a large training program was being undertaken with such a giant step. All previous transitions were on a methodical step-by-step process. The pilot graduated from one class of airplane to the next step in size, but of the same basic type that he had been flying. It was a period of adaptation, and only after this series of graduated moves upward was he permitted to get into something that is turboprop, pressurized, high-performance and high-altitude in its characteristics."

Gilley picked it up again. "But in this case," he added, "we were taking people whose total experience was with the C-119, a twin-engine, low-level, unpressurized, fairly slow and thoroughly conventional piston airplane—and moving them directly into the Hercules. Frankly, we had more than a few second thoughts about this.

"We are still a little dazed with the spectacular success we had in transitioning to the Hercules. We had without exception complete success in moving the initial Air Force pilots and crews into this airplane. And this was in the face of an expected minimum number of training accidents. The Air Force explained that, based on previous experience, there should have been at least two or three airplanes wiped out during the early transition training.

"But it didn't happen. We came out of that program without even a single serious accident. And *that* stands as the greatest testimonial of all to the Hercules."

Well, *almost.*

There was one other incident which still brings contrite looks whenever it's mentioned.

A team of Lockheed crews had flown several Hercules to the Far East and down into the Southwest Pacific area. At each stop they provided the opportunity for local military pilots from the different countries visited to fly the airplane. Dozens of pilots and officials climbed into the pilot's seat to feel the controls and maneuver the Hercules—the kind of demonstration that counts.

At one airfield the Lockheed crew picked up two dozen officers and airmen. Resplendent in uniforms that bristled with decorations, they trooped aboard the Hercules. At cruising altitude, they each took a turn at the controls.

One man, his uniform dripping with insignia and braid, sat at the wheel, flying the airplane for 15 minutes in a steady series of turns, climbs, and glides. His face was wreathed in smiles at the response of the Hercules. Through an interpreter, the Lockheed pilot inquired how long the man had been a pilot.

"Pilot? Oh, no, he is not a pilot. He is our cook!"

CHAPTER IX

Bite a Bigger Chunk of Air   NEARLY A THOUSAND
miles from the western coast of the United States, a long-range
DC-7C airliner is in trouble. Oil pressure in the left outboard engine is a recent memory, and the temperature gauge threatens to
break the glass. With a full passenger complement aboard—men,
women, and a disconcerting number of children—the pilot does not
like to shut down an engine a thousand miles from nowhere. But
he has no choice—it's either shut down the engine or beg for a fire.

The big propeller grinds slowly to a halt as the blades turn knife-
edge into the wind. In the meantime a Mayday signal goes out
from the airliner. It's a precaution only. The DC-7C can fly on
three engines, but if one more goes . . . no one likes to think about
it. The airplane descends slowly, heading for a level of 10,000 feet,
and the crew anxiously waits for sight of their escort.

That will be a brilliantly colored troubleshooter of the United
States Coast Guard. A spanking-new Hercules, adorned in gleaming
white and garish iridescent red paint, and carrying within its hulking body a forest of electronic gear. To the crew of the disabled
airliner the swiftly approaching Coast Guard airplane is an angel
of mercy. From hundreds of miles away its radar will pick up and
"lock on" to the DC-7C, enabling the Hercules to home right to
the airliner.

Another engine might fail . . . or something else. The airliner
might be required to ditch, a difficult decision to make with the
passengers—and a far more difficult feat to accomplish in safety.
But *if* it does happen, that Hercules will be screaming electronically
for rescue craft. It will drop huge liferafts that will inflate automatically, as well as food, medical supplies, and other equipment.

So the "just in case" is an extraordinarily welcome sight when it
appears as a speck on the distant horizon. The Hercules is dropping
like an arrow—a long, curving slant to bring it around and alongside the airliner. And then it is there, a cause for cheering by the
passengers and a long sigh of relief from the crew. The airliner
captain stares at his dead engine and lifeless propeller, and it
doesn't seem so bad now that the Coast Guard is there to help.

The "angel of mercy" slides alongside the crippled airliner with its dead engine. The Coast Guard pilot grins broadly.

And two of the four propellers of the Hercules change from a glistening shine to a darkening blur. They slow to a halt, the broad propeller blades slicing cleanly into the wind.

The airliner captain glances at the Hercules again, and his jaw sags. Speechless for the moment, he bangs the copilot on the arm and points. His First Officer looks out and says only: "I'll be Goddamned . . ."

Maybe that Hercules crew is just plain disdainful of three-engine flight. It could be that they're a bit rankled by being bolted out of a sound sleep by the emergency horn. Or perhaps they figure that there's a unique way to let the airliner passengers know that a feathered propeller really isn't anything to be frightened of.

In this fashion the "two-engine Hercules" escorts the crippled airliner to safety. . . .

The Air Force lieutenant colonel is making his third flight in a C-130A Hercules as part of his transition training in the new turbo-prop airplane. He's delighted with the big machine; more than once he has exclaimed that it handles "just like a fighter."

Today the Lockheed instructor-pilot insists upon practice in absolutely dead-level, on-course flight. The lieutenant colonel sets up his heading and flies rock-steady on his course. Damn, nothing to it with *this* airplane. . . .

The Lockheed pilot, however, is displeased. With mute but telling disapproval he points to the gyro compass. The Hercules is drifting slightly off its course. The military pilot is disturbed. He's flying the airplane with absolute precision. But it's showing a tendency to drift ever so slightly to the left. The lieutenant colonel mutters something about "trim that won't stay effective," and he starts to voice a complaint to his instructor.

The flight engineer leans forward and taps him lightly on the shoulder. The Air Force officer looks back, where the engineer, completely deadpan, is shaking his head and making strange sounds. The lieutenant colonel can't tell if he's choking.

The engineer points out the window. The pilot stares in disbelief. The number-one engine is lifeless, the propeller dead into the wind.

"When the hell did *that* happen?" he asks with an embarrassed look on his face.

The crew explodes in laughter.

"Seventeen minutes ago, Colonel, *17* minutes ago, *that's* when!" shouts the engineer in glee.

A little joke to prove a point about power and inherent stability
on only three engines . . .

An Air Force WB-50 weather-reconnaissance plane in January
1958 disappears in the Pacific Ocean. Last reported position: somewhere near Ulithi Island, in the middle of nowhere. At almost the
same time, the first two C-130A Hercules assigned to duty in the
Far East land at Guam, en route to Ashiya Air Force Base in Japan.
Every plane is needed for search, but the C-130A crews are non-
military—Lockheed personnel ferrying the two Hercules across the
Pacific. No matter; the Lockheed crews don't wait to be asked.
They volunteer for the mission.

The weather is violent. Low clouds, screaming wind, angry and
froth-whipped waves. The rain comes down in torrential sheets,
black streams of water smashing against the two airplanes.

Aboard one of the Hercules is a colonel from the Air Force
weather station on Guam. He's never seen a Hercules before, and
he sniffs distrustfully at the machine. It *can't* have much range with
four jet engines, despite the propellers. . . .

The storm becomes worse and the Hercules staggers beneath the
severe gusts. The airplane bulls its way into the search area, and
the good colonel turns a color somewhat whiter than normal when
the engineer, Ned Ridings, casually leans forward and shuts down
the two outboard engines.

The propellers stab lifeless into the wind. "This kinda shook up
the poor guy for a moment," Ridings recounts. "Appears that he
wasn't used to this stuff. . . ."

After a while the colonel seems to have good cause for that
moment of consternation. The oil pressure readings on the number
three (right inboard) engine fluctuate. The erratic behavior becomes more pronounced.

"I figured . . . what the hell, we'll shut that one down and run
on two and four," Ridings explains. "I fired up number four and
when everything was on the button I shut down number three."

This shakes up the colonel even more. He can't take it with the
storm-tossed ocean only 500 feet below, and engines firing up and
shutting down in such casual fashion. It violates every concept of
safety in flying he has ever known.

"Jesus Christ!" he screams at Ridings. "What the hell do you
people do—just start 'em up and shut 'em down like they're washing
machines?"

The sun is still low on the horizon when a Hercules races away
from an Air Force base in Florida. Normally the airplane heaves

up its nose and runs for altitude. High up the jet engines lose their voracious appetite for fuel.

But this Hercules doesn't climb. It leaves the runway behind, and in seconds the pilot dumps the nose into level flight. The airplane is *low;* trees and buildings flash beneath the hulking body.

The pilot aims for California, and casually says, "Okay—shut her down," to the flight engineer. The engineer moves his fingers on the panel, and the number-four engine sighs to a stop with the propeller blades slicing into the wind.

A little while later the pilot murmurs, "Okay for the next," and the engineer responds with some more finger movement, and the number-one engine gives up its fire. The blades stand motionless.

Two engines shut down, heavily laden with fuel, the Hercules races to the west, staying on the deck—and with California and no stops in between as its goal. A pilot recalls the reaction to the flight:

"It was a hell of a trip. They kept everything just below the airplane—trees, hills, even the mountains out west. They beat up the countryside all the way.

"They've still got warrants out for those guys in quite a few cities, because every town and village and city they passed over, or nearby, people sort of got excited. They saw this big airplane, something entirely new to them, and with a sound they'd never heard before.

"Big airplanes don't fly low—this one was right on the deck. Big airplanes don't sound like . . . well, they couldn't even describe it. And big airplanes don't fly normally with two of the engines dead and the props feathered. The airplane burst into view without warning, howled overhead, and just disappeared from sight over the nearest hill or so.

"Well, what else could all this mean except that this monster was on its way down to a crash? Everyone figured that it had gone out of sight and then smashed into a hill or plowed into a mountain. People by the dozens and then by the hundreds called the police in a big sweat to report the disaster, or they tore off to find the wreck themselves, and when they couldn't find anything—then *they* called the police and wanted to know 'where did it crash?'

"And of course there wasn't any crash, but hundreds and hundreds of people were yelling that there *was,* and many of them were running a wild goose chase looking for the remains of that mysterious big airplane. Like I say, it was a hell of a trip. . . ."

Lockheed was delighted, the Allison company overjoyed, and the Air Force beaming from the performance of their new bird: coast-to-coast, at an altitude where jet engines are notorious for their

Two-engine flight is normal operation for the Hercules on extended-duration missions. . . . A C-130B cruises cross-country with its No. One and No. Four engines shut down and the propellers feathered. (*Lockheed-Georgia*)

fuel-gulping inefficiency, and with two of the Allisons shut down and feathered. No one asked any more questions about engine-out reliability of that new airplane called the Hercules. . . .

Lieutenant Jocko Donlon of the 839th Air Division at Sewart Air Force Base in Tennessee is very fond of his new flying machine. As a pilot of one of the first C-130A transports assigned to the 839th, he suffers green envy from his fellows but nonetheless waxes enthusiastic about the new bird.

On this particular day the airplane is loaded to the gills with cargo, and Jocko Donlon has a flight plan from Sewart into Langley Air Force Base in Virginia. The jet engines purr like kittens, the big props slice the air with ease, and the Hercules eats up miles.

The weather changes—suddenly. Rain is forecast, but the rain gets very big and then it gets very hard. Without warning the

Hercules is smashed with a tremendous barrage of hailstones the size of golf balls.

Of all the sounds in an airplane to separate a pilot from his equilibrium, the worst is an avalanche of hail. Just consider being smashed by a torrent of thousands and thousands of golf balls coming at you at more than 300 miles per hour!

The sound is unbelievable and indescribable. Likely it is worse than going over Niagara Falls in a barrel filled with exploding fire-crackers. The closest I've ever heard anyone come to describing it accurately was an Air Force pilot with a white face who staggered to a wild landing in South Carolina. He had just come through a beaut of a hailstorm and there didn't remain an inch of smooth metal on his airplane.

"It was like I'd stuck my head into a barrel," he groaned, "and then somebody cut loose with a shotgun right next to my ear. Then he did it again—and again and again. The only reason I'm not scared is that I'm too frightened. . . ."

At the time of Donlon's flight, Lockheed had tested the C-130A extensively, but you can't duplicate *all* conditions. And this was the first Hercules that had ever been right in the middle of a full-grown hailstorm. Under these conditions you learn new things—*fast*—about your airplane.

Donlon and his crew learn that pounding hail can beat the day-lights out of the oil cooler ducts of the engines. In fact, it beats those ducts so badly that they twist and bend completely out of shape. And this chokes off the flow of cooling air to the engines.

In no time at all the oil temperatures skyrocket, the seals go wide open on three of the four engines, and the instrument panel lights up with red lights like a control board at Cape Canaveral. Three big, brilliant red lights—each one mutely screaming *"Fire!"*

Donlon hasn't even got time to curse. Not even one juicy, pro-fane word. Immediately he hits the switches to kill *three* engines and feather the props.

This leaves him, of course, with only one engine running. The flight engineer invokes (he hopes) the smiling whim of Fate and squeezes every ounce of power he can from the remaining Allison.

The field closest to the one-lung Hercules is Pope Air Force Base, near Fort Bragg. It is questionable about their dragging in, because that one engine is being called upon to pull a heavily loaded Her-cules through the air.

Donlon eases the nose down. Gravity in this instance is a friend because it means a free dividend of speed. And every bit of speed now is critical. The copilot radios the control tower that they have "some engine trouble" and will need to be cleared for an emergency approach—straight in to the runway and no nonsense about patterns or turns.

Jocko Donlon coaxes the big airplane toward the field. People pour from the operations shack to see the crippled bird. Someone with binoculars shouts that he has *three* engines feathered. More people come running to watch the airplane pound its way down the final approach, and slide onto the runway with a beautiful touchdown.

The Hercules rolls off the runway at the far end (reverse thrust from *one* engine is not in the books) and taxis slowly toward the flight line.

Everybody saw it happen, but no one really believes it. . . .

From the first moments of its existence—as sweeping lines from the pencils of its engineers—the success of the Hercules has been inextricably linked with its source of power. The design of any airplane in respect to its shape, its construction, its appearance can go only so far, and not one step farther, until there are brought into the picture the engines which will impart life to that airplane.

The success of any airplane, notwithstanding all other factors, is in direct proportion to the success of its engines.

Through the history of aviation, a succession of great aircraft has come and gone. This is a matter of record—both statistical and emotional. Yet there is a less conspicuous succession that also comprises a vital phase of this history: the airplanes that were "almost great," but fell by the wayside.

In many, perhaps the majority, of these instances the final blow could be traced to a lack of the power desperately required for these new machines. The airframe design, the sweeping lines of revolutionary concepts that promised revolutionary performance, all these wither on the engineering vine unless there is provided an equally outstanding source of energy.

It is in this respect that the Hercules has enjoyed the greatest of good fortune. The performance of this machine is judged phenomenal by its crews, and this is validated by its record. We have seen certain instances that reflect a brilliant new world of flight as practiced by the Hercules. The incidents with which this chapter began are only several selected at random from a scrapbook bulging with performances that, before the Hercules piled up a record of proof, would have evoked cries of disbelief from even the most enthusiastic and experienced of pilots.

The test pilots and engineers who nurtured the Hercules from its embryonic stages to the globe-girdling mastery that it now practices daily have spelled out in their own words, again and again, the key to that success.

Leo Sullivan, accepted as one of the nation's outstanding test pilots, described the intrinsic promise of the Hercules during the time that he deliberately abused the airplane. He called it a matter not of improved performance, but of "a completely new regime of flight." Expressions that once reflected pilots' dreams took on reality in their reports of "fantastic advantages in thrust capability."

Above all, it was a "wonderful thing to know what lay beneath your hand. All you have to do to get power is move that throttle, and you get an instantaneous . . . response."

Instant power the pilots call it. Another test pilot puts his feelings differently. He goes right to the basics of flying, to those moments on the edge of disaster. "You always have the power to get out of a jam if things start coming unglued." To men who have flown for years on the edge of "just enough power," and attended the funerals of their fellow pilots who failed to gain that much, that one sentence is a ringing speech.

The growing wonder that attends the continued performance of the engines that provide the heartbeat of the Hercules stems also from sources other than flight—such as the intensive and brutal tests in rough, unprepared fields to which the Air Force subjected the Hercules during its "proving trials."

A pilot recalls those days, and with a touch of wonder still in his voice, he asks if the writer remembers "those operations when we were doing the rough-field and the short-field capability tests? We'd come down with a real crash stop. We'd just slam this thing down on the field, and then the airplane would disappear completely from sight in all the dust that blew up. . . . It just disappears; you can't see a damn thing for all that dust. It fascinates me to think that those engines can eat that much dust and just keep right on going as though they were cruising at 20,000 in perfectly clear air. . . ."

All this—the performance, the reliability, the "instant power," did not exist in proven form when the Hercules began to take shape at the hands of its engineers. The *need* was clearly established, however, when the Air Force in its private meetings made it very clear that what they wanted was—in the early 1950's—"the answer to an almost impossible assignment."

> An advanced, all-purpose, work-horse type, aerial vehicle, that can go anyplace, anytime, without elaborate facility or equipment preparations.

This threw the door wide open for unorthodox techniques and designs to make possible the "almost impossible assignment." Unfortunately, there was precious little waiting beyond that open door except for the need to be filled.

The piston engine didn't stand a chance. In terms of greater power it stood near the end of the line in development. The huge engines that powered the biggest airplanes in the world were a combination of miracle and monster. They were incredibly complex in their manufacture, and exasperatingly troublesome in their operation. They demanded meticulous and frequent maintenance. The final blow to their future lay in their sheer bulk and weight. All these factors combined effectively to place the handwriting on the wall for the piston engine—and to guarantee its inadequacy and its rejection for the airplane so drastically needed by the nation.

The pure jet engine had already swept the country, and the leaps-and-bounds gains in performance, guaranteed by its power, at times overshadowed its limitations. The problems intrinsic to the jet engine quickly cast its selection into doubt. In flight at low and medium altitudes, the pure jet was voracious in its appetite, consuming fuel in a manner to delight the oil companies but demoralizing to engineers searching for outstanding performance at *all* altitudes.

The jet airplanes in flight during the period of initial creation of the Hercules proved to be runway hogs. They ate up thousands of feet of runway in their takeoff runs, and their sluggish, almost painfully slow acceleration guaranteed their complete inability to meet the requirement to "go anyplace, anytime." The pure jet airplane could not be considered as adapted to anything resembling short-field operations.

The role of the transport in limited wars dictated the stringent requirement that the new airplane be capable of operating "without elaborate facility or equipment preparations." One had only to consider the extent of facilities and manpower necessary to sustain the jet engine on the ground to cast aside this possibility.

From the exhaustive studies of engine possibilities there emerged only one source of power that could adequately meet the many and varied requirements to which the new airplane would ultimately be subjected—a marriage of the jet engine in its most efficient form with the propeller also in its most efficient shape. If such a blend could be produced, the "almost impossible" would become only a matter of hardware development. And at the time that Lockheed needed to arrive at its decision, the Allison Division of General Motors Corporation was busily engaged in mixing the "blend."

Lockheed and Allison engineers buckled down to proving hard facts and figures. Behind the selection of Allison lay its years of extensive testing and experience with compact jet engines that were exceptionally light in weight. Even more important to Lockheed was the highly successful test program of an Allison jet engine that had been combined with an outboard reduction-gear assembly.

Right there lay the seeds that could well sprout to the success that Lockheed envisioned. The performance of the engine with that gear assembly meant an especially promising combination of the turbojet engine with the propeller. This was the *turboprop* that could fulfill every stringent requirement of the new assault transport.

As the months passed, both airplane and engine moved along concurrent paths of development, directed carefully toward a final merging of the two. By early 1954 the Allison YT56-A-1 turboprop engine was ready for an accelerated flight-test program.

While the Tactical Air Command worked hand-in-glove with Lockheed and Allison to carry the Hercules from concept to reality, the Military Air Transport Service (MATS) also spurred a more rapid development of the Allison turboprop engine. Performance figures for the new engine as presented by Allison whetted the appetite of MATS, which decided to see for itself and ordered a thoroughgoing evaluation test program.

Thus there began an exhaustive double-barreled effort—engine evaluation with the prototype Hercules aircraft and the initial production run of the C-130A model, concurrently with the MATS flight evaluation. For the latter, MATS provided to Allison two Convair C-131B airline-type transports for modification to accept the YT56-A-1 engines. MATS called for the flight evaluation effort to begin in January 1955, and to end the same year. The 1700th Test Squadron received the assignment to fly 3,000 hours with these engines in this period of time, under all possible flight conditions.

Just as the Hercules in its flight-test program was subjected to progressively brutal treatment, so the new Allison engine was "put through the mill." At the time the 1700th Test Squadron began its program of flying literally around the clock with its experimental power plants, the engine was qualified for only 100 hours of flight before it had to be pulled into the maintenance shops for a complete overhaul. It did not matter that the engine might be running perfectly—it must be stripped down and inspected with meticulous care.

In January 1955 the two airplanes flew a total of 196 hours for the month. Later that year the engines were being run in excess of 300 hours every month, and the total time-in-commission each month rose steadily. Statistics often present figures meaningful only to special groups or interests, but the figures that flowed from the accelerated test program raised the eyebrows of all pilots informed of the effort. For an entire year, working with experimental engines and strict overhaul procedures, the engines flew an average of 4.37 hours every day. This in itself is misleading, for the test program picked up steam as it progressed, and finally the airplanes were in the air for almost 12 hours out of every 24.

There are significant trends in every development program. The characteristics of the Hercules made themselves known quickly to Lockheed and the Air Force during its grueling flight tests, and the characteristics of the Allison engines also provided good cause for rousing cheers. The operational performance of the 1700th Test Squadron—who in less than one year flew their airplanes a total of 3,148 hours—was nothing less than astonishing.

An official evaluation at the time stated that engine operation "during this test was phenomenal, since the engine involved had actually been qualified for only 100 hours before overhaul."

This, however, only partially expressed the true significance of the engine's performance. Again, quoting from the official evaluation: "The 'Y' engines, though not yet qualified by official model test, were allowed an increase of time between overhaul from 100 to 300 hours, which made completion of test on schedule possible. Such utilization and availability of an engine at this stage of development is almost unbelievable."

This was one of the more significant of the trends. By June of 1957, when the Hercules suffered the punishment of simulated-combat testing by Lockheed and the Tactical Air Command, the allowable operating time for the engine between major overhauls had reached 450 hours. Now began a dizzy upward spiral in its demonstrated reliability. Four years later—in the summer of 1961—the Hercules' engines were advanced to 1,200 hours of flight operations between major overhauls. And just about two years more brought another wide advance: the time between major overhauls went to 2,100 hours of engine operation.

These progressive statistics quickly become dry and abstract. However, one needs only to mention such figures to the man on the flight line and in the hangar who has a history of skinned knuckles and cracked fingernails from probing the innards of balky engines, to receive an extraordinarily appreciative response. Engine reliability, especially the length of time that the engine stays on the airplane before it is replaced, means everything to the man who must keep this intricate machinery functioning perfectly.

It is especially important to organizations like the Tactical Air Command, that fly the airplane, and to the nation, that they be able to meet their requirements in everyday *and emergency* missions. Statistics that list total numbers of airplanes produced or assigned to different Air Force, as well as Navy, Marine, and Coast Guard units, are actually quite meaningless. They show only the disposition of those aircraft; they do *not* reveal the truly critical factor: how many of those airplanes are actually in operation? Because those that are not contribute nothing to operational performance.

One of the key factors in value received from any product is the time-in-commission rate of that product. If an airplane must spend an exorbitant time in the maintenance shops, that airplane may well prove to be more of a liability than it is an asset—no matter how brilliantly it performs once it takes wing.

This is a factor little understood, and yet it is all-important to the people who must carry out the missions and meet the needs of their services and the nation generally. It is also of extreme interest to the taxpayer, for success or failure in this area of multi-million-dollar airplanes means, over the passage of years, great dollar efficiency or, conversely, a staggering deficit engendered by skyrocketing costs of maintenance.

Excessive maintenance costs create a truly vicious circle in the budgetary department. Every airplane that flies cargo and/or passengers with our military services operates at a specific dollar-value cost. It requires so much money to supply the fuel, oil, and other "working elements" of the airplane. The faster the airplane moves through the air, the less time is involved in point-to-point travel, and efficiency goes up. Equally important, the less time spent on the ground in transferring cargo and/or passengers and preparing the airplane for flight, the higher the efficiency rate.

When the airplane must be pulled off the line and sent to the hangars for maintenance, it is completely out of commission. It requires physical space and a swarm of maintenance personnel. The shorter the period during which an airplane flies before its engines are pulled for major overhaul, the greater the cost of operating it. Airplanes are designed to fly. They serve their purpose only when airborne. On the ground an airplane is a losing proposition. If the engines must be pulled frequently for major overhauls, you've got a money-chewing bird on your hands.

The fact that the Allison engines in the Hercules now run for well over 2,000 hours between major overhauls is a major reason why this airplane is so economical to operate. There are other reasons, of course, but this is one of the more important.

All airplanes sooner or later must undergo engine changes, but changing the engines on a big transport aircraft is a complicated process that involves a crew of skilled men and elaborate facilities, and that freely consumes time. The United States Air Force and the other military services have an "established direct operating cost with the Hercules of four cents per ton mile." A special report shows further that this has "enabled the Military to move air cargo at a rate under that of many other means of transportation." It also allows them to suffer the least amount of wasted time while sweating out the arrival of critical cargo.

It is for these reasons that the budgetary watchdogs find such pleasure in the Hercules on the ground as well as in the air, and they like to remember an incident in July 1959 which typifies Hercules ground maintenance. A regular Air Force maintenance crew removed all four T56 engines from a Hercules, replaced the engines, hooked up all the wiring and plumbing, ran the engines and propellers through a meticulous power check, and returned the airplane to full flying status. Time required for the entire operation: *five* working hours.

Every engine has certain traits that either endear it to its flight crews and the ground maintenance personnel, or else prompt a stream of purple profanity and undying suspicion. The Hercules is a machine singular in the shouts of praise it has elicited from its flight and ground crews, and for the latter there are in the Allison engine the delights of simplicity of design, swiftness of troubleshooting, and ease of maintenance.

With every increase in mission versatility and scope of operations of the Hercules, there arose additional demands of performance and reliability from its Allison turboprops. The spectrum of operational conditions has been, and remains, a cross section of the weather extremes of the world and an itinerary of most of the global surface. This means operations in the peaks of the Andes, Alps, and Himalayas, where the air is brutally thin and support facilities on the ground are no more than a wistful dream. In the opening pages of this book we saw the versatility of those engines as tested by operations from airfields where the flight crews on the ground sometimes experience a shortage of oxygen.

But this is only one environment. . . . The Allisons endure the soggy heat and humidity of jungle operations. They operate with wondrous perfection in the dirt and grime of remote strips, the blistering heat and sand of the Sahara, the grinding effect of clouds of dust from bauxite ore in the southwest Pacific. They suffer the savage cold of 100 degrees below zero from the North Pole to the

In the summer of 1959 a "regular Air Force maintenance crew removed all four T56 engines from a Hercules, replaced the engines . . . and returned the airplane to full flying status. Time required for the entire operation: *five* working hours." (*Air Force*)

other end of the planet, where they have borne explorers, scientists, and developers on their missions to unravel the mysteries of the uncharted wastelands along the bottom of the world.

Operations under such incredibly varied conditions presuppose overworking the engines and exposing them to severe abuse. Maintenance is not only compromised, but degraded by circumstances to a mockery of the term. The fuel fed to the engines would make an American oilman weep, for it is sometimes substandard and rife with impurities—the only fuel that is available. The engines nonetheless continue to spin with their jewel-like precision, the propellers slash hungrily at the air, and the airplanes sail confidently through the seas that cover all the world.

At the military base in Wiesbaden, Germany, an Allison engineer far from home, far indeed from the plant back in Indianapolis, stands with the writer beneath the wing of a Hercules. "It's all quite simple," he explains. "When you get down to the basics of this machine and what it is called upon to do, the people who produce the engines have only one choice. And that is to impart to the airplane what they know the machine needs, what the Air Force wants, and what will bring the crews to accept placing their lives right on the line."

The shadow of the Hercules stretches long and grotesque in the late afternoon sun. The engineer glances up at the two slim nacelles knifing forward from beneath the left wing. He continues: "Any aircraft that flies constant scheduled missions, and, above all, the unscheduled missions over wide oceans, impenetrable jungle, the Antarctic wastelands—well, you name it, anywhere—hasn't got any alternatives in its flights. It either completes its mission, or it doesn't. The 'doesn't' is not pleasant to think about, and there are few people who really understand just how strong this feeling of responsibility for these engines is with us. Every time the airplanes go out—oh, I know, the record for reliability is very bright and shining—but every time they go out, a little bit of us goes along.

"It's surprising just how many people on our staff, and at Lockheed too, I suppose, once wore the same suit these crews wear. We all flew different airplanes, and there was a hell of a lot of flying and a lot of good people who never came home because we were fighting the kind of air war that will never again be fought . . . but that sticks with you. The memories, I mean. Not clear and sharp, like yesterday, but a feeling inside. You can't remember what all the other planes looked like, or how many sunsets you watched, but you never forget that sinking, lousy feeling in your gut when you're in the middle of nowhere and an engine decides to chew itself to pieces. You don't forget it because you don't know *how.*

"And maybe—" he smiled quickly—"this is good. Maybe it's very good. These kids are flying in a different world and in a different age, but we communicate real fine when we think of how the feeling in the belly is the same with anybody and everybody. So when they come back after beating the living bejesus out of these engines, and swearing by instead of *at* them—why, it's a nice thing to know. A very nice thing indeed. . . ."

Sometimes a writer feels the need to support sentiments such as these with unsentimental statistics. A few provide an exciting realization of what is meant by a term so easily abused—reliability.

During the first seven years of fleet operations with the Hercules —flying with our military forces and the Coast Guard under almost every conceivable condition (including being shot up by guerrilla forces in jungle territory)—the Allison engines in the various C-130 models accumulated approximately *four million hours of operation.*

In anybody's language that is a staggering aggregation of time. But it is only the backdrop curtain for a much more significant record. Inherent quality is a promise of increasing reliability, and the Allison engines fulfilled that promise. All engines at one time or another succumb to the many factors that constantly wear and grind at the engine, and the Allison is no exception. But to engineers and mechanics the key figure of reliability is what they call the "unscheduled removal rate." In other words, how often must an engine be pulled from a Hercules, and changed, because of a mechanical fault or failure?

The going rate for the airplane at this time looks like something out of a nuclear reactor handbook. It reads 0.30/1000 flight hours— or the need to remove an engine for every 3,333.3 hours of power plant operation in flight. Taking into consideration the assignments and conditions under which the Hercules must labor, it is a monumental tribute to the intrinsic quality of those engines.

There's a vice president of Allison who looks at reliability in a different and perhaps much more significant manner. When the Air Force, all the other users of the airplane, and Lockheed had completed their survey of the first seven years of Hercules fleet operations, there was one fact above all others that stood out like a blinding light from the stack of technical reports. This vice president saw fit to exhibit some "family pride" in that fact, and he had a little placard made up, which he then hung on the wall behind his desk, framed neatly beneath a picture of the Hercules. That placard says:

During seven years and four million engine flight hours with this airplane, not one accident has ever been attributed to an engine responsibility.

Simple and Complex

The Allison T56-A-7 engine in the C-130B is a sparkling gem of a power plant. With everything running full bore, the engine grinds out a total of 4,050 horsepower—which is nothing less than sensational when one considers the diminutive dimensions of the beast. It is 145 inches in length, and its width is such that you can contain it within your arms. And not outstretched, either, for the engine from side to side has a span of only 27 inches.

There are many different ways to look at an engine, and a thousand more viewpoints from which to consider its merits. But no matter where you stand, it is an impressive fact that 4,050 thundering horses are generated by a package weighing only 1,833 pounds —and one that can operate flawlessly while eating dust or snow, no matter what the temperature, and for more than 16 hours in the air (and much more, if the Hercules could only carry that much more fuel).

Or putting it still another way, each slender Allison whips out 2¼ horsepower for every pound of engine weight. This may not mean much to people more concerned with the horsepower beneath the hood of a chrome-striped auto, but it is the kind of statistic that brings joy to aircraft designers and enables the Hercules to topple world performance records like wheat before a thresher.

Each engine consists of two assemblies—the power section, or gas turbine; and the reduction gear assembly, which has a single

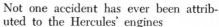

Not one accident has ever been attributed to the Hercules' engines

propeller shaft. The turbine is long and slender, with an axial-flow compressor made up of 14 neatly packaged compressors, which feed air that is rammed together—compressed—into six through-flow-type combustion chambers. Here the fire burns, explosively expands its mixture of compressed air and burning fuel, and sends it howling back to a four-stage turbine. The result of this extremely energetic process is to produce power sufficient to spin the turbine, the propeller shaft, and the fat-bladed propeller, and as an after-thought to kick out a stream of exhaust gases with such force that this also imparts a very solid push to the airplane.

An Air Force instructor, who early in the operational life of the Hercules became one of the very first to check out in the airplane and its equipment, explained the innards of the Allison to a class of eager young pilots.

"Does all this interior assembly of the Allison sound compli-cated?" he queried the students. "Well, friends, it ain't. Just a plain old jet engine that utilizes more energy toward driving a prop shaft and less energy for jet propulsion.

"So what do we get out of this arrangement? We get propeller efficiency downstairs where we really need it . . . and we get high performance upstairs for the long flights. Actually, about 10 to 15 percent of the push from the engines can be chalked up to jet thrust.

"Now, there is another factor in favor of this arrangement, and that is simplicity. No connecting rods to clank and bang. No pistons to push and pull and hammer . . . no rings and no pins. Timing problems? In this engine there ain't none. Fuel problems? None. As a matter of fact, the T56 engine will digest almost anything. Of course, the Air Force likes you to follow the book and to use JP-4 fuel as the recommended bill of fare for your Allisons. But in a pinch the engine can operate on most anything that will flow and that can burn.

"Many of the innovations incorporated within the '130, as they relate to your power sources, will seem quite strange at first. It is my opinion that the very simplicity of the instrument panel will give the average multi-engine driver a shock. The pilot and copilot have a minimum of gadgets to watch. About all they have to cope with are the normal flight gauges. The center of the panel is de-voted to engine instruments. As for a separate panel for the flight engineer, à la C-124, like the feller says, 'They ain't none!'"

The operation of the engine-propeller system of the Hercules is simple. The pilots say so, the engineers say so, the flight handbook says so—until you try to get an explanation in words that do not require an M.I.T. graduate to translate them. The problem here is that there are *two* rather involved interrelationships. Our Air Force instructor explains the basic operation:

"The throttles on the '130 act the way any throttles are supposed to work. Push ahead to go and pull back to whoa! Of course, the arrangement is a bit different from the reciprocating mill setup on account of the fact that on takeoff and in flight *the engines are turning up at 100 percent of their rated RPM all of the time.*

"So . . . when you advance the throttles you are not increasing the revolutions per minute of either your engines or your propellers. You do not increase the RPM one little bit."

At this point the instructor stops for a moment, closes his eyes, and says: "Admittedly, this is somewhat confusing. But only because it represents such a radical departure from what we are accustomed to with the reciprocating engine. . . ."

When a pilot shoved his throttles forward with the reciprocating engine, he did a number of things with that one movement. He increased the flow of fuel to the engine, he raised its operating temperature, and he brought about a great increase in the speed

Secret of the spectacular success of the Hercules . . . engines of tremendous power, amazing simplicity, unprecedented reliability, linked to huge, tremendously efficient propellers. . . . (*Air Force*)

at which the engine operated. He also increased the speed at which the propeller turned—its revolutions per minute. This is conventional and it is quickly understood.

But the turboprop arrangement is not conventional—not at all. The engines always turn at a constant speed. So when the Allison engine is running "full bore," it is whirling within that nacelle at the tremendous speed of 13,820 revolutions per minute.

That engine is spinning around more than 230 times *every second*.

The propeller also turns at a constant speed. But it is not the speed of the engine, and here is where the radical departure takes place. The engines spin at a constant 13,820 RPM. The propeller spins at a constant rate of 1,016 ("A" model) revolutions per minute. There lies the difference with a vengeance. Between the speed at which the engine and the propeller spins there is a specific ratio —it works out to a reduction of just about 13.6. The engine spins about 13½ times faster than does the propeller.

Now we study this subject a bit more cautiously. Since the engine and the propeller are turning at constant speed, how does the airplane get *more* power in flight when the pilot wants that power?

The answer lies in the blades of the propellers. Right there is the final secret of the outstanding performance of the Hercules. To fathom the nature of that secret, it is essential to understand that it is the changing angle—the pitch—of the propeller blades as they whirl through the air that determines the flight power of the airplane.

Few people really comprehend the vital role of the propeller *blade*—or, more specifically, the angle at which that blade cuts the air—in flight performance.

When the pilot of the piston-engine airplane desires to change power, he must be sure that two power controls are involved. His throttle gives him maximum engine power; his propeller-pitch control allows him to utilize in the most efficient manner the power of the engine.

To get more power, he changes the pitch of his propeller blade. He flattens out the pitch—moves it into "fine" position. The blades shift position as they turn, their sharp edges cutting almost knife-like into the air. This means less drag—less resistance to the surface area of the blade—as it whirls. Because of the lesser drag, the engine speed increases. Then the pilot advances the throttle to maximum power (represented as manifold pressure within the engine). Now he has the maximum possible forward *thrust* from the propeller and engine, and the performance improves.

If the pilot were to keep his throttle at maximum power, but changed the propeller pitch so that the blades turned to a 45-degree angle, the revolutions per minute of that propeller would drop drastically. If you place your hand knife-edge out of the window of a speeding car, fingers pointing upward, you don't feel much wind resistance. But if you turn your wrist so that the wind strikes the fully exposed area of your hand—you feel immediately the strong force of that wind. What you are doing, in effect, is to change the pitch—the angle—at which the wind strikes the surface area of your hand.

When the propeller blade is at a "coarse" rather than a "fine" pitch, it presents much of its surface area to the wind created by its rotating movement. To move any object through a resisting medium takes a certain amount of power—and this includes that propeller blade. In the conventional piston engine, we want to rotate that propeller at, let's say, 3,000 revolutions per minute.

We can do so *only* when the engine delivers maximum power, and the propeller is in fine pitch. If the pilot changes the propeller blade pitch from fine to coarse, he immediately increases the drag of the propeller. He is using all his available power. When the drag goes up, it needs more power to maintain its speed. But the engine hasn't got any more power—and so the propeller actually slows down.

The value of propeller pitch may be established in this manner. If an airplane takes off with maximum power and fine pitch, the shifting of the blades to coarse pitch causes so great a loss of power that the airplane immediately is drained of the energy it needs to become airborne. Likely it will never get off the ground—it will crash.

For many years engineers have dreamed wistfully of the ideal relationship between the engine and the propeller. They knew that the fulfillment of that dream lay along only one possible avenue— and that was to enable the propeller blades to bite a bigger chunk of air *without losing any speed while doing so.* In other words, to shift the pitch of the blades instantly into coarse position so that air resistance to the blades increased tremendously. But—and it is a classic "but"—the increased drag must *not* slow down the speed of propeller revolutions.

If this could be made possible, then there could be created a propeller-driven airplane with extraordinary performance capabilities. It would have, first, tremendous power both in normal flight and held in reserve. It would also have that characteristic every pilot holds so dear—instantaneous response to the command of the pilot.

It was a nice dream, but the ideal relationship of engine and propeller simply didn't exist. And until it did, the ideal big airplane would have to remain on the high shelf of wistful hopes.

Lockheed and Allison, in effect, have taken those dreams and those hopes *and made them come true.* For the Hercules, in its engine-propeller system, represents that long-sought "ideal relationship."

That Bigger Chunk of Air

The movement of a propeller produces certain specific results. One of them is to move a certain mass of air from the front of the propeller past the propeller blade, and then hurl it violently to the rear.

A propeller blade is actually an airfoil. It is just as much an airfoil as is the wing on an airplane. A wing functions by creating a lifting force—by generating an upward force of lift that is great enough to overcome the downward pull of gravity, and to permit the forward thrusting force of the airplane to propel that airplane forward at high speed.

The more efficient the engineer can make the "lifting"—i.e., thrusting—force of his propeller blade, the more responsive will be his airplane. The propeller blades are so mounted that their "lift" is exerted in a forward fashion. Thus the lift of the blades functions, of course, as a force to thrust the plane forward.

The trick is to move the greatest possible mass of air past those blades. The more air that the propeller can chew with its blades, the more air it hurls past them and the more thrust it creates. How to bite that bigger chunk of air without losing power or propeller speed is what defied engineers for so many years.

The "ideal relationship," to which Lockheed and Allison aspired in the Hercules, meant achieving maximum possible efficiency of the engines and propellers. If the engines could be spun at a constant and maximum speed, there would never be any time lag in providing power when the engines were called upon to deliver.

But what about the propeller? Here, too, the need was for constant-speed operation. The propellers of the C-130B, for example, turn with a speed of 1,020 revolutions per minute. The propellers turn at this speed *all* the time that airplane is in the air.

When the pilot moves his throttles forward to gain extra power, the movement of those throttles changes the pitch of the propeller blades. This increases enormously, and instantly, the drag of the whirling blades. They are biting a bigger chunk of air, increasing the forward thrust of the blades.

But at the same time the propeller does not slow down in its revolutions. And there lies the crux of it. The intricate gear-reduction assembly of the engine-propeller system comes into play. As fast as the propellers demand more power to *maintain* their constant speed, the engine is squeezed of that power by the gear system. The engine-propeller system, in effect, is shifting gears to draw from the engine whatever power is needed to sustain the RPM of the propeller.

To the pilot the whole thing is incredibly simple. He wants power —so he moves the power levers forward. The propeller blades immediately shift their pitch angle, and the airplane leaps forward. It's as easy as that. The propeller is linked to an engine that keeps operating at 100 percent of its rated RPM—13,820 RPM. Or, if the engine overspeeds—operates at more than 100 percent—the propeller will increase its bite of air and, correspondingly, increase its power drain on the engine to maintain the constant-speed operation.

For the pilot, then, events boil down to basics. For greater power, move the throttle lever forward. The blades bite a bigger chunk of air, they increase their thrust, and there's power for takeoff, greater speed, climb, maneuvers, or any other need.

To reduce power, retard the power levers. The propeller blades shift into a finer pitch, they narrow their jaw grip on the air, and the gear-reduction assembly linking engine and propeller "shifts down." At the same time, the demand on fuel in the engine abates and economy is gained.

Simplicity Is So Complex

The operation of the engine-propeller system of the Hercules as described is, the writer must confess, misleading. It is disarming, because it presents the "ideal relationship" so long sought as the essence of simplicity. On the face of it, this is true enough. But as most professionals are aware, behind every "beautifully simple" device or operation stands an intensive development effort. More to the point—apparent simplicity often conceals the complexity that makes the whole thing possible in the first place.

It would be a gross disservice to the engineers and technicians who labored for many years to produce the "heartbeat of the Hercules" to ignore the incredibly precise and complex operation that must be sustained whenever the pilot demands his "instant power."

To meet this need the writer turned to a man who is both a superb test pilot and an equally capable engineer—a man we met earlier in these pages—Walt Hensleigh.

He doesn't mince any words on the subject, and his is a deep perception of the manner in which this equipment functions.

"When a piston-engine pilot comes into the '130," Hensleigh explains carefully, "he has absolutely no sweat in *flying* the airplane. It's a dream to fly, and as the other pilots have indicated, it's the easiest big airplane in the world for transition. But just about the *hardest* thing for a pilot to do in his transition to the '130 is to learn, intimately, the operation of that engine-and-propeller combination. Because there is the heart and soul of the wonderful performance we get from this machine. . . .

"To understand this system—and I mean to understand it thoroughly—is not an easy thing to do. I don't think there has ever been a system installed in an airplane that was any more complicated than the engine-propeller marriage in the Hercules. It takes a lot of doing for a person to know down inside the guts of that system just exactly what does what. There is both hydraulic and electrical operation.

"Sometimes they operate independently. Other times, they operate jointly, and then the system may even reverse itself to compensate for special conditions. On top of all this, the system can even shut itself down without any prompting on the part of the crew when it encounters a situation that would otherwise damage or even destroy the engine-propeller combination. The whole thing is amazing. . . .

"I want you to understand that I'm driving hard on this point. Learning to operate this airplane and its power sources is one thing, and that is *not* at all difficult. Proficiency comes quickly in this respect. But learning *why* the systems operate the way they do is something else again.

"In order to trouble-shoot any problems—not to fly the airplane—the flight engineers and the pilots must *know* the system and the how and why of it. When they start digging into the insides of the system, they start walking on some intricate eggshells.

"We have what I'd call, basically, a hydraulic-control scheduling of fuel, for the fuel controls of the engines. But then on top of the hydraulic system there is also an electronic trimming system. This is automatic, and it does the fine tuning, you could say, of scheduling the fuel into the engine.

"On the propeller—" Hensleigh took a deep breath and plunged— "well, the propeller RPM is controlled basically by the hydraulic system, *but* . . . in addition to that, it is trimmed so that the props remain synchronized, *plus* an additional electronic trim to keep the propellers sync-phased. You know the difference between synchronization and sync-phasing . . .

"Don't you?

"Well, synchronization demands that all the propellers turn at the same scale . . . the same time scale. All the blades are turning together. In sync-phasing, the objective is to retain the same blade relationship between the propellers. We do this to reduce vibration and noise in the airplane. . . .

"The blades of each propeller maintain a certain relationship to the blades of the other propellers. To attain this condition, the electrical control system cranks them over until everything is exactly as it should be—each blade in relationship to the other.

"It's obvious that when you start getting into all those systems, why, then you have a real complicated piece of machinery. But it's not complicated on the same basis or the same scale as anything we have ever used before. The 'old' complications required the flight crew to adapt and to bend to their needs. The—well, let's call it the 'new' complications—the new setup does not require this. It's automatic. Like I said before, the pilot doesn't need to know all this to fly his airplane, any more than the driver of an automobile must know every mechanical process of the thousands of parts of his vehicle. But the difference is that the pilot *wants* to know these things—or he should want to know them—because he's not just tooling down the turnpike. When he gets problems, they may come over the middle of the Atlantic or somewhere in the desert.

"Anyway, to continue . . . besides the systems we've mentioned, there is the very important interrelationship between the pitch of the propeller blade and the fuel control to the engine. This is what determines the power—the bite of the blades into the air.

"Both the propeller and the engines are always working to stay at 100-percent operation—all the time. They are built as slaves to this requirement, and 'instinctively' they fight to meet this need. If the system suddenly overspeeds, or exceeds 100 percent, then the propeller automatically chews up a lot more air to slow down the engine. The engine, at the same time, eases the strain on itself by cutting down the fuel supply. It's trying to slow down its operations, to damp its fire slightly.

"And *this* is where the overlapping of interrelationships begins to complicate things. . . .'"

Everyone in the pilots' briefing room stared at Walt Hensleigh with something bordering on awe.

"If you get a fuel-flow drop in the fuel control and the engine starts falling off in speed . . . well, the propeller automatically shifts its blade pitch to take a smaller bite of air, so as to pick up the speed of the engine. Right here is where the flight engineer has to be *sharp*. What he assumes to be affecting the engine because of the fuel-control system might not actually be caused by this system at all. It can be the propeller that's the skunk in the woodpile.

"These two systems are actually working against each other all the time, instead of working *with* each other. In other words, there's a governor control that acts as an orchestra leader and tries to get everybody working in tune, even though the brass might be drowning out the strings, and the drums are rumbling away for their share of attention.

"But when you get down to it, the complications of the system are worth it a thousand times over. Because this is what allows the '130 to perform as no other airplane in the world can perform. Besides, this is the kind of brain-bucket work the pilot doesn't necessarily *have* to know. He doesn't need to know a bit of it to fly with skill and with competence.

"All he needs to know is that he rams those levers forward, and the answer comes back to him with a great kick in the pants. You can't beat that 'instant power.'"

And from Here . . .

In the many conferences and flights from which this book grew, a dissenting voice on the Hercules or its Allison heartbeat was long conspicuous by absence. There is a great temptation on the part of any writer to remain solely with the sparkling side of things, and the facts of the Hercules story make this a compelling temptation indeed. The truth of the matter seemed to be, however, that the critical voices simply could not be found. The acclaim for the machine was universal, the pride was fierce, and an experienced writer knows when he must no longer press on for "material." The crews of the Hercules have in the past exhibited some good-natured violence when doubting Thomases questioned their feelings about their birds.

So it was somewhat surprising that the voice that bade me hear the "other side of the story" belonged to none other than Leo Sullivan, Lockheed-Georgia's Chief Engineering Test Pilot. His was a touch of grumpiness on one point. It is Sullivan's position, in fact, that the Hercules is being held back by circumstances from outperforming itself. That, the writer must confess, was a most interesting viewpoint.

"We've been flying this thing since 1954," Sullivan said, "but the power of the engine has been increased by only 300 horsepower on takeoff. Traditionally, airplanes maintain a constant increase in their power, but we have just not done this with the Hercules.

"I suppose there's the problem of balancing off the short-field requirements with the dollar budget. Everything in this business is a compromise, of course, but knowing the tremendous performance of the airplane now and, above all, knowing what some more power would do to its ability in short-field takeoffs . . . well, it just irritates us somewhat."

The "us"—the other pilots and engineers—nodded in mute assent. Sullivan continued:

"Increased power means extending the longevity of the product through maximum possible usability. This is the history of about every really successful big airplane ever built.

"The reason any major product finally slips out of the picture is that it lacks the capacity to extend its flight envelope, to continue to increase the performance spectrum in all regions.

"In the case of the '130, the takeoff capability is still, beyond any question, the best of *any* large airplane in the world. But our engineers want to boost more cruise speed into the bird. They want to take the airplane at maximum gross weight to 30,000 feet and more, and fly above almost all weather.

"But with the power remaining essentially the same, and the weight increasing by an additional 47,000 pounds . . . well, something has to give. The cruising altitude and speed at maximum gross weight *must* suffer a bit. The ceiling becomes 22,000 feet or so instead of the 30,000 the pilots want. . . ."

Military crews have flown the old C-130A model in "normal" operations to 38,000 feet, and sustained this altitude for hours. They have flown the Hercules to 43,000 feet and at that point called it quits—not because the engines couldn't pull higher, but there seemed little reason to continue into a region which, medically, demands space-equivalent survival equipment.

Leo Sullivan is, of course, entirely correct in his comments. The engine has increased over the years by only 300 horsepower. Lockheed, the military, and, above all, Allison agree that with increased power the airplane would astound even its most enthusiastic supporters. Sullivan also provided the answer to the enigma of this lack of additional power in the Hercules when he spoke of "balancing the short-field requirements with the dollar budget."

But what of the Tomorrow in the life of the Hercules? Is there a sharp increase in power in the airplane's future?

It is already available, although the mating of the power plant with the airplane must await decision by the Department of Defense. But just as an indication . . .

The Navy's Lockheed P3A Orion, "kissing cousin" to the Hercules (and developed from the Lockheed Electra II commercial turboprop airliner) is already flying with a slight modification to the

Allison T56 engine. Burdened with an undisclosed but staggering weight of many tons of electronic gear, the Orion uses water/alcohol injection at takeoff, or for any emergency situation, to squeeze an additional 1,800 horsepower from its four engines. Hercules pilots look at nearly 2,000 horses more for their airplane, and they lick their chops in greedy anticipation of what this would do on a takeoff roll.

Beyond this immediately available modification there lie what Allison calls the Phase III turboprop engines. An Allison official explained to the writer that "any basic design has its absolute structural limits, and apparently the Phase II engines—in the Hercules, the Electra, and the Orion—are at their 'modification' limit. Now we're in the Phase III design, and we like very much the looks of what we are testing."

Phase III means an air-cooled turbine design, and the higher operating temperatures which this will make possible mean also a guarantee of greater outpouring of power. The new engines are operating with turbine temperatures at takeoff of approximately 2,000°F., and the temperature of the gas stream of the engine is already at 2,700°F. All of this, spelled out on the runway, means boosting the engine from its present rating of 4,050 horsepower to about 4,850 horsepower.

In nice round figures—that's more than 3,000 high-spirited horses extra per Hercules.

And beyond *that* . . . ?

Hercules drivers already look forward with anticipation to engines known as the T56-M9 and M5. Very technical sounding, but only a title to tremendous power. The preliminary tests of these engines—lighter in weight than those now on the airplanes—"have assured a standard sea level performance of approximately 5,980 horsepower. . . ."

Twenty-four thousand horsepower in the Hercules. "Damn!" exclaimed an exuberant engineer. "Wouldn't that just chew the hell out of the air?"

CHAPTER X

The Weapon   THE LOCAL TERRAIN

in the small Asian country is an abuse of the word. Steep hills
rear up from the ground in random profusion. From a distance in
the air the area gives a strange sense of familiarity. The hills look
like huge Dragon's Teeth, the concrete barriers once sown along
Germany's western borders as protection against marauding American tanks. Whatever the comparison, they present a hellish appearance to the pilot of a big Hercules whose mission is to land
in the midst of nature's obstacles.

The strip assigned to the crew for bringing in the Hercules is
not an airfield. It is just an open space squeezed in among the
hills. It is an open field of weeds, of sand and gravel, and layers
of thick, choking dust.

It seems impossible to *land* a big airplane in this space. The
Hercules pilot, nevertheless, is convinced he can get into the field.
The procedure will be to rumble the Hercules down an invisible
line in the sky—full flaps, gear down, hanging just above the edge
of a stall, propellers chewing air at a rate guaranteed (if the pilot
does not make even a tiny slip, which is under these conditions
unforgivable) to sink the airplane onto the grass field.

To a landing? No, not that. The luxury can't be afforded. The
airplane will descend to earth in a controlled crash.

It is one of the most unnerving experiences in flying. The writer
has several times sat in the right seat of the Hercules during such
a maneuver; several times I have stood behind the pilots, clutching
for dear life at metal supports, as well as being lashed with a
strap to prevent my hurtling forward into the windows. The impact is so great, the deceleration so severe, that it is impossible
otherwise to keep from being whipped forward.

In the Asian country, the pilot circles the open field. A native—
bless his soul—has worked with American airmen in a war long
ago, and he has watched Americans come into small fields. He has
built a small fire that produces much smoke, and the pilot of the
Hercules is grateful for this clear indication of the direction of the
wind.

He sets up the airplane. Speed way down, flaps down, gear down, propeller blades pitched *just* so. In the flight deck the crew rechecks seat belts and shoulder harnesses. In the huge fuselage the scanner and cargomaster strap themselves down, brace for the impact they know is coming.

The Hercules falls out of the sky in an impossible descent. It is moving so slowly that gusts of air bring the crew involuntarily to tighten their stomach muscles, to tense. It is a twinge of fear that every pilot feels when a gust slaps a wing down and it comes back slowly, when control response is sluggish because of the dangerously low airspeed—and every instinct a pilot has screams to him to accelerate his airplane.

The Hercules falls like a great wounded creature of the sky. It drops past a dangerously close hill slope, and then the field is beneath the gear. It is not a landing. The airplane slams with bone-jarring force into the ground. The wings groan in every fiber; and then they curve downward, a frightening bend of the entire wing, like a wing with its bones broken and about to collapse. Instantly dust springs up. The sound of the machine changes to a frantic bellow. The propeller blades dance in their mounts and reverse their normal direction. The pilot slaps the throttles forward and the Allisons surge with power. The scream of whipped air bursts away from the huge roiling dust cloud on the field. The Hercules is nowhere to be seen; only that thick, twisting mass of dust.

The copilot's teeth snap together with an audible click. Blood flows from his lip. The airplane lurches forward, the invisible hand of reverse thrust and maximum brakes, the effect of low-pressure tires digging into the field . . . all of this pushing it back, holding it, cutting the landing roll down. Only 700 feet from the point where the gear pounded into the field the Hercules is no longer moving. The dust blows away slowly.

"*Goddamn* . . ."

More an expletive than exclamation, the flight engineer whispers the word. It is comment enough for everybody in the flight deck.

This is the nature of a short-field "landing" in the Hercules as it is employed by the Air Force, and by other services in lesser numbers, in remote areas of this world. It is the maneuver necessary in areas where a query as to the nearest airport evokes snickering laughter, because such a thing just doesn't exist. It is one of the very special characteristics of this big airplane, one carefully planned for in its design and in the plans laid many years previously by the Tactical Air Command.

It is the type of maneuver that sometimes evokes a mixture of laughter and pride in the Hercules crews. On a landing such as

"You dump the '130 in past the trees and hills and then you don't just land—you make a controlled *crash*-landing . . ."

that described, at an advanced military operations base "somewhere in south Asia," an Air Force Hercules pounded down its approach line and thundered into the ground. And, as is customary, the scream of propellers issued forth from the boiling dust.

At the far end of the field a colonel of the United States Marines watched the impact. His eyes widened as the landing turned into a terrible crash. He saw the wings bend crazily downward. Dust flew in all directions and enveloped the airplane. From within the swirling dust came the ear-stabbing cry of screeching metal. The wind blew gaps in the dust and the colonel saw metal flying both to the left and the right of the blurred outline of the airplane.

The colonel didn't waste any time. He hit the crash alarm and people came running from all directions. There was a chance they could save the crew. Cursing, the colonel jumped into a jeep and went tearing down the field.

Twenty minutes later, the "wreck" zoomed upward from the dirt field, soaring skyward in a power-singing climb.

The Hercules did not, of course, end its life with a crash. It was that same controlled crash maneuver. The metal "flying both to the left and the right" of the airplane was, in reality, jeeps pouring down the rear ramp of the Hercules, loaded with equipment and men. From a distance, through the dust, it seemed a tragedy rather than a standard operation.

The crews still grin at the memory of the "terrible accident.". . .

In the family scrapbook of the Hercules, the record of meeting all its requirements, of standing up to every claim ever made for the airplane, is *almost* unbroken. The Hercules wears a mantle of pride for its unmatched performance in operating from short, rough fields. But in its earliest days of testing, under the Air Force program of "field suitability" studies—which within the industry is known as the "Prove It" program—the Hercules ran into difficulties.

Operations from rough and unimproved fields of dirt, gravel, grass, and, above all, of soft sand have foundered many a superbly performing machine. Despite its performance under other conditions, the big airplane is simply bucking fierce obstacles when it attempts to operate with absolute reliability under conditions that would snare helplessly even the small airplane.

The Hercules didn't fail by much. In fact, to describe as a failure the performance of the airplane in its initial attempts to qualify as an assault transport often prompts belligerent retorts from its crews. Nevertheless, in the fall of 1957 the Hercules stood temporarily as an "almost ran" in a category that no airplane of large size had ever succeeded in entering.

The original Air Force specifications required the Hercules to be able to land on "hastily prepared" runways. This calls for crude leveling of a field. It is still a rough field that falls within the category of "unimproved," but it does require some attention by men on the ground. The Hercules passed these rugged tests with flying colors, exceeding its demands with an operating weight on the ground of 108,000 pounds.

Then there came a new requirement. The Air Force wanted the Hercules to qualify fully as an "assault transport," and this meant the airplane must be capable of landing and disgorging troops and equipment, and flying out wounded, on "rough and unprepared terrain." At Eglin Air Force Base in Florida, there is an area set aside for special treatment. It is one of the biggest torture racks in the world. Here the terrain has been deliberately chewed up and made otherwise extremely rough for an airplane. It guarantees extremely difficult conditions.

It is paradoxical to list the performance of the Hercules in these tests as a "failure." Hercules 3010, the tenth airplane off the production line, amazed observers, broke records like a man running the mile in three minutes, and established unprecedented standards for running big airplanes into unimproved fields—and getting them out again.

In one series of tests the airplane, weighing from 102,000 to 110,000 pounds, was dumped onto the "torture rack field" of soft sand. Inside the flight deck the crew was hammered and shaken like a rat being given the fatal treatment by a terrier. The wheels sliced furrows so deep that the average airplane simply would have bogged down, and couldn't have gotten out without the help of a bulldozer or two.

It dug furrows a foot deep. Despite the gouges in the sand, the Hercules still was able to taxi as required, to make a complete turn where it had landed, and to take off again. This was in January of 1957. In the ensuing months the airplane again and again repeated its performance. Still with its gross weight of 110,000 pounds, it was able to slam onto the sand field and come to a dead stop within a distance of only 947 feet. The takeoff runs *averaged* only 1,500 feet with the 110,000-pound weight.

Then the Hercules added another 6,000 pounds to its cargo load and slammed to a landing on an emergency field built of pierced steel planking. Landing distance—1,242 feet; takeoff distance—1,729 feet. Then the airplane moved to sod fields and regular hard-surfaced runways.

The Hercules ended its tests with the crews rubbing aching posteriors and checking for loose teeth—but with a proven capability in rough-field operations that heralded a new era in combat operations.

But that failure . . . ?

An official report of Hercules' rough-field tests noted that wheels dug furrows so deep that the average airplane would have bogged down and could only have been extricated with a bulldozer or two. (*Air Force/ Lockheed-Georgia*)

The tests revealed that although the Hercules operated as desired from the rough fields with a weight of 110,000 pounds, that very weight was exceeding the structural integrity of the nose gear. As the airplane slammed down and rolled through the rough and sandy surface, the gear was subjected to steel-piston forces. The Lockheed engineers probed that gear and the Air Force people did the same, and they both came to the same conclusion. While there had not yet been any structural failure of any kind, continuing to smash at the nose gear with the 110,000-pound gross-weight airplane made it inevitable that before long something just had to give. Somewhat downcast, despite the record-shattering performance of the airplane, the Lockheed people trooped home.

The specifications called for meeting the "assault transport" requirements with a maximum gross weight of 108,000 pounds, and absolutely no questions as to even *future* compromise with the gear. But the early C-130A model was restricted to a maximum gross weight of 102,000 pounds under the rough-field conditions. More than one engineer muttered darkly about "a lousy 6,000 pounds," but their under-the-breath complaints meant little to the Lockeed front office. The Hercules must not only be able to meet all specifications; it must do more. The front office said quietly that the Hercules was to be an assault transport under the most stringent of Air Force demands, and that the job had "damned well better get done quickly, and better than anyone expects."

The engineers went to work, the Hercules picked up some more muscle, and the crews went back to the bush-covered, sandy loam fields. Their airplanes were clean and shiny, and the Air Force observers took out their notebooks and started jotting down figures —especially about the complete simulated combat mission. The Hercules would be required to slam its way into the field, taxi to the side of the field, pick up a 25,000-pound cargo load, fly it to a destination 500 miles distant, and then come barreling back to the "sandpile." And it had to do this at the "guaranteed" weight of 108,000 pounds.

The Lockheed pilots and engineers grinned at one another, looked straight-faced at the Air Force observers, and whipped through the toughest requirements ever laid down by the Air Force for a big airplane. They did it with a gross weight of 116,000 pounds— four tons *over* the requirement—and they did it again and again and again.

By no means was it easy. Quite the opposite. Beefed-up nose gear or not, those suitability tests were *brutal.*

Lockheed test pilot Vern Peterson and his engineer, Bob Brennan, didn't appreciate their assignments.

"The first day we arrived at Eglin," Vern recalls with a grimace, "we took a jeep and rode up and down the field where we and the other crews were *supposed* to land the airplanes. My God, what a place! It wasn't just sandy. Oh, no. It had piles of deep, soft sand everywhere you went, and to make matters worse, wild brush sprouted haphazardly all about the sand.

"Jeeps were sinking deep in the sand, and some of them got stuck. And here we were getting set to fly airplanes through this stuff at weights up to 116,000 pounds? I do not mind telling you that we were a little perturbed about that field. . . ."

Peterson thought about the "obstacle course" elements, added to a field which was "about 4,000 feet long, which was more than plenty for the Hercules. But on each end they had trees and in addition to that, to make the test more difficult, I guess, the Air Force people put up a 50-foot-high obstacle directly on the end of the runway! They stuck up two high poles and strung a wire between them with bright flags, so we wouldn't run into the wire. But sometimes I thought we were sure going to fly *under* it. . . ."

That was the introduction. On the second day Peterson "made a taxi run to see how the airplane handled on the big sandpile. We rolled off a parking stand and the plane was rocking wildly back and forth, and Bob and I were looking at each other. Just looking at each other . . ."

They ran down the field, testing power settings, reaction and feel of the controls. They slammed into obstructions and hard spots, and the nose gear came screeching up as far as it would go and then pounded hell out of the bottom of the airplane. Peterson and Brennan tried to stop the vibration in their skulls resulting from their teeth being clattered together by the jolting airplane.

"The fact is," explains Peterson, "I got a couple of jolts in the seat of my pants that I still remember. Right in the middle of this 'runway' there was a hard road that cut across our path; we came booming down along the sand and whanged into this road, and *BANG!* we thought for sure that the gear was going to come up right into the flight deck with us. We ran up and down until we reached 80 knots, holding the bird down, and then we stopped.

"Bob and I turned around again to look at each other. We shook our heads—somewhat sadly—and together, word for word, it just came out in unison: 'Boy, this is going to be a bitch.' And we were right—it was.

"The funny thing about those tests . . . our first exposure to the takeoffs and landings, especially under the maximum loads, absolutely convinced us that we were going to tear the hell out of the whole front end of the airplane. The shocks are fantastic; it just didn't seem that anything could stay together under that beating. But after a while, and we marveled at this, things settled down to a routine. . . ."

The "routine" included a merciless beating of the Hercules. The final phases of the tests demanded five days of punishment. Weighing 116,000 pounds, the Hercules *sank deeper than 20 inches* into the sand during rollouts. The landing gear doors were dragging four to six inches in the sand at the end of the rollouts. The crews climbed down to study the scene, and shook their heads in wonder. There was not the slightest touch or even suspicion of structural damage.

They learned—with Air Force crews alternating at the controls—different and novel methods of control on the ground to keep from being stuck. "We found that if we didn't keep the aircraft rolling after we came in for the landing," Peterson said, "and the brakes were set so that they were just skidding in the sand, we could get into a bit of a mess. If we came to a stop that way we'd build up such a huge pile of sand in front of the main gear that all the power in the world couldn't get us out. So we developed a new technique. Just before we came to a full stop, we released the brakes, whipped on power, and just let her go level and stop by herself. No sweat; that way she would always move right out when we fed her power."

Other tests ran concurrently with those at the Eglin torture rack. Hercules transports flew in the worst of winter weather to the Far North, where they tackled glazed ice for runways, snorted their way through deep snowdrifts, and bulled their way into the air with a trumpeting cry of triumph. Other Hercules splashed down on steel planking—and "splashed" is meant literally—laid on swampy ground. The low-pressure tires, and the single-tandem main gear on each side meant good load distribution over a wide area, and a "classroom mark" of A+.

The "Prove It" campaign by the Air Force shifted into high gear, and hundreds of experts in the business hammered and poked and stressed and generally did their best to prove that the Hercules could *not* do its assigned tasks. Failure in their efforts resulted not in unhappy looks, but in wide grins, for such failure was a sign of brilliant success on the part of the airplane. And to do their job they flew to Europe, Alaska, the Caribbean and Panama, and throughout the United States.

Hercules No. 12 flew 41 hours out of 49, as Air Force crews working in series trooped in and out of the airplane. Objective: to subject the airframe and the engines to maximum possible utilization under the worst demands that might be put upon them. A Lockheed technical representative who went along on the tests,

Rough-field tests (*above and below*) with the Hercules included landing rollouts with the airplane at 116,000 pounds, in which the airplane sank deeper than 20 inches into the ground. (*Air Force/Lockheed-Georgia*)

snatching sleep aboard the airplane, laughed aloud and sent a telegram back to Marietta: "No. 12 is wearing out the crews as fast as the Air Force can supply them. Please send lots of stay-awake pills. . . ."

Hercules No. 3 (in order off the production line) went to an Air Force crew that received the cheering assignment of battering the airplane to its maximum allowable flight limits—and then going beyond this figure to determine critical stress loads. The crew soared to 30,000 feet and ran through a long list of maneuvers. Confidence in the airplane grew visibly among the crew. They decelerated in the air.

Down came the landing gear. The flaps went to takeoff position (a low-speed configuration *only*). Then the pilot dumped the nose, built up to a descent rate that raised eyebrows among the veteran test crew, and fell right out of the sky.

Other Hercules went through jet-penetration—maximum-rate—descents—really unwinding the spring. "A jet penetration in the '130 as a standard operating procedure will give you a thrill the first time you experience it, much more so than a jet fighter descent," reported one pilot. "Probably this is because of both the attitude of the plane and the physical sensation. Frankly, it feels as though you were going to fall right through the front picture windows. We didn't accurately check the angle of dangle, but with gear down, flaps full down, and throttles back, you find yourself standing on the rudder pedals. The rate-of-climb indicator shows 1,500 feet per minute down, but surprisingly enough, airspeed is 145 knots [167 miles per hour—the *landing* speed of modern jets]. Now if that isn't a screwy way to penetrate. . . ."

The Air Force wasn't through with beating up the Hercules on rough fields. They wanted more STOL (Short Takeoff and Landing) operations, and they didn't want them from only their specially prepared torture rack at Eglin. "Diversity and the unexpected," chimed one officer, "is the stuff from which proven airplanes are made." With that remark hanging in the air, Lockheed test pilot Jesse Allen began a gypsy tour of bouncing from field to field in an operation that guaranteed the "completely unexpected conditions the Air Force wanted."

Jesse Allen recounts some of the details: "We've had some pretty wild touchdowns. More than once we saw stars from the impact and it felt as though the nose gear was going to come right up through the floor into the cockpit. . . ."

The tests included other areas of engineering. How well could the wing, which is constructed with integral fuel tanks (it is known to the industry as a wet wing), withstand the punishment of flexing, bending, and distortion? One way to find out, of course, was to accumulate all kinds of blows and smashes against the airplane.

"We landed just about everywhere," Allen said. "Many of the places had drainage ditches and holes you couldn't see . . . and you just never did find out until you hit those things with all the force of slamming right into a stone wall.

"Funny . . . but the landing gear seemed to take the landings better than did the crews. The jolt is impossible to describe. Sometimes we would come into a situation where we didn't dare subject even the Hercules to the punishment that resulted. We would hit some fields with the main gear and it seemed like the airplane would tear itself to pieces. The hammering and vibration was so bad you literally couldn't see clearly. And when that happened, you just whack those levers forward and the bird is back in the air. *That's* when you appreciate 'instant power.' . . ."

The results of all the rough-field tests established new standards for the industry and new performance goals at which the competition stared with blanched faces. Lockheed's decision to go to the high-wing design proved itself repeatedly in fields where the airplane rocked dangerously from side to side. When the plane jolted its way along the fields the bottom arc of the propeller tips was

Hercules pounds its way along rough, sandy field and bursts into the air. Takeoff roll—less than 800 feet. (*Lockheed-Georgia*)

almost six feet off the ground, and *that* was a critical factor in success. Not simply to clear the ground, either—but so the props wouldn't have to chew their way through brush and other oddities strewn about the fields. Another important factor: the whirling blades create a tremendous suction, and if they were too low this would snatch up rocks and loose debris from the ground, probably causing severe damage to the blades and demanding their replacement. Just one more item of built-in reliability . . .

At its assault transport weight of 116,000 pounds, the "old" C-130A could rumble along through the air at 90 knots, just above its stalling speed. Pilots at first flew slower and slower until they approached this speed, and like a man stepping gingerly on the thinnest of ice, they finally flew at the edge of stalls—under control. This meant the greatest possible accuracy in maneuvering into the small fields, a maneuver facilitated by the hydraulically boosted controls, which eased the pilot's task greatly. And the pilots had a few kind words to say about the Hercules' new flexible wing— an innovation for a propeller transport that reduced "hunting" in turbulence (yawing of the nose from side to side), and took the worst bumps out of gusts.

That wing, incidentally, had known little peace since the first section rolled off the factory line. It underwent grueling tests (some of which have been discussed in preceding chapters) within the Lockheed plant, which only set the stage for the Air Force to add its own brand of torture.

"You ever watch kids bouncing on the end of a long diving board?" asked the Air Force test director. "First one kid goes out and he jumps up and down as hard as he can. Pretty soon the board is vibrating like a bowstring. This is so much fun he calls his gang, and then there are three or four kids out there until the board is groaning like an old band saw. If the lifeguard gets there in time to kick 'em off, maybe he can save the board before it finally breaks. And if it's a really good board, it won't break."

He smiled with a glint of sadism in his eyes. "*That's* what we do with the wing of the Hercules. The Lockheed people actually conduct the tests, and we kibitz so that no one gets sentimental about the bird. Of course, our 'kids' weigh several hundred pounds each. . . ."

Since the fuel tanks of the Hercules are integral with the wing structure, there's a complete absence of rubber or any other material to form the tanks. Instead, the production-line people seal all joints and rivets against leakage with a special rubber-compound sealant. That's fine—but will it stand up under temperatures of nearly 200°F. above zero, and down to 90° or so below zero? Will it stand up without leakage when the wing is being battered and twisted to the point where the pilots wince at the sight?

The special tests turned the Hercules into what the crews wryly called the Lead Sled. Tons of lead were stacked up on the wings. Technicians suspended lead blocks from the engines to simulate additional stress and loading. And then special jigs applied additional bending and twisting forces, while the wingtips fluctuated up and down through an eye-popping arc. One such test ran for 14 hours—with 210 loads of varying force running the Hercules through the gauntlet.

When it was all over, an engineer informed a Hercules test pilot that the wing had proven itself completely, and under the worst of conditions guaranteed that it wouldn't leak. Just back from Eglin, the pilot rubbed his aching posterior and snarled: "You're telling *me?*"

At Pope Air Force Base in North Carolina, 92 fully equipped combat troops marched into the gaping hold of a Hercules—and we mean *marched*. No climbing through doors or up steps; double-file right through the yawning rear cargo ramp, like a whale swallowing the long line of soldiers. Along with them came a team of medical observers, and then the crew—a total of 104 men aboard the airplane.

Thirteen minutes after takeoff the pilot leveled the Hercules at 25,000 feet and headed for the "combat area" 2,000 miles away. Inside the big hold the air pressure level remained steady at an altitude of 8,000 feet. Temperature just outside the fuselage—52 degrees below zero. Inside: an even 70 degrees.

"Ninety-two fully equipped combat troops marched into the gaping hold of a Hercules . . ."

Approaching the landing area, the Hercules plunged from the sky, simulating maximum descent under combat conditions. It roared over trees and thumped down on a clay strip. Before the wheels stopped turning, the rear ramp was down and the troops were pouring out to establish an "advance battle base." The Hercules crew moved swiftly through their airplane—converting the troop transport right on the spot into a medical evacuation airplane. Troops carried aboard 74 "patients" stretched out on litters, secured the litters to their racks. Doctors came aboard, the ramp closed, and the Hercules was winging back to home base. A few days later the Air Force repeated the operation with the same results.

Two Hercules "without prior alert" were assigned to an "emergency" supply mission. Within six hours they delivered 185 tons of ammunition, artillery weapons, and varied supplies, as well as hundreds of fully equipped troops, to a "forward combat area,"

A single anti-tank weapon weighing 22,250 pounds is chained to the floor of a C-130A Hercules. Tremendous cargo capacity and versatility of the Hercules are dramatically evident in this scene. (*Lockheed-Georgia*)

departing each time from the "battle zone" with the airplane filled to capacity with 74 litter patients plus attendants.

Dozens of simulated combat missions were flown from advanced rough strips in the midst of heavily wooded areas. In another test to determine the Hercules' capability in combat delivery, two aircraft made nine flights within a period of three hours; each Hercules shuttled seven to 16 tons of ammunition, artillery, and supplies during each run into the "combat zone."

Other missions included repeats of the 2,000-mile journey with at least 92 troops aboard; there were several missions over a distance of 1,000 nautical miles, at the close of which each plane disgorged 64 paratroopers.

The performance of the airplane as a combat weapon had to be judged not only in its ability to haul heavy and bulky loads into emergency strips, but also as to the *time* element involved. One Hercules especially closed the book on this question by roaring into an improvised strip and off-loading a large truck, a 155mm howitzer, ammunition, and ten soldiers; the airplane then loaded 74 litter patients and two attendants. Time spent on the ground for both unloading and loading, without shutting down the engines: exactly 30 minutes.

In the most critical of emergencies, could the Hercules cut down sharply on its own unprecedented ability to get out of short fields? How would the airplane "spring out" of the worst of emergency strips with rocket-assist bottles attached to the fuselage? The answer left onlookers with gaping mouths.

Leo Sullivan was at the controls, running the props to maximum thrust, standing on the brakes. Finally he jumped the brakes and gave the airplane its head. Almost at once the Hercules bounded to 50 knots, and at that moment Sullivan triggered the eight rocket bottles. Brilliant flame spat from each side of the airplane, a tornadolike roar bellowed across the field, and almost as quickly as he ignited the rockets, Sullivan was hauling back on the wheel.

Distance from start of takeoff roll: 440 feet. Speed: 70 knots at liftoff. Sullivan didn't take off in the usual sense. He pulled the Hercules into an impossible climb, and the airplane—*still accelerating*—burst upward at an angle of 45 degrees! Twelve seconds after firing the rockets the Hercules was flying on her Allisons alone, the earth far below, and the empty bottles tumbling toward the ground.

The Air Force employs four different types of rocket bottles for emergency takeoff power. Lockheed built the adapters of the Hercules to take any one of the four rocket-bottle types, assuring

Takeoff distance with rocket boost
—440 feet

that emergency takeoff power could be installed at virtually every Air Force facility, anywhere in the world.

The tests increased in tempo. In North Carolina a force of Hercules transports roared low over mountain country. Figures plummeted doll-like from the transports, then jerked abruptly in the air as white canopies unfurled. Minutes later, doors in the airplanes opened and the great ramps lowered. A bulldozer and then a shower of construction equipment burst away from the airplanes and drifted earthward.

More than 330 crack fighting men of the 101st Airborne Division's Engineer Battalion dropped into wild country. The rugged surface of the terrain abounded in huge rocks and trees. The men worked around the clock, hacking and gouging at the stubborn earth. Twenty-six hours after the first men stepped out of the Hercules, a rough strip 2,500 feet in length lay like a scar through the undergrowth. Dust spilled outward in all directions as one Hercules after the other poured onto the field, bringing men, trucks, artillery, and armored vehicles.

Flying out of Eielson Air Force Base in Alaska, a Hercules underwent what Air Force crews called "a savage mauling" for ten weeks to determine how well the big new bird could stand up to the rigors of the Far North. Air Force pilots manhandled the Hercules in temperatures that on the ground plummeted to 50 degrees below zero. They let the engines stand in bitter cold for long periods and then fired them up without any preheating—and don't think that this didn't make every mechanic for miles around sit up in open-mouthed wonder. For the record of operations in

Heavy equipment air drops (*above and below*) of bulldozers, road-graders, trucks, and other vehicles include 352 tons of equipment air-dropped by Hercules into open country in Kentucky. In 26 hours, men of the 326th Engineer Battalion, 101st Airborne Division, completed a rough airstrip 2,500 feet in length. (*U.S. Army Signal Corps*)

the northland up till then was a sorry story of heating balky and frozen engines for as long as several hours to bring them to life.

The pilots deliberately ran across runways and plowed into snowbanks. At times the Hercules looked like an enormous earth-chained bird snuffling and snorting its way through drifts of snow, with great clouds of misty white blasted back from the snarling propellers. From this inhospitable surface the airplanes climbed to some of the greatest heights yet achieved by the Hercules—soaring more than seven miles into the stratosphere, and then maintaining altitude on long missions at high cruising speeds.

The Hercules flew a bewildering variety of missions and assignments—as a military supply ship, paratroop transport, emergency field operations rescue plane, and flying hospital to handle disasters in remote areas. Pity the poor paratroopers bundled bearlike into thick clothing who bailed out of the Hercules on combat maneuvers. To augment this work, the Hercules dumped by parachute such items as trucks, howitzers, a field ambulance, food containers, and dozens of supply packages.

They didn't do much maintenance work out in the open. A man had perhaps four or five minutes at the most in the worst of the weather; then he either stumbled back to shelter or he was in deep trouble. To prove a point, however, while the thermometer plunged and the wind screamed, Air Force and Lockheed technicians went through the Keystone Cops comedy routine of dashing in and out of a heated shelter, working in snatches to remove a propeller from the airplane. They proved their point—they removed the prop, replaced it with another, hooked up all the systems, and completely tested the airplane for flight.

Farther south, at Bemidji, Minnesota, the wind also howled and the snow gathered in great drifts . . . and another Hercules set its own brand of world records in an operation called Project SLIDE. This represents Snow, Land, and Ice Development Exercise,

Landing tests with ski-equipped Hercules on snow

and it meant a development program that sent veteran aviators away shaking their heads in disbelief. For *this* Hercules looked like an abortion made up of a huge bobsled with wings. It was the first Hercules to thump its way around on all kinds of ice-crusted snow on the biggest skis ever stuck on an airplane.

To complicate matters, the Air Force insisted that the ski-equipped airplane must also be able to operate from a normal runway—a dry cement or asphalt runway with the skis retracted to expose the wheels—and land a few thousands miles away where the earth was thick with ice and snow. And, said the Air Force, we *need* those airplanes, and we needed them yesterday for operations along the Greenland icecap—where other planes were floundering and tearing their metal structure into mangled shapes.

The skis developed for the Hercules were huge affairs—each main ski weighed 2,000 pounds, was five feet wide and 20 feet long. Hydraulic pressure permitted the pilot to lower and retract his skis so that he could operate on his wheels *or* the skis as the situation demanded. Their flat bottoms resembled the design of sports skis, and were coated with a special plastic to minimize friction when the airplane stumbled into deep and wet snow. On icy snow the Hercules took a lashing from particles whipped back against the fuselage; the engineers built special fiberglass panels to ease the battering of the metal. And to compensate for the lack of tires that normally cushioned shock landings, they installed powerful air-spring shock absorbers on the skis to keep the crews from snapping their teeth painfully when the airplane banged down on unyielding snow fields.

But it is a wild way to fly an airplane. It is bad enough to slam into the ice ridges which can't be seen until the seat under the pilot slams with piledriver force into his backbone. Even the huge skis and the shock absorbers couldn't dampen out the terrific impact of the ridges, and more teeth got jarred together than the pilots want to remember.

The "real hairy moments" came from crosswinds. They are heart-stoppers with an airplane that weighs nearly 60 tons on its skis, that has a fat body and a huge, broad tail, and the wind is doing its wicked best to blow exactly at a right angle to the machine. A crosswind of that type when the airplane is on flat and slick skis atop a snow surface is *murder*. Sometimes it is a race to see which will win—the airplane in its headlong plunge down the skiway to become airborne, or the wind shrieking to blow it sideways into the thick snow at the side of the runway (to beggar the word).

Whatever the problems, the Hercules emerged from its ice-covered development thickets in fine fettle. The Air Force promptly christened the ski-equipped C-130A as its new C-130D, and issued an official and frantic call to Lockheed to get a dozen of the new airplanes ready for service *at once.* The potential of the new airplane in the Arctic had fired the imagination of the men to whom Arctic supply movements meant nothing but agonizing headaches, and the Hercules appeared to them as a great bird that would solve their problems. Events would justify their hopes beyond their wildest dreams. . . .

There were other tests, however, that continued on a day-and-night basis. How would the Hercules do in dragging through the sky really difficult-to-handle equipment? There was, of course, the acid means of finding out. The Department of Defense handed the Hercules its next assignment, and the groans from the crews were audible for miles.

The Air Force and the U.S. Army Engineers' Research and Development Laboratory teamed their talents into what promised to be the roughest challenge yet to the Hercules. They assembled 110 separate and different items of engineer equipment, and 32 different engineer field units—and told the C-130A crews to "move 'em! Faster, better, safer than anyone else—and in places no one else has ever been able to get in with an airplane that can carry this stuff."

No one had ever planned that the Hercules would be dragging heavy engineer earth-moving and road-building machines through the skies—but this was part of the assignment. The loading crews gave vocal thanks for the 4,300 cubic feet of space within the airplane, and set to the task at hand.

Once again the Hercules came through in a fashion that already was building the reputation of a "Can Do!" airplane. The transports loaded large trucks carrying tons of the Engineers' famed portable Bailey Bridge sections, airlifted them at 320 miles per hour, dumped them into rough fields—and within a few minutes after screeching to a halt rolled out the trucks and their ponderous cargo.

Again and again the Hercules repeated their performance. They staggered up and down from the rough fields with 18-ton D-6 bulldozers. They hauled wheeled asphalt plants, road graders and scrapers, heavy road rollers, crane cabs, tractor-excavators, 35,000-pound trucks, and everything else the Army brought along. And consistently the heavy cargoes rolled out of the rear of the airplane in time periods measured in minutes.

And to top off this cake with a special icing all its own, the Hercules transports then dragged tanks and armored vehicles through the skies, dumped them onto open fields. The tanks and

Huge Air Force jet-fuel tanker (capacity 5,000 gallons) rolls under its own power into Hercules during cargo-capacity tests (*above*). Jeeps, anti-tank guns, recoilless rifles, and Army crews loading up (*below*) in Hercules fuselage, for advanced field trials. (*Upper photo: Lockheed-Georgia; lower photo: Air Force*)

vehicles came roaring out of the airplane even as it rocked on its shock absorbers—came out with weapons cocked and ready to fight.

One of the most unusual assignments ever given to the Hercules —which began during the first weeks of its "Prove It" tests with the Air Force—was to fly support for the flight program of the X-15 rocket aircraft. This was support in a manner unprecedented, and it is one of the stories about the Hercules that in some unexplained manner has never reached the public.

The hypersonic X-15 flew from Edwards Air Force Base in California, and performed its maneuvers at thousands of miles per hour over a countryside that for the greatest part is naked mountain and raw desert. The area is also rich in dry lake beds— their surfaces powdery at the extreme top but as hard and flat beneath as the best of airports. In an emergency the X-15, like other research aircraft, could be dumped onto one of these lake beds by its pilot. One never knew, however, if that emergency would be accompanied by damage to the aircraft or, much worse, fire. For the aircraft would be far removed from any immediate help— separated from it by many miles of desert and mountain.

Until the Hercules came along, and began its tests at both Edwards Air Force Base and El Centro, California. How this changed things may be attested by an example.

The X-15 during one flight encountered difficulties; many miles over the earth the pilot jettisoned his fuel. At the moment it was questionable that he would be able to glide all the way back to Edwards. The decision was made on the spot to land short of Edwards in a dry lake bed, a move that always sets a high-strung emergency force into action.

From El Centro a Hercules boomed its way through the blistering hot air, the pilot holding the transport down on the runway to compensate for the weak lift of the superheated air. The Hercules lifted in a long, flat climb, accelerating rapidly as the wings clutched at the increasing speed.

As the black X-15 sailed down from the edge of space, the silvered transport streaked low over the desert floor, taking wicked blows from the heat that rippled upward. The airplane headed directly for a mountain range and the pilot eased back on the control yoke, slanting the Hercules to skim the jagged ridges. The X-15 eased down; the Hercules flashed over the ridges and then began its slight downward race.

Both airplanes rushed toward a common goal—one crippled, the other on an errand of mercy.

The X-15 came in hard and fast, nose cocked high, the two

aft skids screeching as they chewed into the desert floor, throwing back a huge plume of dust. As the black airplane thundered along the lake bed the four-engine transport wheeled around, cutting onto the desert floor at an angle that in its landing roll would bring it closer to the X-15, which now was slowing down rapidly.

The black airplane slid to a halt. The Hercules screamed energy from full reverse thrust of the propellers, sending dust flying in all directions. From the billowing dust at the rear of the transport, red lights flashing, siren screaming, *a fire engine burst into view and careened across the lake bed to the crippled airplane*—a fire engine loaded with water, with foam, wrecking and rescue equipment, and an experienced crash crew.

Again and again the Hercules has gone out on alert call, loaded with the fire engine and rescue equipment, and carrying paramedics if the occasion so worsens that even minutes are precious. The doctors spill from the airplane with the means to aid the pilot even as the Hercules starts on its emergency descent to land near the X-15. Just one more assignment . . .

There remained several final items on the "Prove It" list of the military. What about bulk cargo, for example? How would the Hercules handle this item—as important as any other—when put

Hercules rescue mission for the X-15 . . .

to the test? The flights with road-building equipment answered all questions in that department, and almost as if to establish the same capability in operational use as well as under test conditions, a Hercules of the 322nd Air Division at Evreux-Fauville Air Base in France turned in an emergency stellar performance.

A call had come in from Adana, Turkey, requesting "extremely urgent" shipment of a huge generator that matched its bulk with a weight of 28,700 pounds. The first attempt to airlift the generator—with a piston-engine transport—failed. The Hercules at this time was still spanking new to regular European operations, but it was pressed into service for the job.

Crewmen loaded the generator into the airplane at Laon, France. At an average true airspeed of 346 miles per hour, the Hercules lugged the special cargo to Adana—a distance of 2,281 miles non-stop, in well under seven hours for the mission.

Sometimes sheer bulk can be more of a problem than weight, and it was this that on many occasions had interrupted cargo operations, or demanded the use of several airplanes rather than one.

In Georgia, workmen lined up on a loading ramp 21 turboprop engine containers. Each container measured nine by four by four feet and weighed 1,260 pounds. In addition to the containers they piled into the aircraft nearly 3,000 pounds more of cargo, for a total of not quite 15 tons. The Air Force assigned the job of moving the entire cargo load to Indiana to *one* airplane.

The weight didn't bother the loading crew. But they were concerned at first with the sheer bulk of the cargo—because that single shipment contained three containers more than could be carried in a railroad boxcar. The Hercules did the job.

Hauling cargo isn't the most romantic part of flying; it is, however, a critical element of military logistics. And as we have emphasized previously, the speed of cargo-transfer operations in loading and unloading an airplane is a major factor in the efficiency and cost of those operations. For example, the average loading time for a cargo transport is about three hours. Often it runs longer. On a constantly moving cargo operation, 50 airplanes require at least 150 hours to be loaded (and this doesn't consider unloading time or the total man hours involved because of large work crews).

The huge cargo ramp and loading space of the Hercules greatly facilitated this task. But it wasn't good enough, and as the "Prove It" tests ran their course, Lockheed accepted the fact that even the Hercules system could be improved. The engineers dusted off their slide rules, conferred with the cargo people, and they whipped out what was then, and still is, a dream come true in the cargo business.

The answer was a new pushbutton system that injects 35,000 pounds of cargo into the capacious hold of the Hercules in *40 seconds*. And the system can work in reverse, yanking the same load from the airplane in the same incredible time.

The Air Force came and looked at the new system, and their accountants once again departed the factory bubbling over with high budgetary spirits. Extensive tests established conclusively that the new Hercules system slashed manpower requirements for loading operations by 40 percent and, perhaps even more important, cut the "idle ground time" between flights—when the airplane doesn't earn a nickel for its user—*90* percent.

Probing all factors of ground operations, hundreds of tests were carried out at different fields, with new crews, and under a variety of conditions. The Hercules consistently turned in a performance of being mechanically loaded and unloaded in an average of 15 minutes.

The new system permits military installations with priority cargo to have it prepared for shipment and waiting on prepacked pallets. Delivery freight is mechanically hauled from the airplane, and reloading is done in the same manner. In this fashion the Hercules delivers point-to-point cargo as though the crew were slinging about mail pouches. But the new "pouches" are the prepacked cargo pallets each weighing 7,000 pounds. These are placed on rollers either in warehouses or directly on the loading dock. They are rolled speedily onto a truck equipped with rollers on the truck bed. The truck backs up to the Hercules, an electric winch is attached to the pallets, and they are then hauled into the airplane, which also is equipped with rollers on the floor.

In a cargo compartment that is 41 feet long, and with a clear width of ten feet and height of nine feet three inches, this is the type of cargo operation that delights anyone in the business. The comment of one Air Force logistics officer, "For the first time we're loading and unloading cargo in a manner different from the way people carried stuff on and off Cleopatra's barge," eloquently expresses the significance of the new system.

With minor changes and adaptations the cargo operation reached amazing efficiency. The after ramp can be lowered to any position desired by working a switch in the cockpit, or at the cargo entrance proper. This means it can adjust to ground level for drive-on vehicles, or to any one of many truck-bed heights for the direct straight-in transfer of palletized cargo. With these features go the refinements of built-in snatch blocks and the movable electric winch. Got smaller cargo units as well? A wide forward cargo door swings up and out of the way to permit loading or unloading simultaneously at both ends of the aircraft.

And just as important to operations—considering a record of buckled floors, and "runaway" cargo in turbulence that had destroyed previous transports—the floor was built with the highest strength ever recorded in a transport. Here the loaders were provided with an over-all 20-inch pattern of 10,000-pound tie-down fittings, as well as tie-downs for 5,000- and 25,000-pound cargo loads. And just to add a note on versatility—this is the same facility that carries troops, litter patients, tanks and bulldozers, and even iron lungs (with power and servicing units built right into the Hercules' systems).

There remained one final category in which the Hercules was required to prove its capabilities—hurling great loads of cargo and equipment from the airplane in flight, for safe parachute descent to the ground. Leo Sullivan has described briefly the flight characteristics of the airplane in air drops during the early tests. But there was much more involved in the process of graduating to higher weights, not the least trying feature of which was the blistering heat on the ground.

Many of the tests were conducted at El Centro, California, which lies in the center of the Colorado desert, 60 miles west of Yuma and ten miles north of the Mexican border. "It's hot, dusty, and barren," groaned a Lockheed technician assigned to the test program, "but once you become accustomed to oppressive heat and choking dust in the middle of barren country, it's 'not so bad.'"

The first Hercules assigned to El Centro were the sixth and 13th models off the line. For weeks cargo loads of different types and weights poured from the open ramps of the airplanes. "They dropped just about everything out of the end of the '130s that you could think of throwing out of an airplane," Bill Smith, a Lockheed engineer, commented. He explained also that the crews made most of their flights "in the early morning, due to the terrific heat. The temperature went to 130 degrees at times, but the average was bad enough—about 120 degrees. So we tried to get on the road by no later than six o'clock every morning, and then devote the worst hours of the day to preparations for the following day's drops.

"Our biggest problem was that heat; it was absolutely brutal. The airplanes were parked out on the ramp and they soaked up the heat like sponges. We weren't running any power equipment on the airplanes, and with no air conditioning they just got hotter and hotter during the afternoons. We recorded temperatures inside the aircraft of 175 degrees, and you can't take *that* very long.

"Sometimes a man had to crawl inside the wing to inspect a system or make a repair. No one wanted to do that during the day and no one wanted to send him there, because the thermometer went up to recorded temperatures of 225 degrees. A man inside there—and a couple of times it was necessary to send somebody in—was good only for a very few minutes or he'd collapse. So we tried to do all repair and maintenance work no later than sunup if possible. By ten o'clock it was already 115 degrees. . . ."

In the summer of 1956 the early production models of the Hercules began to sneer at the record books that listed the greatest weights successfully extracted from an airplane and lowered safely by parachute to the ground. The first "heavyweight" loads parachuted from the Hercules included huge road-grading machines; it proved a startling sight to see one of these monsters sailing down from the sky. In fact, one of the road graders provided an even more startling sight when its parachutes tore free, leaving the great machine to descend entirely on its own. It smashed into the desert floor with a deep *Whump!* that people heard miles away. When a wrecking crew arrived on the scene, they shook their heads sadly, pushed the pieces into a depression, and heaped sand over the mess.

But only this one time did a road grader meet such an ignomini-

Huge military cargo load is hauled by parachute from the open ramp of C-130A Hercules. The powerful Lockheed assault transport holds the world's air-drop record at 41,740 pounds. (*Air Force/Lockheed-Georgia*)

Dramatic photo shows massive truck load (plus mounted recoilless rifle and ammunition) at moment it clears the rear cargo ramp of a Hercules during an air drop. Note the open parachute pulling the load free. (*Lockheed-Georgia*)

ous end. Soon afterward the crew prepared the Hercules for a new world record. From 2,000 feet, an extraction chute hauled the cargo load from the airplane. Six billowing chutes boomed open, and 27,000 pounds floated to earth. Lockheed chalked up not one but *four* new world records in air-drop performance.

Weight wasn't the only criterion of judgment. A single C-130 in ripple-fire fashion heaved an M-55 gun mount, a 105mm howitzer, and a jeep into the air to be successfully lowered by chutes. Right after this drop another Hercules dumped a 19,000-pound road grader and a 7,500-pound 40mm gun mount—a total of 26,500 pounds. Then came the single-load drop of 27,000 pounds.

This wasn't the heaviest load for the early summer of 1956. Another Hercules copped two more world records by releasing 18 A-22 containers, in which small shipments of practically any type can be packed. Eighteen parachutes cracked open beautifully, and the Hercules went down on the record books for a single-mission drop of 29,000 pounds.

The Hercules was just starting to flex its muscles, as Charlie Jackson, Lockheed engineer on the project, recalled. "As far as the heavy drops were concerned," he said, "at one time we dropped a full cargo compartment of A-22 containers. Each container is approximately five feet square and about six feet high, and they completely fill the cargo compartment. And do they move out once we cut 'em loose!"

The trick in getting the bulky loads out of the Hercules in real jig time is to have them roll out along the rail system of the airplane floor. The load skims over roller conveyers and is guided neatly by the airplane's rail system right out the gaping cargo hatch.

"When we loaded those 22 containers," Charlie Jackson explained, "we placed 18 within the airplane and four more on the ramp. Getting set for extraction, we lowered the ramp until it was ready, and then we 'let go.' The typical time for those containers to clear the airplane from the moment the first one started moving was something less than five seconds. . . ."

It wasn't much later when the Air Force lost its world record for single-load air drops from the Hercules. This loss had an ironic aspect to it, for the new record went to Britain's Royal Air Force, which air-dropped a single load of 32,000 pounds—from a Hercules!

"Old Faithful," the sixth Hercules off the production line, was still hard at its drop tests in El Centro. The Air Force and Lockheed had learned a lot about this business of dumping unprecedented loads through the air by parachute. Hercules 3006 came to the rescue of the Air Force record claims by heaving a single load of 35,055 pounds from its yawning cargo hatch.

The experiments with the C-130A models continued. New flight techniques developed from the tests. Soon a Hercules droned at 130 knots, 5,000 feet over the El Centro drop zone. The load that howled past the cargo ramp weighed 40,500 pounds.

Pilots argued that the speed wasn't great enough. The Hercules went back up to 5,000 feet, this time cruising at 150 knots. Two tremendous extraction chutes jerked taut at the end of a long line, and dragged mightily at the load inside the airplane. The new world record stood at 41,650 pounds.

In 1960 a C-130A dropped 41,740 pounds—not much more of a jump, but a flight to prove the new drop techniques now considered perfected by the pilots.

Apparently the experts had done their work well. The world record for the single-load air drop stood at 41,740 pounds from the Hercules when the Air Force called quits to the program. They

Under realistic "combat situation" tests, GI's use muscle power to push a pallet-loaded jeep on ball-bearing rollers into a Hercules prior to air-drop exercises. (*Air Force*)

sent the Hercules home to Marietta with honors. More important— the new air-drop capability had become a standard procedure for the Air Force, anywhere in the world.

The "Prove It" campaign for the Hercules ended officially with its complete and unqualified acceptance not only for all planned and specified missions, but in others for which the need arose even while the test crews put the airplane through its paces. The unprecedented versatility inherent in the design of the Hercules became increasingly evident as the weeks and the months went by, and the Air Force responded enthusiastically to this evidence by expanding its demands upon the machine.

By mid-1957 there were Hercules transports serving throughout the United States, in Europe, and throughout the Far East. Other Hercules moved in groups to special assignments where there existed a critical need for their unique performance capabilities, such as the force of 12 ski-equipped airplanes that roared into Greenland and fanned out in operations through the great northern country.

The aircraft sped on missions into the Caribbean and through South America. They carried huge loads into the Mediterranean and then crisscrossed the African continent. Many of these missions of the late 1950's could not even have been forecast, and were never considered in the original design or proving tests of the airplane.

But one need did exist, paramount among all others, and it represented the fulfillment of the original purpose of the Hercules. The working machinery of the Composite Air Strike Force (CASF) within the Tactical Air Command was not only a reality, but kept ready to be released when needed, to almost any point on the globe. As quickly as the Hercules transports could be dispatched to the troop-carrier organizations within the Air Force, as swiftly as they could be moved into the primary position for hauling weapons and cargo, the Tactical Air Command displaced its existing machines.

Test pilot Leo Sullivan minced no words when he stated flatly that the Hercules did not simply extend existing capabilities. To him the airplane heralded an entirely "new regime of flight."

Under the impetus of accelerated Air Force production orders, Lockheed-Georgia pushed the rate at which the machines rolled out of the great factory in Marietta. Once the Hercules reached the Tactical Air Command in numbers sufficient to form a solid operation fleet, TAC wasted no time in taking the next major step. It quickly established the Hercules as the logistical backbone of its far-flung military striking forces. And as events were to prove, the airplanes had arrived just in time.

CHAPTER XI

The Longest Arm THE TACTICAL AIR COMMAND
is not simply an Air Force. So brief and mundane a description
would be an insult to the incredible diversity and meaning of its
operations. Tactical Air Command—TAC—is a machine, an extraordinarily intricate and complex engine that functions with meticulous efficiency on an everyday, normal basis. While it performs
in this manner, living on a "hot" standby alert basis every 24 hours
of every day, bristling with everything from napalm to nuclear
warheads, it conducts that "everyday business" on a scale to stagger
the imagination and bog down the mind in statistics.

At the same time it is ready, always, to release its trigger of
awesome power and unleash not one but an overlapping matrix of
strikes against targets ranging from a single enemy foot soldier to
huge industrial complexes, should this prove necessary.

Strangely, though, the record would show that TAC's greatest
strength is a combination of its mission fabric: a superb blending
of the weapons that are poised with the "weapons" that function
every day of the year. It should be noted that among the latter are
those two-edged swords—the machines that carry fighting men and
guns or, just as efficiently, such cargoes as food, medicine, doctors,
et al.

TAC is the housekeeper on 14 sprawling military installations in
this country, and its men and machines conduct round-the-clock
operations from a total of more than 100 bases. Twenty of these are
in 12 foreign nations around the world which TAC crews have at
one time or another learned to call "home," and this total of bases
does not include many auxiliary operating sites. Certainly, it's impossible to include in this number the hundreds of open fields and
sandy stretches from which TAC's assault transports operate as a
matter of course.

TAC is a command within the greater structure of the United
States Air Force, and yet at its fingertip disposal there are more
than 128,000 human beings, of whom some 56,000 wear the insignia
of the Tactical Air Command. These are people with a deeply impressive variety of skills, and TAC will stand uncompromisingly on

the fact that this is an intermeshing of talents unmatched anywhere else in the world.

The term Tactical Air Command brings to mind as many different concepts as there are people who hear the words; perhaps still dominant is the "dead as a dodo" notion of tactical airpower as a relatively limited air weapon system with short range and confined largely to making less harrowing the infantryman's task of occupying a particular hill or field.

The "industrial plant" of TAC stands on the auditing sheets with a hardware value of more than six *billion* dollars. And this is not in idle machinery, either, with the greatest weight of this value chained vulnerably to permanent ground installations, as has been the classic case of the military organization. Within the framework of this command there are more than 2,000 crack warplanes, extending from the constantly expanding fleet of different Hercules models to new fighter-bombers that sunder the skies with blasts from 1,600-mile-per-hour sonic booms. Tankers, fighters, fighter-bombers, attack bombers, reconnaissance aircraft, weather planes, command aircraft, troop transports, assault transports, and still others . . . all of it sustaining that two-edged sword of carrying food and medicine to hapless children within a disaster area, or of honing that razor-sharp readiness to cut military targets into slag heaps.

The two-edged sword has been progressively sharpened through the last several years. It has become a terribly important factor that distinguishes one mighty air command from another—as in the distinction between the intrinsic mission of the Strategic Air Command and the goals of the Tactical Air Command.

SAC for many years loomed as the overwhelming giant of American airpower. By necessity of budgetary weaknesses and by virtue of some strategic myopia, TAC could be found on the scene ready for action, but in the background.

All this has gone by the boards. The stirrings of a vast and significant change are still reverberating through the environs of the Tactical Air Command. It is a change that has come not overnight but in a progressive fashion, dictated in its format without the slightest question by the man who sits at the desk of TAC's commander.

This is General Walter C. Sweeney, Jr., to whom a desk is somewhat less comfortable and certainly more frustrating than that to which he is better accustomed—the flight deck of a huge jet tanker or bomber, or the confining space of a supersonic fighter-bomber. To the Tactical Air Command General Sweeney has brought not simply the touch of hard professionalism, but the impact of a driving force that to no small extent, without any deprecation of his predecessors, has made everyone in the airpower business sit up and take sharp notice of the stirrings that have changed the very fiber of TAC.

The Strategic Air Command is a ramrod outfit, an absolutely no-nonsense operation with which the entire world is thoroughly familiar. It is an elite outfit that has for many years stared the toughest opposition smack in the eye, leaving not a shred of doubt as to the awesome power packed into the swollen bellies of its huge bombers. And among the best of the elite were striking forces made up of the immense B-52 bombers, each a half-million pounds of airplane and thermonuclear hell skimming the edge of earth's heavy atmosphere.

The best of the elite . . . and for years much of its force operated under the sure hand of General Sweeney. In 1948 General Sweeney served as Director of Plans, Strategic Air Command. In 1953 he commanded the 15th Air Force of SAC, and in 1955 he was commander of the Eighth Air Force of SAC.

Within the Strategic Air Command the bomber crews practiced again and again and again until they were honed to unbelievable precision and tautness in their tasks. Every SAC crew knew with haunting familiarity its exact target on the far side of the Iron Curtain. They spent weeks, months, and even years in runs over simulated targets that approximated closely the characteristics of the "real thing." It has been a task formidable in its scope, but also one that has been "right down the line," with no question marks as to missions or assignments.

This concept of airpower is to the crews of TAC a marvelous luxury. In comparison to this mission assignment, TAC is a nightmare of responsibility. It is not at all "right down the line"; it is, rather, a constantly shifting kaleidoscope of complexity. The targets for the crews may be selected out of many thousands of possibilities, and TAC crews know only that the direction in which they may be required to fly on a no-notice, instant-readiness basis can be found among the 360 degrees of any compass.

General Sweeney insists that the term "professionalism" in the truest sense of the word must be an integral element of the fabric from which is woven the capabilities of TAC. In this respect he not only desires but demands levels of skill unprecedented anywhere in the world. It means skill requiring such effort that it wrings pilots and crews dry; no excuses are accepted when failure to any human extent may be avoided. It means a methodical whipsaw drive to excel in raw combat capabilities against any opposition that may

TAC Commander General Walter C. Sweeney, Jr., before takeoff in 1,600-MPH F-110A Phantom II fighter for checkout flight. (*The Martin Company*)

be encountered—operating in the assignment vacuum of "anywhere and at any time unknown to us."

Sweeney is determined that no matter what the cost in matériel or in sinew, there will be no sagging at the seams when the heat is on and TAC suffers the acid test of win—or die. Under such conditions in this day and age not only men's lives, but the safety of the nation and perhaps even that of civilization is involved. It must be emphasized that this approach to tactical airpower in the new concept emanates from the man who accepted nothing less from the most powerful strategic heavy bomber force in existence.

The laws of his airpower command are hard and fast. You can either do the job, or you cannot. The time to lay bare the faults and the weaknesses is *now*, before people must be forced to die because of the inadequacy of preparations that could, and should, have been conducted in a more professional and capable manner.

Carrying this thought a bit farther, the writer's own impressions after extensive exposure to the intricacies of TAC are that Sweeney's staff is hell-for-leather on slicing the fat off the fighting force which they conceive TAC to be. The extent to which they pursue this concept is to the limit of endurance of both the men and the machines they employ to execute their missions. It goes farther than this, of course, for concepts and strategy to an appreciable extent dictate the final effectiveness of any combat organization. This is perhaps the shortest distance to the goal of a battle outfit that, despite its complexity and size, is just as sharp and professional at its work as the smallest cadre that seethes with the *Gung Ho!* fighting spirit.

The people who make up the Strategic Air Command, in a mixture of weariness and great respect, rated General Curt LeMay, its former commander-in-chief, as "a tough boss but a hell of a clutch player." The record carved by SAC through the years of an absence of nuclear war speaks for itself. The "new" Tactical Air Command now exhibits the kind of muscle the United States has needed desperately.

General Sweeney is, bluntly, shooting for the moon in his goals. There is no question of his grim determination to make his command "better organized than SAC, tougher than the Marines, and with a better military bearing than the Army." This has made more than one faint heart quiver at the thought of the wicked schedules necessary to achieve these goals.

But it is working. It is working with a swiftness and sureness that is breathtaking. The finest tactical air weapons in the world to support these aspirations have played a major role in its success; of this there can be no doubt. TAC at one time brooded darkly over its status as a "hand-me-down" air force; its funds, equipment, aircraft, manpower, matériel—the gamut of necessity—always ran second to the Strategic Air Command and other organizations.

This is now history. Every fighter wing in TAC but two are supersonic, and these wings include the deadliest machines ever to rip through the skies. They are weapons like the Republic F-105 Thunderchief, a one-man airplane larger than a twin-engine airliner, but capable of 1,350 miles per hour and endowed with an unbelievable power of devastation. Moving in increasing numbers onto the scene is McDonnell's Phantom II. This is not an airplane in the familiar sense of the word. It is a twin-engined, two-man monster of a fighter and fighter-bomber that screams with a fury of sound during takeoff that stabs like icepicks into the ears. Ponderous in size, it defies the tradition of the runway hogs and explodes upward from the ground after rolling only 3,000 feet. It does not climb in the familiar sense of the word. Its afterburners spew flame and diamond shock waves and with disdain it rejects the

(*Above*) Bullpup missile blasts away from F-105 Thunderchief fighter-bomber in live firepower exercises of Tactical Air Command. (*Below*) Huge Phantom II fighter being procured in quantity for Tactical Air Command flies faster than 1,600 MPH, carries "staggering" weapons load, and can take off in 3,000 feet! (*Upper photo: The Martin Company; lower photo: Air Force*)

earth and claws vertically for sky. It nudges the regime of flight close to three times that of sound. Its two-man crews return often from flights so high that they witness the curvature of the planet's horizon and marvel at the purple-black of space beyond.

There is, however, an even more meaningful factor by which to measure the stiffening to steel-rod straightness of the TAC spinal column. For many years just about the lowest member of the operational totem pole had been the cargo and troop-carrier organization. Advances in other fields were celebrated with brilliant performance and superb equipment. Fighters and bombers leaped from generation to generation of new machines, and created in their wake an unbalanced structure of tactical air weaponry.

The howling jets plunged into new flight regimes. They soared to unprecedented heights. The manufacturers waxed eloquent, the generals made appropriate speeches, and the press grabbed eagerly for new heroes by rubbing briskly on the new public image of the "Tiger in the cockpit."

The transports, however, continued to plod along. They rumbled through the skies and, if they were overloaded or an engine failed, they sometimes tumbled through the skies. One twin-engine transport which saw service by the many hundreds acquired an unsavory reputation throughout the Air Force. Heavily laden, it courted disaster. When an engine failed under maximum gross weight, or at almost any time during takeoff, the result was a funeral pyre that became distressingly familiar.

Some crews defended the airplane. They insisted that if pilots flew the machine "by the book" and did not overload the craft, it would remain safe. But as invariably happens, it is necessary to overload airplanes, and engines do cut out on takeoff. In due time the funeral pyres began to cloud the atmosphere.

The transports were short-legged in range, slow in speed, and frankly unequal to the need for flight at high altitude. The transport organizations became regarded as the bastard offspring of the various air commands using them, and high morale became conspicuous by its absence.

The concept of the Composite Air Strike Force, and other innovations in strategy still in their budding stage, would never have become reality with these restrictions. The morale of the crews was unfortunately a reflection of the capability of the aircraft, and "low and slow" does not a strategic transport make. The pilots and crews of the swift jets heaped well-intentioned but nonetheless grating derision upon their fellows, and transport pilots began either to assume a defensive stance or to slink away as unobtrusively as possible.

Without a revolution in this area as well as in those of fighters and bombers, neither TAC nor its cherished CASF could attain the heights at which their commanders aimed. But here the effect of the Hercules extended far beyond its logistical value. The new airplane proved to be as much a shot in the arm for the crews and all troop-carrier personnel, as it was for the logistics of TAC and its subsidiary forces.

At Evreux-Fauville Air Base in France, a colonel left no question as to the impact of the Hercules upon his men. When the pilots made their transitions from the C-119 Packets and C-123 Providers into the Hercules, he said, "they developed from transport pilots almost into fighter pilots. The new planes were so much easier to handle, and their power potential had our airplane drivers literally whooping for joy. The flight rooms sounded as if the fighter jocks were holding a free-for-all beer reunion, instead of transport drivers. It seemed as if everyone walked straighter, and for sure they were able to fly in a manner they'd never dreamed of. They flew higher and a hell of a lot faster and they carried whopping cargoes over distances they once could only dream about. And another item that had them chortling with glee was that little ol' radar that kept them out of thunderstorms even when they were

"They were able to fly in a manner they'd never dreamed of." A colonel of the 322nd Air Division in France described the introduction of the transport crews to the Hercules. (*Air Force*)

flying blind. Afer a few of your friends have stumbled into the big storms which spit out the airplanes in little pieces, you come to appreciate little things like this radar.

"The things we could do with this new bird had everyone buzzing, and we knew we'd struck pay dirt when some of the fighter jocks asked to come along for the ride on training flights. Before, we had to drag them kicking and screaming into our ships.

"We could take the '130 up to 12,000 feet, hold it up with the nose in a steep climb until the airplane scrabbled for lift. Finally we'd go into a complete stall. Then—just slam the throttles forward and the airplane never even changed its attitude. The props chewed their way straight on out and up from that stall. It's the *only* big airplane I know of, anywhere, that can do that. . . .

"So when it all adds up, let me state flatly that I have never known a '130 pilot who wasn't unhappy when he left an outfit that flew the Hercules. And I've never known one pilot who wouldn't trample everyone in his way if he had even a slim chance to get back into the seat of the airplane."

Much of the muscle which TAC now flexes with such comparative ease began building before General Sweeney arrived on the TAC scene. Power of such magnitude and flexibility as is now displayed by TAC is not an overnight matter, nor is it the simple result of the combination of two influencing factors—the realization that we were in dire need of such a capability, and the shock that this capability, despite the need, simply did not exist.

From 1954 until 1960, the Tactical Air Command shifted uncomfortably beneath its own critical self-examination and the impact of its new growing pains. Headquarters staffs thrashed out new concepts into which would fit supersonic aircraft and the long-range tankers with which to impart seven-league boots to the fighters and attack bombers. Equally important in creating the new airpower force would be the Hercules, which a TAC planner anticipated as the "key support aircraft in TAC's CASF, providing the 'long legs' in tactical deployments by providing a global range for airlifting supplies and equipment in excess of a 25,000-pound gross payload." In the future loomed a new airlift force that would be comprised of more than 10,000 people along with many hundreds of transports. The muscle of the new airlift support would be the Hercules, with special assignments to the C-123 Provider, a twin-engine, high-wing ugly duckling that could bounce into tiny strips in the middle of nowhere, and get out again—a role it would play with spectacular success in Viet Nam.

Even as it bore the burden of reorganization to meet the new national need of strike power anywhere at any time, TAC engaged in refining its *joint* operational tactics and techniques through both planning and constant exercises in the field. The critical need to bolster military airpower in Europe catapulted TAC into the overseas support business in a major effort; the provision of such overseas support was coupled with the program to stretch the range of jet fighters by aerial refueling, presaging the current global sinew of TAC. The operational phase of the global mobility business began in 1954 with rotating fighter squadrons to Europe on a six-month basis, but it was a beginning riddled with problems that weighed heavily on the shoulders of both headquarters and field commanders—and, of course, on the crews. Through the grim and progressively successful effort, however, TAC acquired a measure of skill and competence that soon enabled this command to stand without peer in the world.

Five years after its initial faltering efforts, TAC within the space of one year deployed more than 1,200 aircraft to overseas bases, accomplished more than 3,500 mid-air fuel hookups in weather both good and "absolutely foul," and made much of the planet Earth its hunting grounds. What had once been hazardous, and even lethal, had become a routine matter. The skill required is no less today, the hazard is not diminished, but skill has multiplied itself until "threading the needle" is taken for granted as a pilot capability.

The year 1955 stands as a critical high-water mark in the transformation of the nation's tactical airpower. That year saw the birth of the 19th Air Force, which would hold the key to the success of the new Composite-Air-Strike-Force concept, and it was also the year of Exercise Sagebrush.

This exercise was the nation's first major military maneuvers under nuclear conditions. Employing more than 14,000 air and ground troops, Sagebrush involved the movement of massive tactical air fleets. Its immensity and depth may be better understood when it is realized that the fighting forces involved greater military strength than could be marshaled by many nations of the world. Significant currents ran through the entire effort, not the least of which was the distinction that an air general—General O. P. Weyland, then TAC Commander—was in over-all command of *all* forces involved.

Spreading over most of the southwestern part of the United States —an area much larger than many countries in which limited and brushfire wars would be fought—Sagebrush provided a vital test of new doctrines, tactics, techniques, procedures, and weapons systems. It transformed theory and concept from paper to actuality, and it proved conclusively that supersonic jet tactical fighters could provide the three basic elements of air support—close fire, counter-

When the orders to "move out" cracked the whip among TAC's units, the crews moved fast, as in this drill. "Within three hours of the alert notice to 'move out,' the B-57s were in the air and over the Atlantic, on their way. . . ." (*U.S. Army*)

air, and interdiction. Equally important was the fact that this conclusive demonstration was carried out with unprecedented accuracy and with a level of flexibility hitherto unknown in airpower employment.

Marring this new and gratifying picture were some unwelcome flaws. In certain areas the application of tactical airpower revealed weaknesses and sometimes outright gaps. Sagebrush not only brought these weaknesses to immediate attention, but fortunately pointed to several possibilities of eliminating them. That is, after all, the intrinsic purpose of so vast and complex an operation.

Strategists are agreed that the other milestone of 1955 was the creation of the 19th Air Force, then a unique innovation and today an integral element of our national global military power. Within TAC there already existed the Ninth and 12th Air Forces which, as conventional subordinate command organizations, faced merely the "overwhelming problems" of building the new image of tactical airpower. The 19th faced a monumental challenge without precedent. Stated in succinct military terms, its mission was to:

> Be prepared to deploy any and all assigned units to any theater or area in the world as might be directed, and be capable of exercising operational control of attached units upon their arrival in the combat zone.

Military men as well as civilians find it difficult at times to see clearly the role of the Composite Air Strike Force (CASF). As we have seen, a CASF exists only as a plan on paper until the time when it is needed. The staff of the 19th Air Force, which is located at Seymour-Johnson Air Force Base, keeps close tabs on available TAC forces and their disposition, and works out the plans for CASF to go to "any theater or area in the world," but except in training work has no direct relationship with the operational forces of TAC *until* a CASF is ordered.

Let us suppose that Strike Command (STRICOM) receives orders from the Joint Chiefs of Staff to deliver a specific military force to a certain overseas theater. The STRICOM commander immediately makes up a list of all the forces he will need, passing on this information to TAC headquarters. TAC in turn orders the 19th Air Force to establish a CASF of a particular size determined by the military situation.

At this point the 19th Air Force changes from a "paper air force" to one in actuality. The staff pull from their files the preplanned package of a CASF that fits the requirements handed down by TAC headquarters. Immediately the 19th Air Force flashes the word to the necessary organizations throughout TAC included in the selected plan—fighters, tankers, troop-carrier units, and so on—informing them that a CASF has been ordered, and that from this moment on they are under the direct control of its commander—who is the Commander, 19th Air Force. The fighters and bombers immediately start to move out, while tankers from other bases prepare to rendezvous with them for aerial refueling.

Simultaneously the CASF commander orders the troop-carrier planes to proceed to preassigned Army stations such as Fort Bragg, North Carolina. These stations—part of the Strategic Army Corps (STRAC)—have already been notified by STRICOM to prepare troops for immediate deployment. As fast as the Hercules transports land, the troops pile aboard, and the Hercules take off for their overseas destinations.

The commander of the CASF exercises complete operational control over the CASF while it is en route. When the CASF arrives at the overseas theater, it automatically comes under the command of the military officer who commands in that particular area of the world. This unified theater commander may order the CASF commander to operate as his immediate deputy in charge of all air operations, or he may assign someone on his own staff to carry out this mission. It depends upon the local situation.

Simultaneously with the deployment of the CASF, STRICOM

continues to feed more fighting forces into the overseas theater, or simply keeps them poised for immediate deployment. The CASF commander operates under direct orders of TAC headquarters until he is overseas.

The commanders function in constant coordination with one another. STRICOM exercises deployment control of all TAC and STRAC units until they are out of the country. The CASF commander exercises—on behalf of the TAC commander—control en route to the overseas area. In the overseas area, the unified theater commander has full control of *all* military forces in that theater. He operates under the direct control of the Joint Chiefs of Staff. The TAC commander (1) fills the needs of STRICOM in ordering deployment out of the United States, and (2) maintains world-wide control of other TAC forces, assuring their availability to any unified theater commander as needed.

The concept of the CASF was well established (see Chapter III: "The Flexible Blueprint") by the time Major General Henry Viccellio accepted command of the 19th Air Force. Probably no general in American military history had ever been surrounded with a *smaller* permanent force, for Viccellio and his entire staff counted up to less than 100 people. But they were crack men, every one of them, and in their skills and knowledge second to none.

General Viccellio had entered military service in 1934 after attending William and Mary College in Williamsburg, Virginia. Two years later he graduated from an intensive pilot training course as a commissioned officer and fighter pilot. During World War II he served in various combat theaters of the South Pacific, and on the basis of his demonstrated skill as a pilot and grasp of tactics, in mid-1943 was named chief of the fighter and air defense branch of the Army Air Forces, Fighter Division.

After World War II Viccellio played a major role in developing new weapon systems and tactics at the Air Proving Ground Command at Eglin Air Force Base, Florida. Later he attended the Armed Forces Staff College at Norfolk, Virginia. From 1947 until 1949 he commanded the 82nd Fighter Wing at Manchester, New Hampshire.

In 1949 he became Chief of Plans for the Tactical Air Command; one year later he was assigned as the Chief of Operations for the Eastern Air Defense Force of the United States. Then came an overseas duty tour in Europe; it was upon his return that he received the command of the 19th Air Force.

As the prime architect of the CASF concept and the first man to translate the idea into reality, General Viccellio had to map acceptable plans for reacting swiftly, maintaining maximum en-route speed, and reaching a distant overseas area with his forces *ready to fight*. This constituted the heart and soul of the entire CASF doctrine, and the arteries through which the lifeblood of the CASF flowed were the communications channels fanning out from an airborne command post.

The entire responsibility of the 19th Air Force is *control*, as sharply distinct from everyday *use* of men and the hardware with which they function. The headquarters has no logistics, personnel, or administrative responsibilities other than those normally associated with its permanent staff of about 80 people. It commands no units except during an actual CASF operation—during actual combat deployment and operations. It is thus free to expend all its energies and talents on the problems of the Composite Air Strike Force—which include planning for deployment and employment, training units for their roles in CASF forces capable of deploying to anywhere in the world and fighting there, and, finally, planning and training for the 19th to deploy itself and to command the CASF.

The writer spent much time with the headquarters element of the 19th. Major General Maurice A. Preston was the commander; tall and capable, he wears insignia not often found on Air Force commanding generals. The 50-year old officer had recently gone through the rugged paratrooper course at Fort Bragg, North Carolina, and astonished the "youngsters" by taking everything the paratrooper school had to dish out. Before he returned to his desk at Seymour-Johnson Air Force Base, the Army pinned its paratrooper wings on Preston's uniform—the first Air Force two-star general ever to wear the badge of the Airborne.

As this book went to press, Major General Preston was assigned to new command duties in the Far East, and Major General Viccellio, the "original architect" of CASF, returned as the commander of the 19th Air Force.

The top staff of the 19th are either now, or soon will be jump-qualified. The majority of key officers have reached this rather exclusive fraternity within the Air Force, and those not yet through the course are slated for the "bumps and knocks" of paratrooper school.

"This staff sends people out into all types of country to jump," General Preston said dryly. "We must commit thousands of paratroopers, engineers, and other men to jumps over terrain that can be wild and rough. My people cannot ever hope to *know* what this is like unless they have shared in the actual experience. The only way to do this job is to have my headquarters staff right alongside the privates and sergeants and officers of the paratroopers. Once these Army people have seen our people taking the same responsibilities and problems with which they must live on a day-to-day basis, it's pretty obvious that we have the best possible understanding of their needs—and that we can't help but consider their best interests."

Behind the guarded and locked doors of the 19th's war room— its earthbound control center—the writer received a thorough look into the inner workings of this unique command. Lieutenant Colonel Sidney S. Hershberg and his staff went through an elaborate breakdown of the operations that make the CASF a reality. It was a staggering assignment that required a knowledge of every intimate detail of the concept of operations for the tactical air forces, of force requirements, aircraft schedules into the objective areas, target priorities and assignments, ordnance requirements, turnaround times and communications, and support details.

"All of these plans form a complex, interwoven web of coordination," explained Colonel Hirshberg, "which is the hard requirement of success in the joint operations of TAC elements with those of the other services. The communications requirements are unprecedented in their thoroughness and extent—and we've got to plan from the individual field telephone all the way up through intricate tactical air control systems. We function with guidance and homing equipment, all types of radar and radar centers, and air control nets, as well as a complete network of command control on a point-to-point basis. . . ."

One answer to the vexing problem of *speed of response*—the time between a request from a ground force for an attack on an enemy target, and the actual arrival of the airborne strike—has been the slicing away of many of the steps formerly necessary to accomplish such a mission. This is done by means of the 19th's new special organization known as the Direct Air Support Center, which maintains predetermined packages of men and equipment that are kept constantly at the ready. The force can be tailored by the use of "plug in-and-out" units to conform to the scale of any necessary field operations.

In previous communications systems, the request for target strikes moved along an elaborate chain of command. The DASC package, airborne and ready to move into action within minutes of its arrival in TAC Hercules, trims the number of steps in the chain of command. Before DASC, it was often as much as 30 minutes after an airborne strike request before the pilots in the airplanes could start their response. Now the time averages from three to five minutes— a difference that has tremendous effect on the battlefront.

One of the unceasing activities of the 19th is intelligence, and its commander's staff has learned through back-breaking labor never to consider any operational plan as more than a temporary guide-line to their jobs. The complications of swiftly changing interna-tional situations and the constant improvement and expansion of our own military capabilities around the world demand frequent and major revisions of the plans for the deployment of strike forces.

The 19th Air Force commander and his staff keep their fingers on the pulse of activities anywhere and everywhere in the world through studies of every possible intelligence source available to the United States. The constant revision of plans extends from the deployment of a major striking force all the way down the line to the "assignment of a specific gun emplacement for attack with a specified ordnance load, for the first day of combat. The air and ground order-of-battle information on all commands is absolutely essential."

As the "architect" of CASF, General Viccellio was provided the opportunity several years ago to test under the whiplash of a national crisis the thoroughness of his planning and the validity of his concepts.

On the morning of July 15, 1958, the "whistle blew" both for TAC and Viccellio's headquarters. Turmoil seething in the Middle East threatened to explode into border wars and invasions; intelli-gence reported Soviet forces moving up in strength to capitalize on the precarious balancing of governments. Extremists had assassi-nated King Faisal II of Iraq and grasped the reins of government control. Across the border in Lebanon, Communist forces responded to the opportunity and made their bid for a lightning coup against the government of President Camille Chamoun. Russian agents made it clear to the Communist factions within Lebanon that suc-cess in their efforts would bring powerful military forces to support their new and "legal government."

Chamoun issued an urgent plea for assistance to the United States government, and the urgency of that request prompted swift and decisive reaction. Tactical Air Command went immediately on a war footing, and flashed the word to the 19th Air Force "to de-ploy CASF Bravo to Incirlik Air Base near Adana, Turkey." At the same time the Joint Chiefs of Staff ordered Army units to the ready, and dispatched the Sixth Fleet in the Mediterranean to the scene with its warships, tactical airpower from its carriers, and Marines.

In this initial acid test of the CASF concept, the results were startling. Orders commanding battle status cracked the whip through 25 tactical wings. Within the hour B-57 attack bombers in Virginia were moving swiftly to deploy. Crews shuffled charts and computers for the 6,400-mile flight to Incirlik—which would place them right at the doorstep of Lebanon. Within three hours of the alert notice to "move out," the B-57s were in the air and over the Atlantic, on their way.

Within the next three hours the F-100 Super Sabres of the 355th Tactical Fighter Squadron boomed out of Myrtle Beach Air Force Base in South Carolina. The fighter-bombers grabbed for altitude, and in formation set their course to the northeast and Bermuda. From Kindley Air Force Base crews thundered down the runways into the air in KB-50J tankers, pushing with all the power from six engines to carry the 38,000 pounds of kerosene fuel in each plane to a point of rendezvous over the Atlantic with the fighters. Far beyond, from Lajes in the Azores, another tanker fleet readied itself for the air refueling mission.

It was "murder up there," the pilots would report later. Violent thunderstorms churned the sky into turbulence that battered at the heavy tankers and hurled the fighters about like chips on a stormy ocean. Most of the fighters hooked up and continued, but not all. Unable to slide their refueling probes into the long drogues that whipped crazily like maddened snakes, they peeled off and raced for Canadian bases. There they refueled, took off again immediately, and caught the tankers in calmer air.

The CASF Bravo alert sent fighters rolling at intervals down their long runways and into the air. Two Super Sabres of TAC split the dusk with blazing afterburners and start to grab for altitude. (*The Martin Company*)

The majority of the force swept on, sucked in fuel from the Lajes tankers, and cut for Europe. When dawn broke over the Atlantic they were already racing past Spain. Beyond Marseilles they met their third tanker force, took on their fuel, and cut at high speed for Incirlik.

Twelve and a half hours after splashing afterburner flame on the runways of Myrtle Beach, they screeched to landings at Incirlik.

Two hours later they were back in the air on combat patrol missions. More and more fighters joined them, until combat teams "loaded for bear" roared along the Iranian and Turkish borders. The pilots could see units of the Soviet Army moving at high speed toward Lebanon.

The F-100D Super Sabres and B-57 attack bombers soon had other CASF jet company in the air with them. Twin-engine RB-66 reconnaissance bombers and supersonic RF-101A Voodoos sliced long white contrails over the ocean as they went full bore for Turkey. WB-66 weather-reconnaissance planes charted every meteorological phenomenon and pattern along the routes and in the area of potential combat.

Only six hours after the first red alert sounded in Tactical Air Command headquarters, the first elements of the fleet of Hercules transports were well over the Atlantic, land already out of sight behind them. Aboard the Hercules were engineers, mechanics, technicians, and specialists with a hundred different skills. And with the men were elaborately packed "flyaway kits"—special containers carrying the more critical spare parts, replacement assemblies, and other items necessary to make the CASF force virtually self-sufficient in these requirements for the next 30 days.

The initial group of Hercules piled into Incirlik hard on the heels of the fighters. The maintenance crews moved right out to the combat jets to keep them primed and cocked for any combat action. One Hercules bulged with an elaborate communications package that assured complete control over the broad span of radio and radar facilities of all units.

Additional jets and Hercules thundered into Incirlik. Every required item of support, both personnel and equipment, raced over to the preplanned units in the Hercules troop-and-cargo carriers.

Forty-five hours after the "whistle blew," more than 100 aircraft of CASF Bravo were on combat station in Turkey. The Hercules had brought along more than 1,500 skilled personnel and 750 tons of the most essential matériel to support the force.

More Hercules began to arrive, filled with crack fighting men and weapons from the United States.

The United States deemed the situation so grave that it ordered

Through preparedness initial move is made quickly. A line of Hercules (*above*) roll into the loading area of an Army base; note the outboard engines already stopped as they take up positions. Ready on the line (*below*) they wait to board their paratroopers and other soldiers. (*Air Force*)

A CASF alert means men moving in a constant stream through all hours of the day and night. Roused from their beds at four A.M., Air Force technicians board special alert bus to move them to the flight line and hangars. (*The Martin Company*)

additional theater forces to support the operation. United States Air Forces Europe (USAFE) fired off a group of F-86D Sabres for additional strength, and placed all air-sea rescue aircraft on the alert to assist the CASF if needed.

Fifteen hours after the CASF force was fully deployed, 2,000 paratroopers in other TAC transports from England and Germany arrived on the scene. Marines stormed ashore at Khalde Bay in Lebanon. The Navy's carriers deployed out of sight beyond the horizon—but their fighting airplanes rattled the windows of the city as they boomed low overhead.

Once the CASF was in position as a fighting force, it came under the operational control of the Commander in Chief, Specified Command, Middle East, as did all air, naval, and land components. The F-86D Sabres and their bigger brother F-100D Super Sabres maintained an all-weather, round-the-clock combat alert.

After 100 days in the operation, CASF Bravo redeployed to the

The airmen as well as the officers know the sudden moments of unexpected partings. An airman from a C-130 crew on CASF alert bids his wife and daughter a hurried good-by; he may not be home for months. (*The Martin Company*)

United States. *All* aircraft departed Turkey in one day, and were out of the Middle East the next, winging toward the States.

Commanding the Army forces in the Lebanon operation was General Paul D. Adams. The writer's queries to General Adams as to the effectiveness of our deployment in the Middle East drew a direct and meaningful response.

"Many people have asked why the United States sent the quantity of military strength to Lebanon that was deployed," General Adams said. "A fleet, a Composite Air Strike Force, a Marine brigade, an Army brigade, and a logistical command were dispatched to that small country, which is not much larger than a good-sized county in our country. One of the chief reasons the United States was so successful in its Lebanon operation was the fact that there

"There goes Daddy . . . *again.*" A young boy watches his father's airplane roll into takeoff position for a CASF movement. (*The Martin Company*)

was without question enough visible military strength in being in the area of operations to defeat any military force in the area that could be marshaled against it.

"As a matter of fact, I made a remark at the time . . . that at the peak of our dispositions there, I didn't think there was anything *anywhere* in the Middle East that could bother our force a bit. We were that strong. Now, we were so strong that immediately the situation began to change favorably.

"One of the first things discerned was that some armored forces parked along the edge of Lebanon, apparently exploitation forces— I can't imagine what else they could have been there for, because Lebanon was obviously on the verge of collapse—well, after a week of our presence there, I began to observe that there were little withdrawals from these forces. They began to lose their strength with a steady withdrawal and the first thing we knew—they were all gone.

"In other words, the situation had become very clear to the opposition. Everywhere they looked they saw tremendous fighting power. Finally their attitude became one of accepting the fact that 'There's no use to tangle with those boys—they've got the power.' And very quickly the situation stabilized itself, and we prevented what could have become a very large war."

Or, what is considered a classic example of the ultimate goal of any fighting force: "To make the enemy change his mind . . ."

Five weeks after CASF Bravo deployed to the Middle East, the Communists pulled out the plug on the other side of the world. Chinese Communist forces built to alarming strength and threatened the Taiwan Strait holdings of Nationalist China. TAC lost no time in reviewing its plans for limited war in the Far East—an "occupational hazard" in that part of the world.

"It was interesting to note the development of two 'pressure' situations simultaneously, a possibility we had considered very likely," General Viccellio pointed out. "In the absence of 19th Air Force [operating then in Turkey], the 12th Air Force alternate command element received its initial warning alert on 9 August. On 29 August the deployment order was given and CASF X-ray Tango was dispatched. MATS provided the bulk of the airlift for X-ray Tango as well as for the Air Defense Command F-104's that went to Taiwan.

"In addition to the command element, X-ray Tango consisted of F-100, F-101, B-57, C-130, RF-101 squadrons, tanker support, communications and control elements, plus usual support. That exercise, which [was] TAC's first large-scale CASF demonstration in the Far East, proved its worth . . . , our lessons having served to eliminate many bottlenecks. . . ."

The Chinese Communists reacted to the sudden appearance of the powerful combat force with a howl that shook diplomatic corridors the world around. It was a reaction that failed to disturb the CASF operation—because it remained no more than an irritating sound. Only one thing would show whether or not the CASF move had been effective. Would the threatened violence be realized, or would the CASF deployment act as a damper to the aroused emotions of the Chinese?

There was no war—brushfire, limited, or otherwise.

The "longest arm" had emerged from the mists of concept and entered the arena of reality.

The United States, without massive deployment of its forces, without endangering any area by stripping it of its fighting powers, could apply its strength anywhere in the world, as demonstrated

Fighters, bombers, weather planes, tankers, transports, and reconnaissance fighters (*above:* supersonic RF-101A Voodoo) moved out to opposite parts of the world . . . and refueled miles over the middle of nowhere. (*Air Force*)

by CASF Bravo and CASF X-Ray Tango. This was proof, not postulation.

Two situations that almost certainly would have exploded into the fury of full combat—did not. The Communists had pulled both triggers of their shotgun, aiming carefully on opposite sides of the globe. Despite this splitting tactic, and despite the inexperience of the CASF forces under such extreme conditions and demands, the point had been unquestionably proven. From those days on, American policy would remain inextricably linked to the employment of the CASF as an instrument for fulfilling the needs and goals of the United States on an international basis.

The Tactical Air Command, however, gave its weary air warriors little time for celebration. Bravo and X-Ray Tango, along with all their stunning accomplishments, had revealed also a number of serious deficiencies—and the time to assure their correction was "at once."

CHAPTER XII

Hit 'em Harder!   THE POWERFUL STRENGTH
and flexibility of the Composite Air Strike Force system as it
exists today is meaningful praise for the work begun by General
Viccellio and advanced by General Preston. Viccellio designed the
structure and built the framework; Preston filled the gaps and
brought in steel reinforcement to strengthen the entire fabric of
the CASF.

The first two CASF operations dictated several immediate and
drastic modifications of the operating plans of TAC. Those operations showed conclusively that the problems stemming from the
Bravo employment were a direct result of the lack of advance
warning. In 1958 Viccellio envisaged a "certain minimum interval
of alert during which preliminary actions could be taken. Since
this time was not available, all actions had to be taken simultaneously. Troop-carrier movement was somewhat slower than planned
and made it difficult for the Deployment Control Center to maintain tight control of troop-carrier movement, although this did not
impede the flow of tactical aircraft."

The 19th Air Force, in response to the corrections demanded,
shifted its basis of operation to a constant vigil that is maintained
24 hours a day, every day of the year. The alert posture of all
elements which fit into the CASF structure—as well as that of prime
TAC units—is now entirely responsive on a "no warning" basis.

Any advance warning is accepted as a boon on which no one
relies, although such warning can of course ease the requirement
of "instant response" and permit TAC to initiate preplanned actions that increase the flow of aircraft once the decision to deploy
is flashed down to Viccellio's headquarters.

To insure this capability of quick reaction, the staff of the 19th
Air Force has created a system of CASF "combat packages." These
comprise from one to ten tactical fighter squadrons, with associated
reconnaissance, refueling, troop carrier, radar and communications
elements commensurate with the size of the mission to be accomplished.

But even this in itself is not enough. "The arrival of tactical ele-

Red Alert! The crew of the C-135—TAC's Airborne Command Post assigned to 19th Air Force Headquarters—race to the aircraft as the
alert is flashed of a CASF operation. This photo shows a real alert.
(*Air Force*)

ments of the force in advance of the command element was another undesirable feature of the Bravo deployment," Viccellio noted
in a no-holds-barred critique of his own operation. General Preston,
while commanding the 19th Air Force, whipped this problem by
turning to the fastest long-range transport in the national inventory—the Boeing C-135, which is modified to cruise at 600 miles per
hour over a range in excess of 5,000 miles.

This, however, is not all of the enormous benefit of the great
jetliner. It isn't just an airplane to move a number of people rapidly
over extreme range. It has been drastically modified in its interior
as an Airborne Command Post. It is equipped with millions of
dollars' worth of the most advanced communications and electronic
equipment known to exist in the world. It permits the commander
or any members of his staff to carry out continuous en-route monitoring of the progress of the tactical units following behind, and
of the situation in the destination area. These communications provide also the critical links between the deploying force and other
headquarters—including a link straight to the TAC Headquarters
Command Post at Langley Air Force Base, Virginia.

General Preston approached his requirements with a vast background of experience which allowed him to encompass in a sweeping glance the kaleidoscopic nature of his problems—and to move

in the most direct possible manner to their solution. An experienced "B-17 driver" in World War II, he had always felt that the man behind the desk of a force such as a CASF *must* know intimately the requirements of his men in the field and the pressures on them. When he came to the 19th Air Force, Maurice Preston was a rated command pilot, a skilled navigator, a bombardier renowned among his fellow officers, and a pilot who had flown *every* aircraft in the inventory of the United States Air Force.

Then he added the qualifications of a paratrooper.

He also stamped a trademark on his staff which is now known throughout the military. The "Suitcase Air Force," people call the 19th Air Force staff, because they are required always to keep a packed bag at hand, no matter where they are, in order to be able to "move out" at any time the red telephone in headquarters shrills its note of alarm.

The 19th's headquarters involves prepacked "suitcases" on a much larger scale. Its staff—split into two separate "combat sections"—each maintain a "mobility kit" containing supplies sufficient for a month's operation in the field, and which are always ready for immediate flyaway. Thus the gap that lay open in 1958 has been filled. The commander now has within his own headquarters complete control-staff capabilities for conducting two CASF operations simultaneously, as well as an undisclosed number of further command-staff backups within TAC itself.

Again and again operations have emphasized the all-critical role of communications and the importance of "instantly available communications" no matter where the operation may be located. The C-135 (and the 19th's backup plane as well) serves not only as an airborne command post, but also as an airborne Direct Air Support Center (DASC) in the initial hours of an air assault. This new capability of permitting the air and ground commanders aboard the C-135 to coordinate and direct paratroop air-drops, fighter operations, and close air support for ground forces (while simultaneously remaining in constant touch with the en-route CASF units *and* the TAC Headquarters Command Post in Virginia) has both speeded the reaction time and increased tremendously the effectiveness of the CASF.

The lubricant with which all operations must move if they are to succeed is communications. These must not be restricted to the headquarters command posts on the ground or the aircraft assigned to an international mission, but must be on a flexible basis and independent of ground facilities overseas which at any moment may be lost to us. In his critique of CASFs Bravo and X-Ray Tango, General Viccellio repeatedly hammered at the theme that the "re-

Major General Maurice Preston, former 19th Air Force Commander, telephones from his C-135 Airborne Command Post to a ground station during a CASF exercise. (*Air Force*)

liability and security of our command and control communications *must* be improved." The unique C-135 and the CASF backup form only one part of the solution produced by TAC.

In late 1960 19th Air Force personnel conducted several flights of far-reaching significance in a "Talking Bird" aircraft; this was a KC-97 transport bristling with specialized communications equipment to test the concept of the air and ground communications station command post. In more than 325 hours of swift flying, the Talking Bird in its travels touched down at Hawaii, Wake, Okinawa, Guam, Bermuda, the Azores, Spain, Germany, Italy, Greece, Panama, Peru, Chile, Uruguay, Brazil, Ghana, the Congo, Southern Rhodesia, Uganda, Saudi Arabia, Iran, Pakistan, Ceylon, Thailand, Singapore, Australia, New Zealand, the Philippines, Taiwan (Formosa), Korea, Japan, the Aleutians, Alaska, and Canada.

The multiple missions proved so successful that TAC ordered immediate development of Talking Bird aircraft that would be deployed permanently both in the United States and at overseas bases. That development order resulted in one of the more specialized of the Hercules transports series—airborne communications command posts assigned to the Air Force Communications Service, and on duty permanently with combat headquarters commands from Europe to the Far East. In 1962 six of the Hercules Talking Birds moved to their "hot alert" assignments: two Hercules in the Philippines for the Pacific Air Forces, two in France for U.S. Air Force Europe, and two under the operational control of the Strike Command (with which we will soon become more familiar) with headquarters at MacDill Air Force Base, Florida.

One of the most impressive facets of our modern Tactical Air Command, a response to the driving force of General Sweeney and his top staff, is a command-and-communications capability that leaves nothing to chance. The nerve center of all TAC operations is the intricate Headquarters Command Post in Virginia. Here the writer was privileged to accept General Sweeney's seat during a significant "run-through" of TAC's reaction to absolute hell breaking loose in the world.

The Command Post is maximum security, and it is difficult to escape the feeling of grim purpose that pervades the installation. An attempt at unauthorized entry to the nerve center of TAC gets absolutely nowhere. There are several gauntlets to run—not all of which are visible to the intruder—and any one of these gauntlets can and most assuredly will result in a reaction calculated to immobilize the interloper, even if it is necessary to make such immobilization quite permanent.

The Command Post is a deep, wide, and huge installation. It is a facility apt to be misleading to the visitor, unless he is aware of its intricate mechanisms and skilled personnel, who are *not* within sight as they attend to the functions of this extraordinary man-machine system. It is this system that permits General Sweeney and his staff to direct, control, and coordinate the multitude of TAC's globe-girdling, highly diversified missions. The airborne command posts have aided immeasurably in meeting this task.

A double tier of desks faces three rear-projection screens where battle plans, intelligence, logistical situations, aircraft status reports, weather reports, air routes, enemy strength, and other vital and constantly shifting data are displayed *within seconds* at the commander's request—or upon need. On each desk there are glowing telephones studded with the buttons to provide instant global communications.

These are the telephones which can unleash the most powerful engine of war the world has ever known. . . .

The officers and airmen who monitor the continuous flow of information being fed into the Command Post are unbelievably adept in their duties. Sweeney wants no "reverse writing" on transparent walls, which has been the practice at such installations in

The secret TAC Command Post during an actual alert. Third from the right is General W. C. Sweeney, Jr., TAC Commander. (*The Martin Company*)

the past. His facility uses Iconerama changing displays: electronic displays on a series of related screens which provide a constant play-by-play progress report of what is going on *anywhere* within the vast reaches of TAC and the entire planet. There is no fuss, no noise, no spectacular activity. There is the grim and purposeful mission being conducted, and everyone concerned is painfully aware that the stakes involved include the people not of nations, but of the world.

No source of information is left unprobed. On the crucial matter of weather, the Command Post receives some of its meteorological data from the Tiros series of weather satellites. Weather reports also flow from facilities of the United States Weather Bureau and from reconnaissance aircraft flying anywhere and everywhere in the world. The commercial airlines and our Weather Bureau engage in a mutual sharing of weather data between the United States and the Soviet Union; this too feeds into the picture.

The random-select projectors of the Command Post are the fulfillment of visual-display dreams; they house thousands of 35mm slides catalogued in drums. These slides, always kept up to date,

(*Above*) At TAC's Command Post a master sergeant indicates "a late situation report" on master reference charts; information is processed immediately to the Iconerama display and presentation equipment. (*Below*) Weather conditions in any part of the world are shown in up-to-the-minute situation reports at TAC Headquarters Command Post. (*The Martin Company*)

provide immediately the intelligence the TAC staff needs to eva-
luate virtually any situation or combination of situations which
may arise. Within seconds, on the huge screens the projectors flash
preplanned air routes to any point on earth for use in connection
with the decisions that must be made by General Sweeney. Other
slides present data on such subjects as status of forces, the location
of forces at home sites, on maneuvers, or en route. The positive
control system is so far-reaching that General Sweeney can learn
within seconds the disposition of any *single* aircraft assigned to
TAC.

The philosophy of the Command Post was explained by one
of its key officers. "We're here," he said, "to provide communications
on a to-from basis anywhere in the world, at any time, and under
any conditions. Along with this job we must be able to answer *any*
question asked by the commander or his staff; when we can't
provide the answer—" he snapped his fingers—"just like *that,* then
we're not doing our job. I might add that we had better damned
quickly find out *why* we don't have the answer, and get it into
the system immediately."

Beefing Up the Airlift

The CASF deployments of 1958 threw a less harsh light on the
logistics and airlift sinew of TAC than they did on other areas, such
as communications, but there could be no escape from the fact
that the airlift did *not* meet all requirements in the manner desired.
Contained in the critique of the operations was the significant state-
ment: "Payload increases for the C-130 are desirable on a few
critical deployment legs."

Also, in reference to X-Ray Tango, which moved to the Far
East: "In this operation a problem of resupply transportation also
developed. A backlog of cargo built in California awaiting MATS
transportation."

The solution to these logistical problems was already well advanced as a result of efforts initiated *before* the CASF deployments.

During May 1958 the Air Force and the Army provided a telling
demonstration of their prowess with the Hercules transports newly
assigned to them as operational aircraft on a fleet scale. It was
not a maneuver, but specifically a response to an order for troop
and weapons deployment to meet a crisis in South America.

Vice President Richard Nixon, during his visit to Caracas,
Venezuela, had been stoned by a screaming mob. There was danger
not only that this performance might be repeated, but that the
violence would get out of hand and endanger the safety and the
lives of the Vice President and his party. Washington ordered a

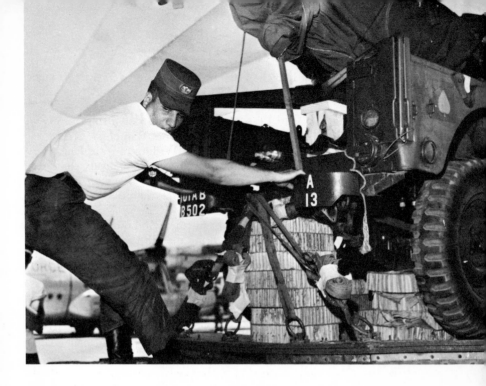

"Instant response" is the keynote of Hercules operations. With special air-drop pallets always kept ready for loading, moving vehicles and supplies onto the pallets and into the Hercules has become a "smooth and swift operation." (*Upper photo: Air Force; lower photo: U.S. Army*)

crack combat outfit into the Caribbean to "stand by," ready to move immediately to the aid of the Vice President, should this prove necessary.

At four P.M. on May 13, a Hercules rushed down the runway of Campbell Air Force Base, adjacent to Fort Campbell, Kentucky, home of the 101st Airborne Division. Within the airplane were 64 "ready-to-fight" paratroopers. And hard on their heels, one after the other, came additional Hercules bearing more than 500 paratroopers from Companies C and D of the 506th Airborne Battle Group.

More Hercules took to the air. In just over 13 hours the transports had moved 577 of the toughest fighting men in the world, *and* their equipment, nonstop over a distance of 1,600 miles. Into Puerto Rico with the troopers came a large helicopter (for the emergency evacuation from Caracas, if necessary, of Vice President and Mrs. Nixon), 44 jeeps, ambulances, light and heavy trucks, seven trailers, three 106mm recoilless rifles, four mortars, 17 machine guns, 22 rocket launchers, 115 land mines, 500 pounds of ammunition, 10,000 pounds of rations, and 650 gallons of gasoline for the mechanized equipment.

It was a "no notice" mission with special meaning to the words —neither the paratroopers nor the flight crews of the Hercules knew their destination until the transports were airborne.

The troopers had good cause to remember the Hercules on the "all-out" flights to Puerto Rico. Several of the airplanes plowed into unexpectedly violent weather over Florida—storms so severe that they towered almost out of sight above the aircraft. With time of the essence there could be no flying around the storms, and the Hercules bulled their way through.

The deployment to Puerto Rico was not a CASF operation, although it moved with all the effectiveness of one. At their destination, the paratroopers slept in a giant hangar right on the flight line, equipment at the ready. The heavy equipment within the Hercules transports remained where it was—and so rigid was the alert that the flight crews remained within minutes' time—on their feet and running—of their airplanes. Not until the Vice President's airplane had safely departed Venezuela did TAC call off its alert and order the paratroopers returned home.

At the time of this operation, the 314th Troop Carrier Wing, from Sewart Air Force Base, had known the airplane only one year— when the first Hercules arrived at their home base in Tennessee. The changes coming in the Hercules already anticipated the needs laid down explicitly by General Viccellio. Minor modifications improved the characteristics of the C-130A model, but one change especially improved the performance of the airplane. Engineering crews installed a pylon beneath each wing, and onto each pylon went a large teardrop-shaped fuel tank. As a result of the new pylons the airplane increased its range by several hundred miles.

The *big* change, however, came in the form of the new C-130B, which gained an increase of 300 horsepower in the thrust of each engine. As has been mentioned, the Air Force looked to the new C-130B more as a long-range passenger/cargo transport than for service in medium-range assault operations, for which it intended the C-130A. Specifically, the mission requirement was an increase "down the line" in range and weight-carrying ability.

Under normal conditions the airplane proved entirely capable of flying cargo payloads of 36,000 pounds nonstop over a distance of 2,300 statute miles or, with a slight decrease in range, bringing the cargo load to 40,000 pounds. On short-haul trips the C-130B went to 45,000 pounds *without* overload conditions. "And who ever heard," commented one officer, "of any airplane in the field that *doesn't* get into overloading when the chips are down?"

The variations in range-performance proved equally important, especially when flying into areas without refueling capabilities. The '130B proved itself adept at flying a 20,000-pound payload for a distance of 2,000 statute miles, landing to disgorge its cargo, taking off and flying back to its home base—*without* refueling.

There are factors other than flight performance which measure the effectiveness and versatility of any airplane, and in these areas especially the C-130B received a rousing welcome from the crews. Vibration and noise dropped appreciably with new insulation and adoption of the shorter-diameter, four-bladed propellers. But even more important was a complete redesign of the crew flight deck to compensate for the long missions envisioned with CASF and other operations. The B's front office included 40 square feet of window area for wide-range vision, easing problems of air-drop operations, formation flying, and "landing in the bush country." New Nesa glass windshields provided maximum visibility under all possible icing conditions, and arrangement of the crew positions drew huzzahs from the operations rooms.

It seems strange that a hard-bitten military assault transport should also be described in terms of "spaciousness, comfort, and convenience" for its flight crew, but the C-130B model brought these features to the men who would have to fly missions over multiple stages of from 5,000 to 12,000 miles. Into the flight deck went much more floor space, more comfortable seats, double-deck crew bunks (*very* spacious), lavatory, and a galley complete with an oven, hot food containers, refrigerator, and sink. All these are

There are many things about which pilots wax enthusiastic with the Hercules. Not the least of them is the unprecedented range of vision assured the pilot by some 40 square feet of window space in the flight deck. (*Air Force*)

important factors to crews who must spend weeks and perhaps months working under field conditions considerably less than "passable."

In the ensuing years the C-130B would prove itself capable of range well in excess of the new performance guaranteed to the Air Force. Long-range missions which took advantage of favorable wind conditions stretched flights to 3,000, then 4,000, and finally in excess of 5,000 miles nonstop.

Continuing field operations produced a new concept of logistical support for the C-130B—a result of critical shortages of fuel for fighters in advance bases during strike operations. TAC and Lockheed modified several Hercules into portable gas stations, and then ran field operational tests with their new system. The results had even the old-timers abashed.

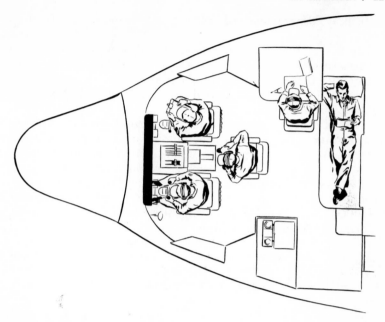

"Spaciousness, comfort, and convenience"—flight deck of C-130B

Two Hercules roared into an open base; aboard the two transports was a total of 50,000 gallons of fuel, a special hydrant fueling system, and all personnel necessary to operate the equipment. Almost as soon as the propellers of the transports whirled to a stop, nine Super Sabres of the 354th Tactical Fighter Wing screamed overhead, pitching hard and fast into their approach and landing patterns. Thirty minutes after the nine fighters smacked their wheels onto the concrete, they were refueled and taxiing out for takeoff.

In a 1960 combat exercise, a fleet of C-130B Hercules provided a prophetic display of the increased power of the airplane over long distances. In Banyan Tree II, "waves of Hercules thundered over Panama—spilling more than 1,000 battle-ready paratroopers with heavy support weapons into a narrow drop zone."

Six nations from South America participated closely with TAC in the full-dress rehearsal, and the men who descended from the skies spoke in several different languages. American paratroopers came from the new Strategic Army Corps (STRAC); with 64 fighting men in each plane, the Hercules raced nonstop for a distance of more than 2,000 miles to release the paratroopers. Hard on their heels came other Hercules, each airplane air-dropping by parachute as much as 38,000 pounds of vehicles and weapons into the drop zone.

Banyan Tree II, and literally dozens of other exercises extending to forces involving more than 70,000 men and hundreds of warplanes, proved the versatility of the Hercules in meeting almost every situation within the United States and abroad. Not every situation, but *almost*.

Lockheed called in the Air Force for some closed-door huddles. There had been a significant change in the disposition of American military forces, and a revolutionary new concept of applying pressure at trouble spots anywhere in the world. Successful as were the Lebanon and Formosa operations, they weren't successful enough. *Time*—time to move bodies of crack fighting men—was everything. The United States reorganized its military commands and arranged them in a new order.

". . . waves of Hercules thundered over Panama—spilling more than 1,000 battle-ready paratroopers with heavy support weapons into a narrow drop zone."—Report from Banyan Tree II. (*Air Force*)

Paratroopers of the 82nd Airborne pour from Hercules in Banyan Tree II over the Rio Hato maneuvers area. (*Air Force*)

In September 1961 the new line-up showed seven unified commands as the basis of American military power. These included the Pacific, Alaskan, Caribbean, Atlantic, and European commands, and the North American Air Defense Command (NORAD). Now there was something new—*Strike Command.*

General Paul D. Adams—World War II Ranger, division commander in Korea, ground forces commander in Lebanon—brought his four-star rank to the top desk of the new command. And with the advent of Strike came a startling new philosophy. No longer does the commander of any individual service exercise operational control over any of his combat-ready forces. In every instance where the need exists for the use of such forces, they will do so under the direct control of one of the specific or unified commands. And in the middle of it all is Strike Command—which goes several leagues farther than the operational structure created by General Viccellio, though it was foreseen clearly by the "CASF architect."

Analyzing the CASF operations of 1958, General Viccellio criticized the "lack of accepted interservice procedures for the conduct of joint support operations. . . . There was a period during the initial phase of the operation when air support operations would have been hampered to some degree by lack of accepted joint standard procedures. The solution to this vexing problem is obvious, though difficult. Over the years the Army and Air Force have been developing air support doctrine, tactics, and procedures. These are still far from complete agreement in all details. . . . Participation in joint forces is obvious from our experience and from hot-spot geography. I think that even some of our CASF people were surprised to be operating with land and sea units . . . but it must now be apparent to all that unilateral action by any one component will be very infrequent. The refining of our cooperation procedures . . . is an obvious need."

The response to this "obvious need" is one of the most gratifying steps ever taken by our country. It is a powerful extension of the original CASF concept, and it is free of the restrictions of divided commands attempting to merge their structures into a single unity. To achieve the latter, the Joint Chiefs of Staff ordered the formation of Strike Command, and placed at the disposal of General Adams and his staff all of the combat-ready forces of the Continental Army Command and the Tactical Air Command.

This includes for the Army two corps headquarters, eight divisions, and the combat support and technical and administrative forces necessary for backing up these divisions. For the Air Force, the Strike Command component available through TAC included the three numbered air forces (Ninth, 12th, and 19th), and more than 40 squadrons of reconnaissance, tactical fighter, troop carrier, and tanker aircraft.

It may come as something of a surprise to airpower adherents to discover that Air Force staffs, which in their tactical organizations now come under Strike Command, have received their new subordinate status with deep satisfaction. The public—and much of the press—have had it deeply ingrained in their thinking that there exists between the Air Force and the Army a fierce and unrelenting friction. This appears to be so when doctrine and strategy are argued in the public light, but often the goals sought by the two organizations are much more similar than either party realizes.

At TAC headquarters, leading staff officers made it clear that the organization of Strike Command represented a step long needed for the welfare of the United States. "Strike Command is the answer to a long-time requirement," explained a colonel on General Sweeney's staff. "It forms the apex of the triangle that brings together the highly specialized forces of TAC and the Army to provide a flexible and selective strike force, the like of which has never been seen before. That force can move swiftly and with

unbelievable power and flexibility to meet any threatening situation. It's what we might call the balancing of forces and the
operational concepts for their employment. It allows the Joint
Chiefs of Staff and the theater commanders a swiftly reacting
combat force—in *depth*—that provides the widest possible choice
of actions in preventing any outbreaks of violence, or of blunting
an attack once the enemy has decided to go all the way. What we
have here, really, is a limited war deterrent force with the same
credibility that both we and the U.S.S.R. have afforded our strategic
nuclear deterrent. . . . It doesn't matter a damn what service hat
the top man wears. This may sound like a DOD speech, but we
are literally working as a single team to do a single job."

We are familiar with the Tactical-Air-Command half of Strike
Command. To rifle a powerful composite force to any point of
the world in the shortest possible reaction time, General Adams
hits the red alert signal within the Strategic Army Corps (STRAC).
This is a balanced force of eight divisions, with supporting combat
and logistical troops. If the Joint Chiefs of Staff dictate our movement to any point in the world, General Adams can commit any
part of STRAC, from a company to all eight divisions, as the situation demands.

Following the CASF concept, the STRAC force can act quickly
wherever it is needed because of the strategic reserve nature of
STRAC; with a geographical location in the United States, rubbing
shoulders with TAC's troop-carrier wings, it remains uncommitted
but always ready for rapid reaction.

General Adams explains that from STRAC "we can tailor a
force for any situation; and this force—whether it be a company
or an entire corps—can fight in any type terrain such as the Arctic
wastelands, deserts, jungles, or mountains."

Few military commands understand so deeply as does General
Adams the foundation upon which our new deterrent forces must
stand. Again and again he has pushed for increased mobility for
our national military strength. "Mobility is a function of mass and
velocity," he explained recently to a select military group, "and
therefore cannot be resolved in terms of mass or in terms of speed
alone. . . ."

General Adams has established the hard-and-fast rules by which
the Strike Command must move in order for it to be effective on
an international basis. Strike is kept always on a "primed and
cocked" status in order to execute its mission of swift reaction
anywhere in the world. Thus an extension of the hard-and-fast rule
in terms of airlift is clearly an extension of the general's no-nonsense
approach.

"Ready to load!" Crack Army troopers prepared to roll heavy equipment into C-130s of the 315th Air Division at Naha Air Base on Okinawa. (*Air Force*)

General Adams' convictions on the matter of airlift have necessitated much of American industry and the military moving smartly into line. He leaves no questions of failures *after* a mission, to be answered in critiques, but slices right to the heart of the national problem.

As in this incisive appraisal of national needs:

> No matter how powerful a military force may be potentially, it is useless if it cannot be delivered to the right point in time to employ its strength usefully in accomplishing the military mission. The requirements for speed and strength, related to the [enemy] submarine threats that exist in the world today, place the greatest premium on airlift and [have] made airlift a vital element in the mobility of our General Purpose Forces. It is only through airlift that substantial forces can be initially lifted with sureness and with adequate speed to arrive in the objective area fast enough to meet fast-moving and sensitive military situations that arise in the modern world. . . .
>
> Broadly speaking, an operation of the nature we have in

mind requires two kinds of airlift—strategic and tactical. The strategic airlift is comprised of large transports capable of lifting large numbers of men, materials, and supplies swiftly into the operational area. Tactical airlift is required if the actual entry [into] the objective area has to be made by parachute assault, or if that contingency is a probable requirement. This is mandatory because military forces being employed on missions of this nature must initially arrive at the objective in a fighting posture.

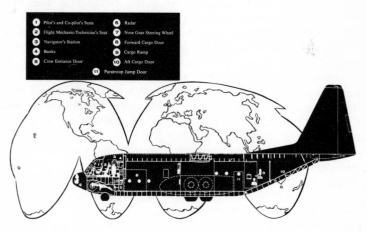

Airlift both tactical and strategic, and with one airplane—the "Hardware facilities" of the Hercules

General Adams insists that his command headquarters, no less than his combat forces, maintain a "fighting posture," ready at all times to take part in airlift and paratrooper operations. The mission of Strike Command includes the responsibility of planning and conducting contingency operations anywhere in the world. At any moment that the Joint Chiefs of Staff direct such a mission, Adams and his staff *must* be equal to his combat teams in mobility and airlift capacity.

"That is why our entire Headquarters and the Joint Communications Unit are air mobile, capable of moving all personnel and minimum essential equipment by air to any objective area by C-130-type aircraft. The entire Headquarters would be air-landed or, if required, advance elements could parachute into the objective area, to be followed by the air-landed echelon."

The 19th Air Force, in constant preparation for control of CASF deployments, isn't the only "suitcase" military headquarters. The

Strike Command's headquarters staff have learned to live in a manner far removed from the everyday world, for Adams insists that the only way in which his staff can *know* that all contingencies lie within its powers of solution is by constant demonstration of that fact. As such, the headquarters staff at frequent intervals, day or night, may receive a no-notice emergency alert order. The designated members of the staff *must* report within 30 minutes at the outside, and be ready to "move out" to . . . well, just about anywhere in the world.

The lesson has been well learned. Each member of the Strike Command headquarters staff has three bags always packed and stored near the MacDill flight line. One contains items for "general use." The second is jammed with Arctic gear, the third with equipment for the tropics. Not until the man receives his emergency orders does he ever know which bag he will grab on the run.

Strike Command's deputy commander, Air Force General B. K. Holloway, sums up this capability: "We are going to stay as small and alert as possible and try to be at all times lean, mean, and ready to go."

The 150,000 rangers, commandos, paratroopers, guerrilla experts, ski troopers, ordnance specialists, engineers, and other men who constitute the backbone of the ground elements of Strike Command are in need, as General Adams has explained, of "two kinds of airlift—strategic and tactical."

The 1958 CASF operations, involving deployments of almost 10,000 miles, demonstrated the need for improved range-*and*-heavy-cargo characteristics in the Hercules. With the entire Strike Command headquarters staff committed to global deployment in the C-130 aircraft, the improved performance became a critical requirement. The C-130B model represented a significant step in the right direction, but it did not succeed in going quite so far as the Air Force and Strike Command desired.

Which is why Lockheed-Georgia and the Air Force went into their closed-door huddle. They came out with a "vastly improved tactical *and* strategic airlift capability" in the form of a single aircraft—the spanking-new C-130E. The Air Force handed Lockheed an "initial order" for 99 of the new transports with a plea to "get 'em out *yesterday*."

On April 6, 1962, the first C-130Es for operational duty with the Military Air Transport Service (MATS) and Tactical Air Command were delivered to Charleston Air Force Base, South Carolina. Few airplanes listed officially as transports have ever received the unrestrained enthusiasm that greeted the new C-130E.

For it wasn't simply a new transport. The United States during

Profile of a working giant with
seven-league boots—the C-130E

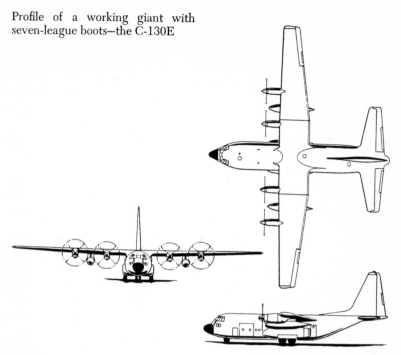

the Korean War had come to appreciate the need for a long-term
program of airlift modernization. It wasn't a plan to be imple-
mented overnight, but one that would stretch over a working
period of from 13 to 18 years. The first giant step in the modernization program was the Hercules itself, in the form of the C-130A
and C-130B models and all their many derivatives. Then—next in
line—came the C-130E.

General Curtis E. LeMay flew to Charleston Air Force Base to
place the new Hercules transports officially in operational service,
itself an unusually significant move for the Air Force Chief of
Staff. LeMay referred to the C-130E as "the second stage of this
program—airlift modernization." Modernizing a nation's airlift
capability means, of course, the displacement of older transports—
and in this instance it meant the removal from the MATS unit at
Charleston of some other Lockheed airplanes. The aging C-121
Constellations that had seen many years of constant service stepped
aside for the newest members of the Lockheed family.

The attention afforded the movement of C-130Es into both
MATS and TAC raised some questioning eyebrows. Most people

think of MATS as a military airline—an organization that performs the military role equivalent to that of the commercial lines. Nothing could be farther from the truth, for carrying passengers in its transports is only a minor element of the vast responsibility of MATS. It has a national airlift mission in the truest sense; MATS serves the needs not only of the Air Force, but of every government and military agency.

The question arose of employing Lockheed's Electra as a MATS transport. It mounted the same engines as the Hercules, carried a great passenger load, could range 4,000 miles, and was appreciably faster. These were characteristics intended and adapted to commercial airline needs. But the Electra can't hold a candle to the versatility of the Hercules, and it was never intended to do so. Airlift modernization means designing your product for its job and, if you're good to begin with, you may end up with everything you started out to get and a great deal more—as happened with the Hercules.

LeMay views the C-130E Hercules as giving "real substance to our determination to have flexibility in dealing with conflicts ranging from counterinsurgency to open warfare." With a total fuel capacity of nearly 10,000 gallons, the C-130E quickly demonstrated its abilities as a strategic transport. Carrying 24,000 pounds payload—in any form—it can fly nonstop for 4,600 statute miles. General LeMay put the performance in another light when he revealed that in simulated combat situations the new Hercules had proved its ability to "overfly the Atlantic with a payload of 27,000 [now 34,000] pounds. Carrying the same payload, it can cross the Pacific with only one stop. This is at a speed of six miles a minute. Twelve hours after takeoff, troops can be at their European destination. With this kind of speed we can respond to new situations rapidly and decisively."

And to General Adams of Strike Command the C-130E came as an "illustrious addition" to the line of Hercules transports; he described the earlier models of the airplane as "the old reliables of the airborne trooper."

Blanketed by the high speed-and-range characteristics of the C-130E was another performance attribute which the military felt was as vital as any other. The airplane would lift from the ground at 155,000 pounds gross weight, fly more than 4,950 statute miles—and then land on rough and unimproved surfaces less than 3,000 feet in length. *That* was what the military considered as the ingredients of strategic airlift with meaning—because the best of the long-range turbojet transports at their destinations were still chained to a requirement of 7,000 feet of excellent, paved runways.

Latest in the famous line—the C-130E Hercules, designed for long-range global airlift missions with heavy cargo loads or paratroopers ready to spill into target areas. Besides its other capabilities, its tight turns, steep climbouts, and other fighter-like maneuvers have brought acclaim from pilots. (*Lockheed-Georgia*)

With the E model assigned essentially to strategic airlift, but also enjoying combat-area versatility, Strike Command gained all-important flexibility through the use of its different types of Hercules. It had transports for operations from rough fields no more than 1,500 feet in length for constant resupply of combat forces, and it could also fly long-range strikes and give logistical support with heavy cargo loads nonstop across the Atlantic and one-stop across the Pacific.

What this means to the man on the firing line can hardly be overemphasized. When a grizzled old master sergeant who had fought through North Africa, Europe, Okirawa, *and* Korea first met the Hercules, he walked around the brute with a mixture of open suspicion and an attitude of "what the hell is *this*?" Finally he turned to the ranks of rawboned young troopers behind him and said: "Men, watch your step, or this thing is gonna bite you."

Months later, with two dozen jumps from the Hercules behind him, with extensive experience on combat maneuvers with the airplane, he evinced a deep feeling toward what it meant to him—as a soldier.

"I'm as fond of air support—the fighters and such—as any man who ever wore this uniform," he told me. "I've had Thunderbolts save my neck in Germany, and the jets save our lives in Korea. I know air support from the best possible of all positions, and I *like* it. But there's another thing to consider in this business."

He looked up at the Hercules looming over us on the flight line. "You know," he went on, "it takes as much airlift with machines like this one to bring in enough fuel to let six fighter planes make *one* sweep—only *one* sweep, mind you—in a single day, as it does to supply completely a battalion of 2,000 crack soldiers in the jungle or the mountains for the same period of time. And, mister, when you fight the kind of wars they're fighting today, I'll take the hardware and to hell with the go-juice. Those fighters can't come down below the treetops in the jungle to see what's going on. . . ."

Shortly after the '130E went into active service, the Air Force ran special tests to see what the new weightlifter could do in terms of hauling cargo under "emergency conditions." Originally the airplane was to reach its limit at 40,000 pounds payload. This went up slowly but steadily to 45,000 pounds in the airlift tests. And the Big E—to the surprise of many people, because there had been no increase in power—boosted the acceptable operational limit to a payload of 56,000 pounds.

Almost as if to prove that there is nothing guaranteed in this business except the unexpected, the Tactical Air Command called in Lockheed-Georgia engineers for the now familiar meetings to add to the flexibility of the Hercules. We have seen the extraordinary and multi-faceted growth of the airplane; now the troop carrier people wanted to endow the C-130B model with added assault-transport characteristics. This would enhance even further the already formidable assault power of the Strike Command.

At Sewart Air Force Base in Tennessee, the 463rd Troop Carrier Wing moved out of its long, flat, and beautiful runways into what GI's unlovingly call the boondocks. Every pilot of the Wing—and other units at Sewart—had demonstrated outstanding proficiency in assault takeoffs and landings. But this had been done from concrete runways marked off to simulate a strip 1,500 feet long.

"Not realistic enough," said TAC. "Get 'em out in the boondocks and do the same thing under *actual* conditions. We want STOL

[Short Takeoff and Landing] capability with no question marks."
The 463rd did exactly that. An enterprising headquarters officer
remembered an old training runway in the midst of an isolated
forest area. No one had used it for years. Its surface had virtually
fallen apart as weed and heavy brush pushed upward and chewed
the runway into an obstacle course that slowed a jeep to a crawl.

The Hercules went in to a "jungle strip" in the full meaning of
the word. Fifteen hundred feet and not a foot more was the allowance for the pilots. And *not* under empty conditions either.
Each time the airplanes slammed down onto the strip they grossed
a weight of more than 120,000 pounds.

Could the airplane possibly do better? And with its weight up
to 135,000 pounds? Groans could be heard from the engineering
offices where the lights burned far into the night, but they came
up with still better performance. The pilots took one look at the
modified airplane and promptly tagged it with the ungracious title
of "Boondocks Bird."

The engineers increased the deflection of the flaps and speeded
up their rate of operation. They modified the rudder and ailerons
slightly, and then added—of all things—a 22-foot-diameter drag
parachute to the tail. The pilots listened; when they heard that
they were to release the parachute *in the air* to steepen and slow
down their rate of descent before dumping onto a field, they shook
their heads in dismay.

They also shook hell out of the airplanes. Operating under maximum weight conditions, the Hercules again and again thundered
into tiny strips, and boomed out of the clearings. The final results
showed a significant gain in assault capability. Despite its ponderous weight the modified C-130B could pile onto a strip only 1,400
feet long, dump its cargo, load on new cargo, and be out of the
strip within minutes of touchdown.

The Air Force Systems Command came to see the Lockheed-
Georgia engineers, and this time even the redoubtable engineering
staff raised their eyebrows en masse. The Air Force wanted a test
program begun immediately as a result of studies they had conducted since 1958 with BLC—Boundary Layer Control. They gave
Lockheed *carte blanche* to plan its own development program.

Lockheed pulled the seventh production C-130B off the flight line
and rolled it into a hangar for extensive modifications. They slung
two T56 jet engines (no props) beneath the wings, and hooked
the engines to stainless steel air ducting that ran from wingtip to
tip. "This gave us a system of high-energy air blowing across the
flaps and control surfaces," explained Jesse Allen, Lockheed test
pilot. "It produces high-energy lift to help the airplane fly at very

low speeds—so slow, in fact, that without this assist the Hercules would fall right out of the sky. When we get into the slow-flight regime, air normally separates from the wing—and you're on the verge of a stall. We use the extra jets to suck air in through nozzles and then blow the high-energy air across the control surfaces and the flaps—maintaining full lift at speed that's normally impossible to attain and still keep flying. In other words, we don't permit the separation to take place." To compensate for the expected low speed, Lockheed added 40 percent to the rudder area, drooped the ailerons, and doubled the travel of the flight control surfaces. Other changes were slight, but significant for the revolutionary test program to come.

Lockheed test flights with Jesse Allen had the engineers and flight crews walking around with wide grins—and in absolute silence, until Lockheed could demonstrate the airplane in flight and during takeoffs and landings, in competition against a modern short-field-capability lightplane.

"Flabbergasted" is the only word properly to describe the reaction of the observers. On the date of the test—in the middle of summer—the temperature soared to over 100 degrees, and the wind subsided to a dead calm. Heat and no-wind conditions are the things that make every pilot pay the closest attention to his flying, for these rob him of the lift he needs for flight.

Operating from jungle and forest strips—the "Boondocks Bird"

The lightplane sailed toward the runway at only 70 miles per hour, a lazy descent in which the 2,500-pound airplane seemed to float earthward. The wheels touched and the pilot slammed on his brakes. Only 600 feet farther the light plane jerked to a stop.

The Hercules came into sight several miles from the field, in a gradual descent toward the runway. It came, and came . . . and came. *Slowly.* It approached the runway with exactly the *same speed* as the light plane—70 miles per hour. The nose dipped suddenly and the Hercules grabbed for the runway. Jesse Allen slammed on the brakes and reversed the propellers; the engineer killed the boundary layer airflow.

One hundred thousand pounds of airplane screeched to a stop *in less than 450 feet.*

Jesse Allen taxied back to the start of the runway. He applied full power, the engineer tripped the BLC system into operation, and Allen "cut loose."

In 730 feet the Hercules bounded into the air, climbing at a steep angle. Later the Hercules and the lightplane began a side-by-side minimum-speed pass across the field—and the lightplane couldn't stay with the Hercules. The pilot flew at his minimum speed until his stall warning yammered at him. Still he pulled away from the Hercules while the Lockheed crew grinned at him.

Jesse Allen has brought startled expletives from other pilots who have watched him perform "square turns" in the air with the Hercules. "It's the only airplane in which I've ever been able to make a level turn," he explains. "Normally, to make a good turn you've got to bank the wings—but with *this* thing you just kick the rudder, your wings stay level, and she comes around smart and snappy in the turn. . . ."

Was the performance satisfactory as regards STOL? More than satisfactory, everyone agreed readily—especially since the projected production model—the C-130C—would be able with more powerful BLC engines to land and take off in less than 500 feet.

As it happened, the C-130C—the 50-ton airplane that could do things a pilot wouldn't dare try in a Piper Cub—never went into production. Leo Sullivan wisely said that an airplane of the size and performance of the Hercules is "the result of a fantastic chain of circumstances." As a production airplane, the C-130C would be comparatively expensive. Rough estimates showed the Air Force that they could purchase perhaps two C-130E transports for the cost of one C-130C model. The Boundary Layer Control system was a "backbreaker" for mass production, and high cost was the only solution. Then there was the problem of operating the C-130C in rough fields with great quantities of dust, grass, and other debris swirling about. This could partially choke the BLC nozzles and interfere with the flow of high-energy air.

The Air Force was the customer. If they wanted the airplane, Lockheed could guarantee taking off and landing within a space of 500 feet on virtually any type of terrain.

The "circumstances" of cost and possible rough-field problems with the BLC system dictated the decision not to place the C-130C in production, but to continue with the airplane as a research vehicle.

But what about that increased airlift/mobility equation for ground combat forces that both the Air Force and the Army sought? The answer was to come from a source unexpected by the trade or the military. At Wilmington, Delaware, a skilled team known as All American Engineering had come forward with a startling proposal. Lockheed and All American, with the official blessings of the Tactical Air Command and Strike Command, prepared further to revolutionize the air mobility of our global strike forces. Their new technique of "instant extraction" would soon become world-famous.

CHAPTER XIII

The New Warfare   WE HAVE SEEN THE
evolution of international arms and the pressures in the world
today nurtured by this evolution. A host of fluid and intermingling
factors produced first the Strategic Air Command, and also the
climate for the development of the intercontinental ballistic missile
and the Polaris-armed nuclear submarine fleet. The solidification
of counter-strike power between the United States and the Soviet
Union prompted both nations to seek the "secondary factor" approach to pressing national desires and, under special circumstances, to attempt to resolve those desires through restrained application of military strength. The results, of course, are the limited-
war concepts out of which grew the Composite Air Strike Force,
the Strategic Army Corps, and, finally, from both these approaches
to the national need, Strike Command.

The philosophy which guides any major effort such as that of
Strike Command cannot be obtained from computers or from
statistics. There is no electronic panacea to relieve men from weighing a multiplicity of factors in their struggle to reach the right and
proper solution to a problem. Certainly the computer must find
electronic despair in its inability to compensate for the total un-
predictability and irrationality of human behavior.

In this respect, then, Strike Command must inevitably be a reflection of the man who stands at its helm, and from whose management and leadership there are created the attitudes and the capabilities of that command. No man can be indispensable in any effort so
vast as this; nevertheless Strike Command is to some extent a
personification of its commander, General Paul D. Adams.

Good fortune permitted General Adams to shuffle his busy schedule for a most rewarding meeting and conference with the writer;
the essentials of that discussion are thus available to us here and
now. It was a rare meeting with a rare man; unstilted and wide-
ranging in his thinking, exhaustively knowledgeable as to his
responsibilities, General Adams gave what I believe is the most
penetrating analysis yet made of the factors which dictated and
sustain Strike Command.

I inquired of General Adams the methods and the procedures by which he and his staff were able to mold the final form into which Strike Command and its forces must fit—the process by which final decisions could be made as to weapons, equipment, and the tactics of employment particular to Strike Command.

The general revealed that for many years prior to the actual creation of United States Strike Command in 1961, military leaders had actively studied the problems inherent in such a force and had supplemented their studies with exhaustive field tests and maneuvers by which they could establish a yardstick for future guidance. General Adams explained that with a small group of planners, in the mid-1950's, work had gone on—

". . . for about a year on smaller things to see what we could accomplish. We staged an exercise called Pinecone in the spring of 1957 and in this exercise we moved all the typical units of a corps . . . a three-division corps, into an airhead. This followed the normal routine of a tactical air operation to hit the enemy area, and then an airborne assault into that area. Then came the movement of the corps itself. We worked it out with great care on a time basis, with the commitment of the airlift aircraft, carving out an airhead in the 'attack area.'

"We established an airhead that was big enough to provide a low density of our forces as a defense against attack by nuclear weapons, and we poured into that airhead all the essential elements that one needed for such an operation.

"Here and there, because of the airlift nature of the operation, we had to step down one size, say, on a particular piece of equipment. For example, it's natural for the engineers to prefer the biggest bulldozer they can get for their work; the bigger the bulldozer the better the engineers like it. Well, the big 'dozers they have today simply do not move easily into airplanes. We stepped down from a D-8 to a D-6 bulldozer, which really didn't interfere with the engineers' mission in the field.

"One of my commanders . . . well, he absolutely believed in the 155mm Long Tom artillery field piece; he believed it was the greatest weapon of its type ever built. And it *is* an outstanding weapon, except that you can't get them anywhere except on a ship; so we made a general across-the-board substitution of 155mm howitzers for the Long Toms. And, frankly, I believe that for ordinary combat you're probably just as well armed.

"Many people like the Long Toms primarily for counter-battery work; it has excellent range and it is an effective harassing weapon. I've never found counter-battery too effective. I've seen many reports claiming that the enemy batteries were silenced from our counter-battery fire; sure, they quit shooting, but an hour later they would be back again shooting as they had been before. That kind of thing never impressed me very much. The only way to go after an artillery battery that I know of—unless you can see it and obtain good visual observation of it from the ground—is to bore right down in there and then cover it good with your firepower."

We discussed the history of airlift in Strike Command. In this respect I wanted to know how the Hercules fitted into the growth of the command. I asked General Adams: "Did Strike Command begin with a heavy commitment to use the Hercules?"

"The answer must be yes and no. The '130 we all recognize as probably the best troop-carrier ship that ever came down the road. It is a good strong ship . . . you could almost say that it is a ship that put a new turn, so to speak, in airlift operations— particularly the air-assault type of operation; we could see this coming as it was being developed. At this time I was at Fort Bragg, in the 18th Corps, when it first came into operational service. We participated in the original and widely varied drop tests.

"I think we made some 5,000 jumps from those airplanes, with every one of the jumps photographed. When it ended we knew just what we had with the airplane. Outside of flanges on the doorway to deflect the wind a bit for the man as he exits from the airplane, I don't believe that anything substantial had to be done to that airplane from the time they turned out the first one to fly until today."

Question: "Does Strike Command make unusual use—in terms of quantity, that is—of the recoilless type of weapon because of its light weight—more so than other Army groups would?"

Answer: "This is a sort of preferred weapon for anyone. It meets the needs for swift movement. It is light in the sense that you can haul a pretty powerful weapon on a jeep. You can carry it a short distance by hand, and it is relied upon right now as one of the principal anti-tank weapons in the Army. Of course, along with that goes your capability of busting bunkers and other hard targets that you can't damage adequately with routine artillery fire. But with the recoilless weapon you must have a direct line of fire at the target to use it with any real effectiveness."

Question: "Is Strike Command—troops, artillery, tactical air, and all other elements—equipped with nuclear warheads?"

Answer: "We have a number of units that have what we consider as nuclear capability; they have been trained to high com-

Over the drop zones. General Paul Adams of Strike Command calls the C-130 "probably the best troop-carrier ship that ever came down the road. . . . You could almost say that it is a ship that put a new turn, so to speak, in airlift operations. . . ." (*Air Force*)

petence in the use of tactical nuclear weapons, and they have the means to deliver these weapons. The preponderance of our forces, however, are considered as 'conventional' forces. I believe they have adequate means of tactical delivery in both the Army and the Air Force. Now, we maintain these capabilities very carefully, and in our maneuvers and exercises we give ourselves a workout along conventional lines to be sure that we are not trying to solve everything with one kind of weapon.

"So we have extensive exercises for our troops and ourselves; for a good part of these activities we use more or less conventional tactics and then—later—we get into and permit the play of atomic weapons in our maneuvers. In doing that we are keeping up our capabilities to work either way."

Question: "What do you consider to be a standard size in terms of a force that you would commit to an operation, as opposed to a minimum or maximum effort; what would be your average-sized force to respond in a certain area to what is defined as a national emergency?"

Answer: "That is a difficult question to answer, but we do, of

Formation air drop . . .

course, function with a system to arrive at such an answer. First we have to size up the situation into which we must move. You can see readily that there are various types of situations in different areas of the world that would not require too much force.

"I think the Lebanon operation provides a good picture. The whole country of Lebanon was about to collapse from the pressure of bands of internal revolutionists; they had an Army in there that ran about 11,000 people. It had been employed as a peace-maker between these bands of rebels; the Army would just go in and stop the fighting. They would not take sides with any faction but separate them and stop the fighting.

"On the other hand, when we went in there it was impossible to predict whether that Army would turn against us. So it was neces-sary to have a force of such power that beyond any question it could stand entirely on its own.

"You work along that line as the initial move, and next you move into an area where *time* is important; you want to achieve a buildup that is fast enough to give you a superior force on the ground at the earliest possible moment . . . and *maintain* that superiority so that the other man will say, 'Well, hell, I can't keep up with you.' That's just what we did in Lebanon—we put enough force in there to cover all bets. I've remarked in the past that at the peak of our dispositions in Lebanon, I didn't think there was anything anywhere in the Middle East that could bother the force we had . . . we were that strong.

"These are some of the factors that influence the size of the force that you would send into any situation. Now, we work on the basis that we shall send in and build up just as rapidly as we can, what we consider [the] . . . minimum essential force . . . build up in a building-block manner.

"We start off with a force which is comprised of a small CASF . . . it may have three or four squadrons in it. . . . We get them in position where they serve, you might say as eyes, and also as a security force, to cover the input of the other forces. Then you move in; the way we do it when we move by air is by battle-group increments. Each increment would run around 2,000 people and would constitute a battle group with a small engineer unit with it, and a battery of artillery, and a headquarters to run it.

"You put the first one in; then you keep building up until you get what you need in the area of the operation. Concurrently with that, you must send along a certain amount of supplies to take care of them, to be sure they don't run out of things until you can get your logistics operating.

"But with the rather decided improvements that have taken place in the military airlift, primarily in MATS, in the past two years . . . well, you can think in terms of moving division forces and keeping them up to all their requirements. If you then take that capability, and parlay it with concurrent surface or sea movements, you can put a pretty sizable force overseas at a rate much faster than anyone had ever conceived of before, and you can keep building it up just as far as you want to go. There is no limit to what you can do, given time and the dovetailing of these operations. You can go just as high as you want to go after the Joint Chiefs of Staff have decided it that way."

Question: "There seems to be something alive and sharp about the men in Strike Command; both the Army and Air Force people I have seen are highly impressive. Do you have any particular qualification for the Army people who are placed under your command, or are they regular Army groups who receive this duty as normal assignment procedures?"

Answer: "No, they are just the way the Army develops them—they are good units—good men in them to start with, and we've got the best men in the armed forces today that I've ever seen and ever expect to see . . . so you've got something to start with. And the second thing is, I believe this command brings to the body of our military forces a means by which we are able to exploit the combat powers that are inherent in each of the services; we bring them into an integrated team that works together with understanding.

Fresh off the drop zone, a member of the 506th Battle Group, 101st Airborne Division, loaded with ammunition and a new M-60 lightweight machine gun, "moves out" to join up with other forces. (*U.S. Army*)

"I believe in all of this . . . and all combined with a demonstrated way of getting to the scene of the fight that gives these men a conviction that if they are needed, they can get anywhere, and if they get there they can do the job. And I think that this is the foundation of it."

Question: "Has there been a complete modernization of equipment as required by Strike Command? There's been testimony before the Congress that the replacement of older weapons hasn't taken place fast enough. Has this been a problem in any way that affects Strike Command?"

Answer: "It is a problem sometimes . . . but you must understand that problems are generated by modernization, as it were. For example, the ROAD Infantry Division now has a great field of armor and a great number of armored personnel carriers as an integral element of the division. That generates a problem for us in the sense of rapid movement—bringing in all of their equipment. So modernization in a sense can generate a problem for you.

"The lack of modernization in some respects is more a source of conversation sometimes than a proof of real inadequacy in having to get along with the old. The M-14 is a nice rifle—a good weapon with which we had a little trouble at first; like everything else that's machined nowadays, it had some bugs. But when you get those cleaned up you have a fine weapon. As I recall, we had some similar difficulties with the M-1 rifle when it came into service . . . so you have to be ready to meet those things when they come along. The M-14 rifle is a lighter weapon; it's easier to carry and better balanced, and I'm sure that in a day's marching a man hasn't done as much work as he would have in carrying the M-1 for the full day. On the other hand . . . both weapons are absolutely useful and usable in a fight. The M-14 especially is a good accurate rifle and it will fire as fast as a man can aim it. But the M-1 is also a deadly weapon. . . .

"You do want to move forward in terms of modernization. In this respect, for example, we are achieving a common ammunition with our Allies. That alone is important; it might even by itself be adequate justification for producing a new rifle, whether or not you got one that was lighter, or with a smaller barrel. . . . That standardization of equipment by itself is important in a war."

Question: "Will new lightweight alloys and metals give you greater mobility and firepower with less weight?"

Answer: "The new alloys are tremendous; they are hard and they do apply to new weapons ideas. If you could get a lot of this equipment for airlift—your trucks, jeeps, and even your artillery pieces, or parts of them—made of some of these lighter metals, then you could use your airlift for more equipment. Generally when you get into this kind of gear, tonnage is the thing that kills you; *weight* is the problem. So we are anxious to see what takes place."

Question: "I'd like your opinion . . . as to what you believe is the best road to efficient control and use of our 'hard' military strength. Is the future development of the Army leading more and more to the mobile striking force as opposed to general-purpose forces chained to the ground?"

Answer: "I think you can see the increasing recognition of the value of mobility . . . or at least a kind of mobility that you must have as we move on into the future, where things can break out on you almost overnight. Because if you are not there in a hurry, you have just lost that issue."

Question: "Coming along as the third and final phase of the nation's airlift modernization program is Lockheed's C-141 Star-Lifter—the giant turbofan high-speed transport designed for strategic airlift in the truest sense of the word. How does the C-141 fit into the picture?"

Answer: "That enhances the capability tremendously. I have been watching the C-141 with almost the same excitement with which I watched the '130 develop. This is going to be a real piece of machinery on wings. Here is what I hope to see out of the '141, which is a good strategic airlifter. It will lift a load a long distance better than 3,000 miles [1] and I hope, of course, it will be used for strategic-type airlift to position our forces preliminary to an operation.

"It should also make a very handsome assault-type ship for heavy drops, in order to have the load that you want, delivered right where you want it. I don't think it would be very good for dropping paratroops because it is so big. . . . Your patterns would be so long on the ground that you would begin to defeat yourself through scattering of your troops. The C-130 is ideal, just the right size—64 men, 32 out of each door, and you've got your people where you want them.

"Now, you will be able to jump from the '141, of course, but its asset to me—as I see it—in an assault role is for the heavy drop. And I'm looking forward to the time when you can deliver a battle group or a battalion of men out of, let's say, C-130s and get all the other gear there you need in an equivalent number of C-141s; this way it's possible to get a combination of everything that's needed.

"In this fashion we make maximum efficient use of the equip-

[1] The C-141 will lift a 70,000-pound payload for a distance of 4,200 statute miles.

ment, very much like the old pattern of using the jeep and the three-quarter-ton truck for the light loads, and the two-and-a-half-ton truck for the heavier loads.

"I think that is the pattern in which the '141 should be used in the assault role, so that ship then has its best capability for you, just like the C-130B and E models: the E in strategic transport is a superior aircraft because of its greater range. It can pick up the troops at their home base; if you have to make a long move and an assault when you get there—why, you can leave the home base ready for that contingency. Or if you want to pull up the tail of your column, and make a large assault, you can pull these things in close to the staging bases and work your capability up to drop a whole division at one time."

Question: "Your forces within Strike Command must have—if Strike is to be really effective—the same quick responsiveness to a critical situation which the Strategic Air Command has developed so brilliantly. Are the Army units—the people who will do the actual fighting—maintained under the same immediate move-out capability?"

Answer: "They are—except that it has to be done in a different manner, because you're dealing with a different thing, another entity altogether. The way we handle this is to maintain in our divisions what we call the Division Ready Force. These troops are in the airborne divisions, since they move easier with airlift than any other division. They are the people on whom we rely for the immediate, quick move.

"They keep a reinforced battle group on what they call 'Division Ready Force Alert' all the time—and that's 24 hours a day, without fail. They change this, I believe, on a weekly basis. During the period of time that the battle group is assigned to this mission, its first company must be ready to load all men and weapons within 90 minutes from a no-notice, cold start—in other words, the middle of the night, or just getting ready to sit down to dinner, or *whenever* it happens.

"The rest of the force we require comes along as rapidly as the aircraft come in, and we make these moves—unless the plan is to assault—in what we call an 'air screen' column instead of a forma-tion. The other men move up and are prepared to load, as we assemble the aircraft into the loading base.

"Then as that battle group moves out, or at least completes its loading, the next battle group in the division is marshaling to start its out-loading. They keep up with the availability of the incoming airlift.

"It is a one-behind-the-other sort of thing, a continuous flow.

The Airborne—ready to go at any time, day or night. Mass paratrooper drop from Hercules . . .

We never take anything for granted; we practice these things, we check them out. We've never had a single bit of difficulty in getting these troops out, but we also turn our attention to the next force in line behind the Division Ready Force. We do this without warning to be certain that the people right down the line are as sharp as the Ready Force. We take every step to assure that everyone keeps thinking about what has to be done, no matter what the situation may be, and we make sure they don't forget about it.

"When you need a large force, many of these things must be—and *are*—planned out ahead of time. The Joint Chiefs decide for reasons good enough to them—adequate and good reasons—that there is a possibility of needing a certain type of operation in certain parts of the world, and that provides the basis for planning. . . .

"The unified theater commander makes his plans, and if that situation comes along, why—everything is already laid out in great detail. On the other hand, one of the things we have to be ready for is the unexpected. We've got to be able to move quickly if something should blow up somewhere, and we've got to move some forces in a hurry and meet a military mission. We're the ones to do it, and when we're called upon, we have got to have certain drills worked out that we can fall back upon—the kind of drills that we're sure will move a good force into the objective area, supported properly with ammunition, fuel, oil, and items of that nature."

Question: "There are reports to the effect that Strike Command is preparing special units that would meet the national need to get small, versatile groups of men into areas of potential danger. This would provide for eyeball surveillance in cases where aerial reconnaissance couldn't satisfy intelligence—following the World War II pattern of jumping men at night from high altitude, or even getting them in low and slow right over the trees—forces of two or 20 men. Are you working along these lines in Strike Command?"

Answer: "We do not have forces specifically set aside for that activity. Obviously, we must be prepared to meet any need, any situation. We've got people in the airborne of that sort, people we could train very quickly for the task at hand. We demand an awful lot of night work of the airborne; we require a great deal of field exercises and guerrilla work in all environments. The general training of the troops—particularly with respect to Ranger-type training—well, there are plenty of troops available who can do just about anything if you need them to do it, men who have been in the service long enough for us to know completely their character, their stamina. You just *know* them. You can do these special jobs and, knowing our men, it's not too hard to do, either."

Question: "I have a final question—more of a favor, perhaps. I would like to have your opinion on the intrinsic meaning of Strike Command to the United States. Let me extend this by saying to you flatly that the average American citizen is not aware—he hasn't the faintest idea—of the vast changes that have taken place in our national military structure. I'm afraid that the exotic gleam from Cape Canaveral and other areas such as that have clouded the facts of life in terms of the forces upon which our nation depends. Thus my query, in a general nature, for your interpretation in a summary to our citizens."

Answer: "There are three or four ideas which I believe deserve comment . . . and attention. One of them stems from what I believe is a matter of national appreciation of the facts as they are. The Congress wrote into the law of this land in 1958 the reorganization of our Department of Defense.

"The policy of the Congress was to establish means for the unified strategic direction of the armed forces, and for the operation of combat forces with true . . . unified command. This means integrated teams of land, sea, and air forces. That's simply recognizing the fact that none of the services can win a war alone. Except for very special circumstances that result in separate forces such as the Strategic Air Command, you simply must combine different capabilities to meet different military situations that arise in the world today, and we say you must bring into the picture those capabilities that are needed. There simply cannot be any snags allowed in this sort of mission.

"Now, getting specifically to Strike Command, we have fulfilled the intent of the Congress in this command. We have wholeheartedly supported what the people wanted in the way of organization, in the way of operation of their forces, insofar as our command goes. External to our command we hold the responsibilities of being ready to support any other unified command which is also a part of the general scheme.

"We go through numerous exercises to guarantee our ability to do that. If it is European Command, or Pacific Command, that is in need of reinforcement, we *know* we can get it to them because of the exercises we've had to date. We know just how to get it where it's needed, and in a hurry.

"Now this is what I call unity of effort, something in which our people believe. *Teamwork* . . . The second thing is the mobility that is inherent in the leading element of this command, to arrive at the most distant points quite rapidly and commence to execute the military mission upon arrival. And when I speak of the most distant points, I'm speaking of Southeast Asia. We could get a good force out there pretty fast and we can build it up pretty fast, and as our airlift gets stronger and stronger from the input of the '130 and then the '141, I know that we can do more.

"In painting the full picture you must not overlook the tremendous capability that exists in the rather small number of all-jet C-135s that we can draw on from MATS. The '135 fits in nicely and I can best illustrate it to you by moving an infantry unit, for example, from the Fourth Division at Fort Riley.

"We keep them also on alert as a ready-to-go force. Now if we want to move them our problem resolves itself to people; the volume of gear is not the great thing at all. We use the C-135-type aircraft and just a handful of these will move your people. And then you bring along your purely military ship, which is the C-130. We still have to use the big C-124 because we haven't got all the '130 aircraft that we would like to have or that we need. So we bring the military gear, all the armored personnel carriers and the trucks and other equipment along in those . . . ships; with the combination of these you can move a very strong force very rapidly.

"We had a good feel of this last summer in our exercise Swift Strike II. We wanted to work out a problem of strategic reinforcement—what we have to do if we want to send an outfit to Europe in a hurry, send them with all their combat gear.

General Walter C. Sweeney, Jr. (*left*), Commander, Tactical Air Command, and General Paul D. Adams, Commander, Strike Command, compare notes during a major field exercise. (*U.S. Army*)

"We selected the battalions of the Fifth Division at Fort Carson in Colorado. We did a bit of tailoring on some of the gear; we made the decision to leave some of the heavy engineer stuff out. And not a hell of a lot, either.

"We picked up that outfit; it came to more than 8,000 men and well over 5,000 tons, *plus* the equipment. Now, we moved these people from Fort Carson to the maneuvers area in South Carolina. We closed out the entire moving operation in 80 hours.

"But we had troops 'fighting' down there in a very short time. As soon as a battalion assembled and closed in, it was in turn moved right down to the front, and we started feeding them into action right then and there. So that when the last battalion closed in to the combat area, the whole division was down there 'fighting.' That movement took some 80 hours for all those men and all their gear and supplies.

"But it was like a two-edged sword. By the time the last battalion moved up to the maneuvers combat front, the lead groups had already been fighting for at least 48 hours. . . ."

There is an appropriate postscript to this meeting with General Adams, and it did not come from the general himself. At the Command Post Headquarters of Tactical Air Command in Virginia, a colonel explained to me through one incident the meaning of the constant alert which is demanded of the air and ground forces that make up Strike Command.

No one ever knows when the red phone will ring shrilly. No one ever knows whether the call will be a test, a rehearsal, or the "real thing." Defense Secretary Robert McNamara, who fought unreservedly for two years to make Strike Command a reality, is likely at any moment of the day or night to trigger a conference call to *all* the unified forces commanders in the United States and around the world.

During one such hookup conference General Adams, whose phone was picked up almost immediately, watched the second-hand of his clock sweep around as the commanders responded to the alert. The second-hand had not quite moved four and a half times around the face of the clock—less than 270 seconds for a no-notice, middle-of-the-night alert hookup around the world—when every commander-in-chief had reported in.

McNamara's voice came loud and clear over the planet-wide conference call: "Can't we do it in three minutes next time?"

CHAPTER XIV

The New Warfare—Part II   IN THE MIDST OF
the Southland's rolling hill country, a group of men clustered in
a small clearing work feverishly with a strange system of cables
and drums. The clearing is barely 500 feet long. It is absolutely
unfit for the landing of an airplane; strewn with ruts, holes, rocks,
and other natural debris, it would tear to shreds the landing gear
of any airplane. And yet, this same field is about to be used by a
Hercules transport of the Tactical Air Command to unload—without parachutes—three huge palletized cargo loads. One of these is
a truck; the other two loads contain ammunition and other military
supplies.

The Hercules will not use parachutes to place this cargo safely
on the ground—and neither will the airplane come to a landing.
Indeed, it will not even touch the ground. The group of observers
on the side of the clearing knows only that the system about to be
demonstrated has been kept a secret until Tactical Air Command
has completed its tests and proven the system to be absolutely
reliable.

The Hercules drifts into view over distant hills. The airplane
makes a fast sweep over the area while the pilot checks the wind.
Then the wings bank sharply as the transport heels around in a
tight turn. The observers cannot understand just what is going to
happen. They know that the Hercules will not land and it will not
paradrop cargo. Yet its landing gear is down, the huge cargo ramp
door is in release position, flaps are full down—and there are three
palletized loads, each weighing 10,000 pounds, to be dropped in
perfect condition in front of their eyes. It is too confusing for con-
jecture; they wait to see for themselves. . . .

The Hercules slides down a nearby hill, the humped wheels
skimming only feet above the treetops. It flattens out the descent
as it reaches the clearing and drops to only four feet above the
ground. The observers are startled by the slow speed, for the airplane—a regular C-130B model—rumbles through the air at barely
100 miles per hour. And then they *are* baffled, for they see a long
steel hook trailing behind and below the airplane.

What happens next is a blur. The Hercules roars past them; the hook trails behind and suddenly snags on a steel cable raised several inches off the ground. With explosive speed a huge object bursts rearward from the airplane. A howl of power from the suddenly accelerating airplane mixes with a screech of cable and the *whump!* of the object striking the earth. Dust billows upward as the cargo load slides 90 feet over the ground and skids to a halt.

Soldiers rush forward to the cargo, unfastening catches and securing cables. One man climbs to the driver's seat of the truck that appears from its protecting framework of wood and light metal. He starts the truck, guns the motor, and roars off the open clearing. Behind him several men drag the now empty pallet to the side.

Just in time . . . the Hercules rumbles down over the clearing for its second pass. And once again the scene is repeated and the huge 10,000-pound load bounces and skids to the ground.

The hook trailing from the Hercules has caught the steel cable on the ground. Attached to the palletized cargo load, the hook assures that it is literally yanked from the airplane. The ends of the steel cable in turn are attached to two energy absorbers in the ground—planted there by the GI's shortly before the airplane came into sight. The energy absorbers are set in in a sunken housing filled with water. As the cargo load slams forward it drags the cable; the cable movement turns two rotors in the water housings— and the drag action of the water slows the forward momentum of the cargo as it draws out the steel cable. The entire operation takes only a few seconds.

The second load has barely ground to a stop when the truck is back again. The soldiers hook a short tow to the palletized load; the driver guns the truck and drags the five-ton load quickly to the side. Moments later, the roar of the Hercules still booming through the nearby hills, the GI's are hauling the third load extracted from the Hercules.

One must see this fantastic new system to believe it. And even then it is difficult to realize just what goes on before the eyes. There is a wild blur of frenzied activity; a black mass bounds through the air and across the ground . . . it just does not seem possible for the cargo, smashed down onto the ground after being jerked from an airplane at speeds of from 98 to 130 miles per hour, to survive the fearsome jolt.

They ought to give the people who designed the pallets for the extraction drops some kind of medal—for even the post office couldn't damage *their* packaging. The writer witnessed a jeep come hurtling on its pallet out of a Hercules. The pilot had called down by radio, saying that his loader had taped an egg to the jeep

The wheels of this Hercules are inches off the ground and the airplane is flying at 115 miles per hour—as the extraction technique system yanks a huge truck out of the transport for a slam-bang but absolutely safe delivery at a rough, short field airstrip. (*Air Force*)

radiator, and would we check to see how the egg made out? We did.

The egg was unscathed.

The new extraction system can yank packages as bulky and heavy as 14,000 pounds from the airplane—or the same airplane can have three five-ton loads extracted in three successive passes, as was described.

At Sewart Air Force Base, the home of the 839th Air Division, the crews were ecstatic about their performance.

"We have produced some absolutely amazing results with the old bird and this extraction technique," a major chortled as he vented his glee with a walloping slap on the writer's back. "Did you see those loads come whizzing out of that airplane? Hot damn! Talk about pinpoint accuracy—just about anywhere and anyplace!"

Equally enthusiastic, though physically less exuberant, was a colonel from the CALSU (Combat Airlift Support Unit) organization of the 839th. "We can go anywhere," he confirmed, "and that means real close-in resupply support for the combat troops who are operating from rough forward positions. We can do things with this extraction technique that not even the BLC [Boundary Layer Control] could have given us. . . ."

The colonel is correct, for the combination of Hercules and the extraction technique represents literally a vast step forward in increasing the Army's combat mobility.

Or putting it another way . . . take a giant airplane with 30,000 pounds of vitally needed supplies in three palletized loads. Mix in one fairly level area of ground, with troops on that area. Drop the energy-absorption system to them by air. Eliminate all other para-drops—or, if you want to eliminate *any* drops, have the ground units carry one energy-drag system with them as standard equipment. Eliminate all necessity for landing. Just set up the system and stand to one side.

In the space of one hour flat, a line of Hercules can lay down with pinpoint accuracy a quarter of a million pounds of vital cargo, with absolute safety for that cargo.

Use *two* energy-absorption systems on the ground, and take your choice. The quarter of a million pounds of cargo can be slapped down on a dime in 30 minutes . . . or you can double the load to a half-million pounds for that same original hour.

The more that TAC planners saw of their extraction technique and its success—and the more they thought of the experiment with the unbroken egg—the faster they began to work on innovations for their own revolutionary system. They had a spanking-new method of cargo delivery that had Army forces beaming, and now they came up with a new twist in the delivery of troops that assured a major breakthrough in combat-forces support.

The twist was simple. Just take the same extraction technique used for equipment and adapt it to troops. TAC engineers went at their new program with enthusiasm. Under development now are pallets that can hold 12, 24, or 48 men, depending upon the size of the pallet—the largest being 39 feet long, so as to fit easily into the Hercules.

The transport rumbles slowly over the drop site, the extraction technique is employed, and the men are literally yanked clear out of the aircraft and deposited on the ground. How much force is involved? Nothing harder than the stop in an express elevator, and many, many times less than in a parachute landing.

The pallets are about nine feet wide and low-slung, not much higher than the height of a seated man. Each pallet, which resembles a huge toboggan, is covered with a tough but resilient material—as though it were half cocoon and half capsule—for full absorption of shock.

The people pallets, as they're called, will be snatched out of a Hercules at heights up to 35 feet from the ground, and moving at speeds of 115 to 149 miles per hour.

The C-130E model especially will be able to take full advantage of the people-pallet system. TAC officials point out that with these special pallets a *single* C-130E "could deposit two combat platoons —more than 40 fighting men—in the battlefield vicinity." One TAC squadron with the people pallets "could deliver two Army battle groups—approximately 3,000 men—in less than six hours. Under favorable conditions, the rate of buildup could reach 1,500 combat troops an hour."

But the significance of the breakthrough goes beyond battlefield delivery alone. What also delights Army commanders is that the new technique will "overcome difficulties in drop accuracy and the need for reassembling troops scattered over the drop zone. With full cognizance of battlefield difficulties, the pallets promise absolute precision."

The New Warfare—Old Style

The United States each month becomes more deeply embroiled in warfare that, compared to our gloomy preoccupation with thermonuclear bombs and intercontinental ballistic missiles, is a throwback to the days of furious hand-to-hand fighting, slinking through the jungles, and fighting as marauding killers in the night.

And that's exactly what it is. . . .

The "new" warfare isn't. It's the old story of man against man, of superior skill and a lethal character rating winning out over the opposition. It is dirty and uncompromising, with no quarter given.

Extraction technique using "people pallet" . . .

It is a Donnybrook kind of war with fatal consequences instead of black eyes and lumps on the head.

It is a war of individual killers who have adapted everything to their deadly purposes, from strips of wire for silently strangling a man to death in the jungle night, to surplus Air Force training planes rebuilt into murderous treetop fighter-bombers.

There are different names for this new crop of deadly fighting men. In the Air Force they are the Air Commandos, a rakish, unbelievably undisciplined, unmilitary bunch of people who are rewriting the books on slug-it-out-at-close-range air warfare. The Air Commandos are trained at the Tactical Air Command's Special Air Warfare Center in Florida. They are a "quick and dirty" outfit, and their mission is the same as it was many years ago when the First Air Commando Group fought a running, vicious battle with the Japanese in Asian jungles. That mission is to support allied guerrilla forces and the U.S. Army's Special Forces.

The latter are without question the toughest, hardiest group of fighting people in the world today. That's their business. Any man who doesn't measure up to those standards has no business being in the Special Forces outfits. And there aren't any that don't measure up.

The over-all program of the Air Commandos and the Special Forces has been given the blanket title of COIN. This is counterinsurgency . . . the result of our country's firm decision to mount a meaningful offensive against subversion and guerrilla tactics.

But there is a wide gulf—and most people are grossly unaware of that gulf—between limited war and COIN operations. Only under unusual circumstances is this abyss bridged. People tend to lump the over-all mission of TAC, including its CASF system, and the mission of Strike Command, together with COIN in a single package—and they simply do not lump.

Contrary to widespread opinion, the purpose of the Special Air Warfare Center at Eglin Air Force Base in Florida is *not* to fight air-commando wars. Increasing the nation's counterinsurgency tactical air capability is its primary goal. Thus the center splits into two operational organizations—the First Air Commando Group and the First Combat Applications Group.

It's a neat partnership. Under the concept of COIN, the key objective of *both* the Air Force and Army special air and ground warfare units is fast reaction to any situation. But their prime mission is *not* to fight a war; it is, instead, to teach other people how to fight their wars against guerrilla and other forces. Thus the Air Commandos, who have been operating in Asia for several years now, concentrate their efforts on instructing the air crews of other nations in all phases of what are defined as "airborne counter-insurgency operations."

While the Air Commandos fulfill this mission, the First Combat Applications Group is always in the picture, either alongside the Commandos or hovering in the background, always studying and probing for more effective weapons and techniques to pass on to the Air Commandos. It's an endless job of trying to be even dirtier and more effective killers at treetop heights, so to speak, than anyone has ever been in the past—including the frenzy of World War II operations at its peak. The Air Commandos are convinced that the rougher they can be now—the more skilled in lethal use of their weapons—the better chance we all have to keep the host of wars around the world neatly packaged and limited, *without* our small friendly nations disappearing within the Communist maw, as has happened in the past.

It must be noted that most of the airplanes that the Air Commandos use in their savage beatups of Communist forces—especially in Viet Nam—are not all products of the modern day and age. They are both American and Vietnamese airplanes, and certainly they recall the question the writer asked of General Adams about "old" and "new" equipment. For the treetop killers are Invader attack bombers that were flying in combat in Word War II. Their single-engine companions aren't even fighters; they're Trojan trainers adapted to jungle war. The transports are largely the venerable C-47 Gooney Bird and the big-bellied and ponderous C-46 Commando. The Gooney goes all the way back to 1935 for its first flying, and both the Gooney and the Commando were flying Hump operations across the Himalayas in World War II. The only real new twin-engine airplane the Commandos are using themselves is the high-tailed, bloated-belly twin-engine C-123 Provider—and *that* ship goes back to vintage 1949. Oh yes, there is one spanking-new airplane—the L-28 liaison plane. Pick out any field in which a jeep can accelerate to 30 miles per hour—and you've got a landing strip for the L-28. The pilots call it the "Super Spad," considering it as pretty much a "modification" of the Spad XIII fighter of World War *I*.

The First Air Commando Group flew a wild and wicked war in the jungles of Burma way back in 1944. John R. Alison, then deputy commander of the Commandos, summed up their job: "We flew the Burma Raiders where they wanted to go, resupplied them by air, picked them up when they called us, and helped keep the Japanese off their backs with bomber and fighter strikes."

The job in the Asian jungles hasn't really changed much. But we have refined some of the techniques. . . .

There is one incident in the history of the Air Commandos in Burma that is remembered as typifying the spirit of almost unbelievable coordination—or even rapport—among the men. A group of Air Commandos fought to get out of Japanese territory after being dropped short of their objective. One American boy, unable to swim, was being towed by an officer across the Chindwin River at night. Every man maintained absolute and unremitting silence, since a powerful Japanese jungle force was nearby—less than 100 yards away, as it turned out.

For some reason we shall never know, that boy in the middle of the river at night either lost his grip or let go . . . he was swallowed by the black waters.

Through it all, he never uttered a sound. . . . The men today remember the story of this kid. It's their idea of their predecessors.

You've got to see them to believe the Air Commandos. You can find them in tennis shorts and sneakers, or in flying suits, or in bloused-leg fatigues and combat boots. They dress like no one else in the Air Force, and nobody complains—because they fly and fight like no one else. Their hat is the crowning inconsistency; it makes spit-and-polish officers blanch and sometimes they even get quite ill. The hat is made of quilt-stitched denim with a wide floppy brim, and it's as pliable as a cowboy's ten-gallon felt. It can be pummeled and shaped and squeezed and pinned to meet the desires of the wearer. It's perfect for jungle heat and sun. With such complete disdain for official headgear about him, the group's commander wised up. He made the hat official, so that everyone is now in uniform. Except for the combat controllers on the ground up front with the Vietnamese troops—those Air Commandos were already wearing black berets and they refused to give them up.

The Air Commandos are a throwback in everything but their unbelievable skill and efficiency in their work. They're like the American Indians in one respect. Everyone in the Sixth Fighter Squadron, for example, has several jobs to fill. Above all, this is the only outfit in the Air Force that has no written Standard Operating Procedures!

The officers—skilled as pilots and navigators—are people who wear their uniform to *fight*. And they've walked out on both lucrative and rewarding positions to get where they are. Several of the pilots in the past commanded the giant, eight-jet B-52 bombers. There are engineers and schoolteachers; there's one wild man who passed the exams and tests to be an astronaut and then decided to stay with machines that fly with wings and fight. There's a preacher with a degree from West Point, an Air Force commission, and navigator's wings.

How about maintenance procedures and policies? There "ain't none." How could there be with derelict airplanes and museum pieces turned back into topnotch killers?

"In that *Gung-ho* outfit," reported a dazed officer who had visited the Commandos in Asia, "they just don't have rules. They don't even have a place they call a home base. They operate anywhere. They don't have any maintenance specialists, just a bunch of wrench-twisting mechanics. But they can tear an engine down and put it together as if it were spanking new, and just about do it blindfolded.

"Their maintenance boss laughs crudely whenever anyone mentions regulations pertaining to maintenance. In fact, he breaks out into gales of laughter. Otherwise he is very quiet and soft-spoken. Who'd ever think that for years *before* World War II he was a cropduster who did all his own mechanical work in cornfields and on country roads? As far as he's concerned the scenery is all that has changed. . . ."

A mechanic of the Air Commandos—one officer describes them as "a bunch of wrench-twisting mechanics. But they can tear an engine down and put it together as if it were spanking new, and just about do it blindfolded." (*Air Force*)

The Air Commandos were very unhappy that they weren't fully qualified as airborne, that they hadn't "hacked it" as far as paratrooper requirements were concerned. They nearly broke down the doors of paratrooper jump school to get in. Some of them now wear the paratrooper wings. The others waiting in line for admittance filled in the waiting time in what they considered "useful fashion." They started jumping out of planes strictly on their own. Some of the men still waiting for paratrooper school already have dozens of jumps to their credit, not to mention high-altitude, free-fall skydiving skill.

The guerrilla air war in South Viet Nam is a sharp departure from the modern combat tactics of the Tactical Air Command, which has graduated its fighter-bombers into howling giants that weigh as much as a twin-engine airliner. In Viet Nam the operations again the Communist Viet Cong forces have evolved into a tactical air-ground war adapted to the situation, which itself is a unique product of geographical, political, and military factors. The theorists have termed the action "counterinsurgency," imbuing the term COIN with a meaning perhaps out of proportion to the facts; the people in the business and on the scene consider it simply as a guerrilla air war.

In addition to air support so low the planes sometimes clip the tops of trees, there is interdiction of the battlefield, tactical airlift, and reconnaissance. Tactical airlift is not airlift in the sense that most Americans know. Any daylight mission that brings the old airplanes to more than 50 feet above the jungle is considered as a "high-altitude flight," and especially hazardous because of the increased field of fire from the Viet Cong in the jungles and fields. At night the pilots fly in their Gooney Birds and big-bellied Commandos as high as 200 feet—an altitude to make the stoutest heart tremble.

On some missions the Air Force moves in with its C-123 Providers —the only transports that are still officially American, rather than South Vietnamese airplanes. All three types do every job known in airlift and supply; they operate out of dirt fields, drop paratroopers, make assault landings, and to help starving villagers, the airmen throw out of their airplanes live chickens, pigs, goats, and other animals—all of which are introduced to their first parachute descent before ending up over the cooking fire.

The people who fly airplanes with guns—the twin-engine Invaders, the Trojans, and more recently the big and husky Navy Skyraider fighter-bombers—operate around-the-clock against the Communist Viet Cong guerrillas. At Tan Son Nhut Air Base, outside of Saigon, the Joint Operations Center coordinates the frenzied action over the jungles. The pattern in everything is for the Vietnamese Air Force (VNAF) to do the work, alongside U.S. Air Force officers, with U.S. Army liaison officers joining in.

One of the things that make these people a bit more secure in their tactical situation is that there are a limited number of Air Force jet fighter-bombers also in the operations—solidly backed up by small but powerful jet strike units based only hours away. The air war to date is one-sided, with *us* doing the flying and blasting. The moment air opposition shows up—and guerrillas could have air support only from the Chinese or Russian Air Forces—the people in Viet Nam blow the whistle. Then, and not until then, does TAC come into the picture with a deadly Composite Air Strike Force tailored to the jungle area.

Officially the USAF people in South Viet Nam function as advisers and instructors to the VNAF to teach them tactical air combat techniques—to give them the means to fight their own air war. In the process our people go along on the combat missions, and despite official insistence on the "advisory and instructor" status, it is a very thin hairline indeed that separates their activity from combat. Although they act as "instructors," the USAF pilots often fly the airplanes, make the attacks, and wallop the targets.

How successful is this aerial guerrilla mission in the "new" warfare as practiced by the United States with the VNAF?

The effectiveness is best measured, of course, in terms of its impact on Viet Cong tactics, strategy, and operations. It *has* prevented concentration of large forces, which deprives the Viet Cong of the ability to launch any real large-scale attacks. This leaves the Red guerrillas only the harassing but limited effectiveness of small-scale, sporadic hit-and-run thrusts; these can be effective in the opening days of an operation, but only as a prelude to major attacks such as the Communists made in French Indo-China. And to the Viet Cong such attacks are denied.

The fact that the Viet Cong are kept "on the run" is a telling tribute to the immediate responsiveness of applying selective firepower against targets that are mobile and of a fleeting nature. This has been *the* bottleneck in air guerrilla operations, and our experience in the South Viet Nam jungles represents a major breakthrough in effectiveness of tactics. The South Viet Nam terrain ranges from rugged, forested mountains to dense, triple-tiered jungles, or flat and swampy delta country. The monsoons and heavy rains make many areas virtually impassable for long periods of time, and it is in this terrain that air becomes the primary and often the *only* weapon which can be used against the Viet Cong. In previous operations such as these, casualties inflicted by tactical air came to only a very small fraction of the total. The picture has changed abruptly and the percentage is still going up; currently, at least one third, and perhaps more, of all Viet Cong personnel casualties result from the guns of the Air Commando operations.

The Mule Train operation in South Viet Nam has already become a fabulous—although unpublicized—classic of modern times. This is the combat air-cargo operation in that jungle land, and it has proved extraordinarily effective as the literal backbone of the counterguerrilla (or COIN) warfare. Squadrons of USAF-owned and -manned C-123 Providers provide all in-field logistics requirements. The Mule Train operates from the Saigon area and flies a wild and frenetic *scheduled* combat cargo run to all South Vietnamese bases. That's only part of it, for the chunky Providers also bounce in and out of more than 100 jungle "airfields"; these range from former French concrete strips to dirt roads and open pasture. Remote outposts live entirely off the skill of the Air Force crews who drag in at almost treetop height and with pinpoint accuracy deliver the goods—ammunition as well as assortments of live cows and other barnyard denizens. Frequently the airplanes return to Saigon riddled and punctured by Viet Cong bullets. Mule Train crews and aircraft provide the *only* method of transportation across the country for ground forces, logistical supplies, and reinforcements.

The elaborate rules that govern much of contemporary close-in tactical air fighting just do not apply to the contained but fierce Asian war. There simply isn't any open means of telling which side is which. In South Viet Nam a sampan is the equivalent of a boxcar; a dinghy might be compared to a semi-trailer truck; a group of thatched houses to an ammo storage dump or a weapons arsenal. The Air Commandos play the game of distinguishing and striking legitimate targets that *look* harmless. . . .

It's a war with weapons out of the Dark Ages, intermixed with some modern touches. The Viet Cong receive modern arms from North Viet Nam and steal what they can from the South Viet Nam forces. But supply is difficult and the guerrillas are good at their business. So they fight with ancient crossbows and poison-tipped bamboo arrows (they're deadly at close range in the jungle). They use homemade shotguns made of rusted steel tubing, which have a blunderbuss effect. Their mortars are of hollow bamboo poles, their machetes sometimes fashioned from automobile springs. They use foot spikes made of rusty nails and hidden in paddy waters, and a land mine concocted of crockery filled with nuts, bolts, wire, glass, and metal—anything that can hurt, maim, and kill.

Night raids are a favorite of the Viet Cong. Whenever a raid begins the alarm is sounded by radio to the Air Commandos. They roar into the battle area and circle in low swings, releasing a steady stream of high-powered flares which bathe the entire area in a painful, eerie white light. The moment the Gooney Birds show with their flares, the attacks break off.

The fighter-bomber strikes at night are right out of medieval times. When the Vietnamese soldiers pinpoint enemy groups in the darkness, a man is always ready to release a flaming arrow into the enemy concentration. Orbiting pilots watch the arrow streak downward and burn . . . and immediately afterward bullets, cannon shells, rockets, bombs, and blazing napalm rip and shred the jungle.

We've come a long way; we've learned to fight in a manner ruthless and unprecedented in our history. Even the best of our American Indian warriors would look upon our tactics with pride, for the rule is never allow the enemy to rest. Hit 'em and harass 'em, seen or not seen.

Even the Viet Cong soldier must rest during the suffocating heat of mid-afternoon. The heat saps a man of his strength, drains him of energy. This is the time when the Air Commandos tear up the jungle hunting for the Viet Cong. The purpose on these missions isn't so much to kill or wound, and, in any case, the jungle never lets us know the effectiveness of the strikes. But we *do* know that our attacks against the Viet Cong camps keep them running hard during those critical "hard-to-move" hours.

And to keep things lively at night—*without* expenditure of a single bomb or bullet—we call on the supersonic jets of our Pacific Air Forces (PACAF). In the remote, completely hidden Viet Cong encampments, with the men sleeping, the night is split without any warning by a tremendous explosion. The blast jars the ground and brings men scrambling in fear to their feet. It happens, again and again, throughout the night.

The intruder is a jet fighter. Sometimes it flies in the stratosphere, not even a whisper of sound drifting to the earth. The pilot rolls over and dives; in seconds the airplane is well past supersonic speed. Still high above the earth he pulls out . . . leaving a tremendous sonic shock wave racing toward the earth to impact with explosive sound and force in the Viet Cong area. Or the airplane may come in low, flat and level, the pilot pouring on the coal for supersonic flight. The sonic boom from this approach is painful; special tests years ago taught our tactical fighter pilots how to smash windows, break beams, and inflict ringing blows against the ears.

Not a bomb and not a bullet . . . but it plays absolute hell with the Viet Cong, and they never *know* whether it's a sonic boom or an exploding shell that is only the first blow of many to come.

The Mayhem Troopers

Several years ago a small band of paratroopers "violated" their standard procedures for jumps. The airborne troops almost always go in low—anywhere from as low as 400 feet to 1,500 feet above the ground. Their static lines tear open their parachute packs and spill the nylon into the wind. Seconds after the canopies billow open they're on the ground. That's one of the main reasons for the low altitude for jumping—minimum exposure in the air, as well as minimum dispersion on the ground.

The select group of men from the 82nd Airborne Division lined up before the jump door of a Hercules cruising slowly at 12,500 feet. Outside that door the sky was black. The men shuffled into position and waited for the light signal to blaze.

In the flight deck the navigator checked his coordinates. "Jump time coming up in 60 seconds," he said into his lip microphone. The pilot acknowledged, gave absolute attention to his controls. The alert signal came again at 30 seconds, and then the light flashed and the bell clamored in the back of the transport.

"Go!" shouted the jumpmaster. They spilled out of the airplane, no familiar static lines from the back packs to the airplane. No chutes cracked open, no bodies jerked at the sudden deceleration.

The dark shapes plummeted with absolute silence through the sky. Sixty seconds later the bodies fell at 120 miles per hour. More than 10,000 feet had been swallowed up in the long free fall. Two thousand feet above the ground the packs streamed nylon and slapped open.

The troopers thudded to the earth, shucked their harnesses, and in catlike silence grouped together. Swiftly they moved across open country, closing in on a vital radar installation. Before the "defenders" knew what happened, they felt cold steel at their throats. Explosive charges—simulated, fortunately—were already packed into position to blow the installation to flying pieces of metal. The startled guards and technicians stared in wonder as the paratroopers sheathed their knives and melted away into the night, leaving behind them a group of "dead men" and a "totally destroyed" vital installation.

Before the night ended, the paratrooper raiding party had "slaughtered" hundreds of men and left in their path a "swath of destruction."

Not once was an alarm given as they moved in shadow fashion through several military bases in the United States, providing a grim demonstration of their lethal skills.

These troopers were a part of the Army's new Special Forces, professional soldiers to whom premeditated mayhem is as natural as awakening in the morning. They combine the attributes of Rangers, commandos, paratroopers, guerrillas, ordnance experts, and a dozen additional skills and form the greatest "loose" fighting team the United States has ever known in all its history. Experience gained at the price of agony and bloodshed through many wars has been the foundation of their training; and their capabilities have been honed to the temper of fine steel because of the present military needs of their country.

Volunteers for the Special Forces fighting teams join the Seventh Special Forces Group (Airborne) at Fort Bragg, North Carolina. They are already qualified soldiers—able combat men and thorough in their business of killing—*before* joining the Seventh Special Forces Group. At Fort Bragg they receive their master's degree through brutal and intensive training that is designed to make them potent, highly skilled, and with a toughness second to none, as part of 12-man operational detachments. These detachments are the basic elements of the Special Forces Group, which disdains large numbers in favor of merciless efficiency in its work.

These are the men we are sending to remote parts of the world, to jungles, swamps, forests, villages and towns, deserts, mountain retreats . . . to every possible part of the world, from sweltering equatorial jungles to great lands that know only snow and ice. These are our counterinsurgency forces that work in the COIN program from the ground floor up. They are an incredible group of men.

Their efficiency comes from a spectrum of requirements that would have made the crack soldier of World War II reel in dismay. They must demonstrate an assortment of technical skills with ordnance and machinery, as well as with a throat-slicing blade or the heel of the hand—with which they are expected to be able to kill a man with a single blow.

The weapons experts of the detachments are fully versed in the operation and the field maintenance not only of every American weapon that might be used by the regular, guerrilla, and counterguerrilla forces of our allies, but also those that come from foreign lands, especially weapons that will be used by hostile forces. This covers the gamut of pistols, rifles, mortars, machine guns, rifle grenades, flame throwers, bazookas and recoilless rifles, machine pistols, submachine guns, and anything that a man can carry, or use, in order to kill people or destroy equipment.

The Special Forces men, incidentally, are skilled in making battlefield "zip guns"—bows and arrows, crossbows, blowguns, spears, bamboo mortars, and other improvised weapons.

The demolitions experts develop extraordinary talents in adapting explosives for sabotage and for delaying operations against enemy forces; and they can perform the same missions with improvised materials when the high explosives are unavailable. This isn't the kind of operation where the men are burdened with heavy equipment; they're experts at scrounging anything to make weapons. And they have a unique ability to manufacture explosives in the field by mixing fertilizer and a few chemicals. That is why their training includes a thorough knowledge of just what types of chemicals are available in most parts of the world.

The medical aides with the team must be able to perform battlefield surgery, simply because no one else is going to be around to do this work. Besides matching the other men as specialized killers, the medical soldiers receive six months of intensive training at Army medical centers, as well as a unique on-the-job training session at Fort Bragg under experienced surgeons. When they go out into the field, they can—with what they carry on their persons—perform minor surgical operations and take whatever steps are necessary to keep a badly wounded man alive for a long time.

The elaborate cross-training of the men provides each detachment with unprecedented staying power in the field in any mission to which they have been assigned. *Every* man, in addition to his basic skills, is expert in the use of code, in demolitions, in advanced first aid, in weapons.

And every man is a killer with a knife, his bare hands, a sharpened stick—*anything*. They are experienced in judo and karate, in rough-and-tumble, slug-it-out, hand-to-hand fighting.

One of the more interesting pastimes at Fort Bragg takes place in the "Gladiator Pit." This is a circular pit six feet deep and 50 feet across. At a given signal about 60 men go roaring into the pit in a gladiatorial struggle with bare hands and feet. It is a furious, sweating Donnybrook of a fight.

There is only one winner—no matter how long it takes to arrive at this conclusion. The one man who is still on his feet at the end of the mayhem is declared the victor; more accurately, perhaps, he proclaims himself as the victor, since no one else is standing to argue the point.

In March 1961 the Army doubled the units assigned to Special Warfare teams, with heavy emphasis on the training of the airborne troops at Fort Bragg in North Carolina. There is also the Jungle Warfare Training Center at Fort Sherman in the Panama Canal Zone. It is at schools such as this one that the new student killers receive some dramatic lessons from the not-so-distant past—especially about one raid by Merrill's Marauders in Burma during World War II.

On that occasion Lieutenant Colonel C. Johnson led a raiding party against a Japanese bivouac in the midst of the jungle. The Japanese outnumbered the Marauders several times over—and the Americans on their way in to attack *carried no ammunition in their rifles*. Every man had to empty his weapons of any shells.

The weapon to be used was the machete. In the darkness of the jungle night, confusion and chaos would reign. It would be impossible to tell friend from foe. The Marauders swarmed into the Japanese camp and began hacking away with devastating effect. Blood splattered wildly about as limbs and heads disappeared in gory showers and bodies were split cleaver-wise. The rules were grim and simple—cut to pieces anyone who is firing a weapon.

The casualty ratio that night was 40 Japanese dead to each American killed or wounded.

It's a different kind of American today; you learn this as you listen to one rawboned Army veteran telling his new crop of killers:

"A little guy can be a much better bladesman because the machete depends on speed and angle of cutting rather than sheer weight. You've got to whip the blade fast and easy, at an angle of about 45 degrees. Hold it firmly with the thumb and first two fingers, and loosely with the other two. You get the whip action from the wrist. A good bladesman can snap off a small tree—or an arm—with no trouble at all. Like this—"

Flashes of light on steel and a dummy tumbles to the ground in six pieces. . . .

There are talents possessed by this new breed of killers which, along with their other skills, justify terming them the deadliest and most effective combat force in the world. Every man is experienced in *teaching* guerrilla-warfare adeptness to the natives of countries allied with the United States. Every man in Special Forces is an authority on surviving under any combination of conditions, in living entirely off the land. Each man must be jump-qualified as a paratrooper, and his life is an almost uninterrupted course of instruction in jungle, amphibious, desert, arctic, and mountain combat and survival.

And they never know when they'll be routed out of the barracks in the middle of the night, flown to a remote part of the United States where no sane human being wants to be—and told to bail out, without special equipment. It's all part of the course—proof by trial.

The Special Warfare teams work closely with the Air Force and

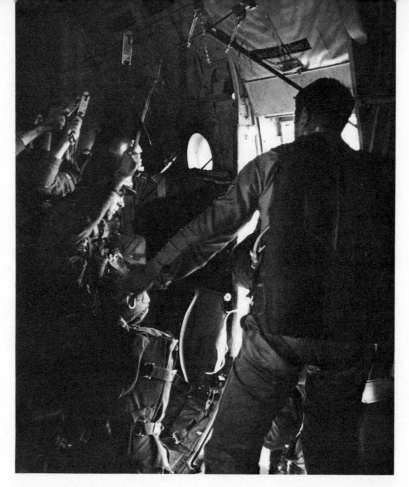

Paratroopers of the Second Airborne Group, 503rd Infantry, 25th Infantry Division . . . prepared to leap from C-130 Hercules in a mass drop during field exercises in the Far East. (*U.S. Army*)

the Navy. They are taught to jump from high-speed aircraft at *low* altitudes, or to go out of a Hercules anywhere from 12,000 to 30,000 feet above the earth. They do underwater demolition work, must be expert swimmers above and below the surface of the ocean, and work with submarines on special missions.

And sometimes they modify their techniques for something new and unexpected, as in the case of the Army's First Special Forces Group (Airborne), stationed on Okinawa. The crews of the Hercules who carry these troopers have worked out a technique that unnerves brave men. The airplanes race at high speed, at 25,000 feet, toward the objectives. And then—they pull the plug. Props in flat pitch (for braking action), gear down, flaps to full deflection, power back, the Hercules transports fall out of the sky in dizzying swoops. At 1,200 feet above the terrain the troopers spill out of the airplane—striking with little or no warning.

But perhaps the most effective skills of the Special Forces teams parallel those of the Air Commandos—in whipping eager local natives into efficient guerrilla fighting teams. The Special Forces troopers train them in the use of weapons, teach them agility and speed in sabotage missions, and how to establish intelligence nets— without which no guerrilla or counterguerrilla force could function with anything resembling efficiency.

These are representatives of the United States trained in a manner almost unknown to our public. Every member of a Special Forces or Air Commando team goes through detailed area and language studies. They learn the attitudes, customs, politics, economic conditions, and other aspects of countries into which they may be sent with little or no warning. Every possible opportunity is provided for the development of their language capabilities, and the linguistic specialists with these teams are astonishing in their ability to cover a variety of languages with complete competence.

Their task is never one without thorns and difficult obstacles. Experience has made it unquestionably clear that the training program in the foreign lands must begin at the very bottom of the ladder, and that to fashion an efficient fighting force of the local military personnel it is often necessary to carry out "basic training of foreign personnel in marksmanship, field sanitation, first aid, scouting and patrolling . . . before they can begin the tactical training to combat guerrillas."

It has required the passage of many years and the fruitless expenditure of men and matériel for us to learn the hard lessons of guerrilla war. We know—now—that in an organized operation it requires from ten to 20 fighting men to neutralize one guerrilla. More than 200,000 men struggled for years in Greece to overcome 21,000 guerrillas. In 1955 the British learned sadly that they needed every one of their 35,000 soldiers to track down and contain 4,000 guerrillas in the jungles and rain forests of Malaya.

The dim and eerie shadow-world of the rain forests and the jungles provides a natural habitat for the Asiatic guerrilla, who subsists on the most basic of food supplies, living off the country. Our counterguerrilla operations are unique in that the United States has learned the absolute necessity of throwing off the encumbrances of massive, unwieldy, and vulnerable supply lines, and drawing upon the previously untapped versatility of combat airlift to sustain men in the field.

The problem of logistics emphasizes this point—which is why our Special Forces teams have concentrated upon teaching their native soldiers to utilize every possible weapon made from indigenous materials. It is a one-sided problem, and the best example of this comes from one specific engagement in which a South Vietnamese infantry battalion fought a shadowy two-day fight in the jungle with the Viet Cong. When the shooting ended and the opposing forces went their separate ways, the Vietnamese learned that of their casualties—and they were not minor—not one had been wounded or killed by bullet or bayonet. It was jungle warfare in its strictest sense—with the Viet Cong reaching back into history for their weapons.

Science properly applied can still beat the enemy on his own grounds—and it's not necessary to fight him on his own terms. We are developing new weapons that defy the experience of combat veterans and shake the imagination . . . such as a small plastic tube that looks exactly like a drinking straw.

Inside that tiny tube is a microjet rocket—a needle-shaped nylon rocket that bursts from its "drinking straw" launcher with an amazing velocity of 4,400 feet per second. At a range of several hundred yards it will tear a gaping hole in a man. It is virtually a silent killer and described by the Special Forces troopers as the "most vicious little weapon ever imagined." The tubes can be clustered to hurl a fantastic barrage of explosive needles at an enemy. . . .

And there's a new type of gas. Not a poison gas, but an explosive mist. Sprayed from portable and disposable tanks, it spills down slopes, hugging the ground, filling ravines, caves, the beds of streams, and any rough terrain. Then—a spark, and the gas explodes with terrible violence, tearing everything within its reach into small pieces.

Just two examples, out of many, of the new weapons . . .

The United States Marines have a Counter-Guerrilla Warfare School in the jungle forest country of northern Okinawa. Thousands of Marines have completed the course, which above all emphasizes self-reliance under jungle conditions.

"We teach our people how to prevent surprise, how to kill the initiative of the guerrilla," explains an officer instructor. "Our mission is to fight the guerrilla—*not* to be one. Our men can't be guerrillas in Southeast Asia, where the guerrilla is able to blend in with those all around him.

"The only place a Marine could be a guerrilla is back in the United States. . . ."

Americans who read today of counterinsurgency and of the great importance placed by our country on this "new" warfare are in for a surprise. For guerrilla warfare not only is not "new" to our history, but it appears that the United States has *more* experience in guerrilla fighting than perhaps any other nation in the world. And it is perhaps for this reason, as well as others, that our men are meeting their new tasks with such tremendous skill and competence.

Guerrilla fighting has been an important factor in our nation's growth. The Minute Men fought not as troops or soldiers, but more as insurgents than in any other role. When necessary they adopted guerrilla tactics that confounded the British and crippled their attempts to eliminate the opposition, for the Minute Men simply melted into the countryside—a tactic which we are just "discovering" to be employed by Communist forces in Asia.

In the campaigns of the south against the British, the American guerrillas drove the English forces wild with hit-and-run tactics. Generals Thomas Sumter and Andrew Pickens joined forces with Lieutenant Colonel Francis Marion and unleashed a perpetual menace that appeared out of thin air, sliced deeply into the British forces, and just as quickly vanished. Marion gained fame as the Swamp Fox. With only several hundred men under his command at any one time, he confounded, bedeviled, and hacked with bloody effectiveness at British forces many times his own strength. He was a wraith that appeared with blazing guns out of nowhere and defied massive attempts to run him down, in the process tying up large forces of the enemy.

In the War of 1812, to protect our flanks and back areas, we formed Ranger units from our frontiersmen to fight off Indian attacks. And in 1848 we smoothly shifted tactics to counterguerrilla operations—by necessity. After the defeat of the Mexican Army and the occupation of Mexico City itself, General Winfield Scott learned firsthand the effectiveness of guerrilla raids that swept down upon him almost constantly from the Mexican hills and mountains. The Texas Rangers and other units were formed into special counterguerrilla forces. They rode day and night in the field to pursue the Mexicans. A system of staggered replacements kept fresh men in the field, eroding the strength of the Mexican guerrillas by their unrelenting blows at the defending bands.

And what student of American history does not know of the legendary feats of John S. Mosby of the Confederate forces in the Civil War? Mosby gave new meaning to the words daring, courage, and skill; his guerrilla tactics remain all-time classics of technique and effectiveness.

In 1900 the United States Army in the Philippines, on Luzon and other islands, fought over a thousand counterguerrilla actions. Many of them were savagely contested and bloody in the results. It was anything but a remote or small campaign, for the Army troops killed 4,000, wounded another 1,200, and captured 6,000 Filipino insurgents.

World War II saw extensive guerrilla and counterguerrilla operations by the United States. Merrill's Marauders fought fierce battles in Burma. In a preview of today's situation, the Army's Detachment 101 teamed up with and trained Kachin tribesmen to fight one of the bloodiest guerrilla actions in history. Even the Japanese were stunned by the ferocity of the tribesmen, who moved with the stealth of cats in the jungle and mountain country.

We had our Alamo Scouts operating with the U.S. Sixth Army in the Southwest Pacific, our Ranger battalions, and our commandos in hit-and-run operations deep behind enemy lines.

But above all else, the training ground for guerrilla and counterguerrilla fighting has always been right here in the United States. For nearly a full century, from 1790 to 1885, the American Army fought what Lieutenant Colonel Hugh H. Gardner describes as "the most fanatical and dedicated guerrilla forces the world has ever known—the American Indians." A century of guerrilla combat between Indians and whites added up to 19 full-scale wars, 69 major campaigns, and literally thousands of bloody, all-out battles.

The tempo of the guerrilla warfare of today even now is shifting all about us. The so-called "small-scale" actions are not that at all. There are 12,000 Americans in South Viet Nam alone. Officially they are advisers to the South Vietnamese. Realistically they are advisers in the thick of combat and in the path of enemy firepower.

Which is why so many of these fine men who wear the uniforms of our Air Force and our Army will never again walk among us.

We have learned, and we are still learning. The guerrilla experience of the United States in the past would seem to favor our role in *counter*guerrilla operations today. The new weapons to go with these men of spectacular capability, combined with airlift facilities the like of which has never been known before, and given even greater versatility through such innovations as the technique of cargo extraction from the Hercules . . . all these things begin to form a new capability for the nation.

General Adams expressed the meaning of that capability; it is no more than a reflection of what took place in Lebanon in the stifling summer of 1958. We moved, and we moved fast; we moved with a fighting force undeniably powerful but nonetheless lacking the muscle and sinew we possess today. Yet it was enough for the opposition to decide, "There's no use to tangle with those boys—they've got the power."

CHAPTER XV

From the Flight Deck On the morning of March 13, 1963, three Hercules transports loaded with supplies stood idly on the ramp of Kindley Air Force Base in Bermuda. The airplanes were primed and ready to go, the weather was beautiful, and the crews, as well as their passenger loads of mechanics and technicians, chafed at the enforced idle ground time. The planned moment of takeoff had become a series of interrupted starts and postponements, of delays thrown in at the last moment.

The culprit in the successive delays was the wind. Not the wind we felt in warm, sunny Bermuda, but at the island of Lajes in the Azores, many miles distant to the east. With our heavy load, Lajes was our scheduled refueling point. At Lajes the sun also shone, but the wind! It howled off the sea with demon force, shrieking across the runways at more than 100 miles per hour. That wind chained the Hercules to Bermuda.

In all other respects we were delighted with the wind. At our planned cruising altitude of 25,000 feet, the wind would rush out of the west. The river of air that flowed eastward would give us a free dividend of speed, anywhere from 40 to 50 miles per hour, added to the cruising speed of the airplanes.

But the winds at Lajes grounded us. The previous night I had talked with an old friend, Captain Gayle Williams of TAC, who had shattered the Bermuda skies with the sound of his approach into Kindley. Williams and another pilot descended in two F-105 fighter-bombers. The razor-winged killers cracked giant whips of thunder as they fell earthward, then whispered skillfully onto the runway. Williams—with whom I had flown for a month in the Thunderbirds jet aerobatic team—shook his head as he described conditions at Lajes. The winds were blowing at 110 miles per hour.

To land *any* airplane under such conditions is not only a hysterical affair, but one that promises fatal consequences to the most minute slip in piloting technique. And sometimes even the best of pilots cannot cope with such a tremendous driving force of air blowing at an angle across the runway, as it was at Lajes. Such winds are treacherous, and shift direction with frightening suddenness; they can flip a wing wildly upward, slamming the other into the concrete. Even with a safe landing the side loads on the landing gear could damage the airplane. A landing under conditions such as these is one long moment of impending disaster.

Under combat or emergency conditions there would be no hesitation to bore right in; and the Hercules pilots have done just that. But ours was a mission of supply and rotation; the Hercules transports and crews were from the 839th Air Division at Sewart Air Force Base, en route to Evreux-Fauville Air Base in France for three months' rotation duty at the home of the 322nd Air Division. A delay would mean juggling of schedules, but that did not constitute an emergency.

With the crosswinds so high, TAC regulations forbade the pilots to take off from Bermuda for Lajes. Major Wilmer S. Wallick, our pilot, had no doubt that he could land at Lajes, and neither did the Air Force. But it was foolish to thin the margin of safety for the airplane, the crew, and our 30 passengers. So for two days we were scrubbed, as the saying goes, and we stayed on the ground.

Major Wallick and his navigator, Captain Alfred C. Bowman, Jr., go off for a private huddle. Few men exhibit the impatience of Bowman to get into the air. He knows our C-130B can overfly Lajes and continue on into Spain nonstop, even without favorable winds, and with plenty of fuel "in the bank" at our destination. Wally drags on a cigarette and Bowman hunches over a long table, the paraphernalia of his trade spread out before him. After a long silence broken only by the creak of chairs and the sputter of matches —slide rules don't make much noise—Bowman studies a mass of figures he has written and looks at his pilot.

"No sweat, Major. We're fat all the way. We could even go on into Evreux if we wanted to give it a whirl."

We could, but we won't. Now we sweat out permission of the TAC Command Post in Virginia. This is TAC's system of positive control of *all* its aircraft to assure that at a critical moment there will never be any doubts or questions as to the disposition of every machine.

First Lieutenant James S. McReynolds—Mac—comes out of Operations waving a sheet of paper in the air. Our copilot grins happily; that paper is our clearance to jump from Bermuda to Spain—not a bad jump for a "medium-range" assault transport weighing 65 tons and perhaps flying partly under still-air conditions (no guarantee of favorable winds *all* the way), but we should arrive over our air base in Spain with several hours of fuel remaining.

At 12-noon sharp Wallick slaps the brakes free and the airplane bangs forward. Staff Sergeant Homer H. Quinn, our flight engineer, sits between and behind the pilots as immobile as a rock, but with his eyes flicking over every dial and gauge, his hands ready to move at once to any control requiring adjustment or attention. Our loadmaster, Staff Sergeant Pyatt H. Cook, has reported all cargo secure and the passengers strapped in. The scanner, Airman 1/C James H. Andring, has made sure all doors are secured and closed . . . a team fore and aft working smoothly.

There are seven of us in the spacious flight deck: the crew of four, the writer, radio and news correspondent Henry Curth on his way to Europe, and a hitchhiker—Lieutenant John R. Rinn of the U.S. Navy. An experienced jet bomber pilot, Rinn is bound for Spain and has grabbed a ride with us. He has never been aboard a Hercules before and he looks about him with a critical and piercing gaze. The men who fly sleek Skywarriors and other jets sometimes sniff down their noses at big transports, but Rinn is not one of them. The size of the flight deck still makes him shake his head in wonder, for he is accustomed to being squeezed into a cockpit and surrounded with a bewildering maze of instrumentation, controls, switches, and armament triggers. Now he can stand, walk around, even lounge comfortably. And with six other people!

Hercules Number 297 streaks down the runway, accelerating rapidly. The needle on the dial swings around to an even 100 and Wallick eases back ever so gently on the control yoke. The nose wheel lifts and its vibration against the runway slides away. A subtle change takes place with the airplane as the changing angle of the wing bends the air closer to the lift desired.

Wallick is that kind of pilot who senses the feel and mood of his airplane. He insists that an airplane always knows better than the pilot when it is ready to fly. So he rotates the nose slightly, gives the wings additional lifting force, and—waits.

Patience is rewarded almost at once. Exactly 21 seconds from the moment he released the brakes (*twice* the time necessary for an assault takeoff) the Hercules fulfills the wish of its pilot and gently rejects the earth. The crew shifts through its motions in flawless coordination. The gear rumbles into the wells, flaps slide back into the wings, doors fold and ease into surfaces flush with the outer skin of the airplane; Quinn makes minor adjustments of pressure lines and valves. Wallick eases the great machine into a wide, curving ascent; McReynolds links the airplane to earth by radio and Bowman already has adjusted his thoughts to the four dimensions of flight—in which position in time *and* space means

(*Above*) Major Wilmer S. Wallick, 839th Air Division, at the controls of Hercules No. 297, nearly five miles above the Atlantic. (*Below*) In the copilot's seat is the author. (*Photos by Henry A. Curth*)

First Lieutenant James S. McReynolds in the copilot seat of Hercules No. 297; "Mac" is glued to his seat—and eating lunch "on the wing." (*Photo by Henry A. Curth*)

everything. The loadmaster and scanner in the rear of the airplane check every visible part of the machine to assure that equipment functions as the instruments read on the flight deck.

This blending of the talents and skills of six men is barely evident. It is a product welded of experience, skill, and a slavish attendance to proficiency. It is a series of subtle and interwoven events, and as it takes place the Hercules answers to the ministrations of its crew and ascends to its lofty kingdom in the skies. The inert, metal assembly is no longer merely an airplane. It is a creature imbued with life, with flight.

This is an outstanding crew in every sense of the word. And they would be the first to remind you that they are only average, and to maintain that there are many crews far more skilled than they. The writer doesn't believe it; but they insist.

At 25,000 feet we enter a new universe of shifting moods and scenes, a world that is treasured by its inhabitants—the airmen. At times during our flight the sky becomes burdened with clouds, with great soaring masses. The scene shifts constantly as the Hercules devours distance.

The planet rolls beneath our wings and the cloud ramparts drift by in a meteorologist's feast. There are clouds of every shape and description as we slide through and along their summits. Bowman remains a willing slave to his computers and his myriad electronic devices; through the navigator's own brand of scientific sorcery he keeps an exact check of our position at all times. And no one is unhappy when he remarks: "We got a push on the tail, Boss . . . we're three-eight-zero knots ground speed."

Our speed over the ocean surface is nearly 440 miles per hour. Our true speed through the air is 305 knots—that comes out to a true airspeed of just about 350 miles per hour. So at this particular moment we've been blessed with that invisible stream of air moving at 90 miles per hour. By sliding into the river we add that much speed to our passage over the surface of the earth. Nice! There's no telling when the stream may veer sharply and dump us back into uncooperative air without favorable winds, or even with winds shifting around to our nose; but at the moment we're fat cats.

From our height of five miles above the earth, looking down through the intermittent gaps and wide spaces in the clouds, the ocean is a hard steel blue in color. Despite our height and the distance to that water we can see whitecaps speckling the Atlantic, and that means a heavy and running sea, an ocean of deep and long swells with the surface lashed by the same winds that howl across the runways at Lajes.

The writer many years ago sailed that ocean as a merchant seaman; that past intimacy with the power of the swells and waves prompts a sudden and keen appreciation of the giant within which several dozen men rest comfortably, unable to comprehend, really, the great speed with which we are hurdling what was once an impassable barrier of this world.

You look out through the windows of the flight deck; with that marvelous greenhouse effect it is hard to reconcile the view and the steadiness of the cockpit with the cavernous hold and belly of this machine, with the rapierlike wingtips, the sleek and hungry reach forward of the engines and their black spinners. But in fact they are no longer entirely black; even at this height there is great moisture, and the spinners at their open snouts are ringed with white whorls against the black. These are rings of ice.

Around us now, in the shifting panorama of nature, is a strange cloud condition through which we ghost our way; I would call it a cirrus fog, with shapes impossible to grasp either with eye or mind. It is, quite realistically, an indefinable whiteness through which the machine passes, emerging from the fog banks with the visible proof of bitter, moist cold on its metal.

(*Above*) Everything is "right on the button" as we cruise high over the Atlantic, en route for an air base near Seville, Spain. (*Below*) "Even at this height there is great moisture, and the spinners at their open snouts are ringed with white whorls against the black. These are rings of ice." (*Photos by Henry A. Curth*)

But it is at night that we plunge into a world not of earth, when magic steals into that space where man and machine together conquer time and distance. . . .

The scene within the flight deck is startlingly unreal. There is, first, the space leading forward through the capacious hold from the most distant part of the aft fuselage. The sides of the airplane stretch back and then slant upward along the retracted ramp. Bright lights, like those of garish automobile sales lots, line the complexity of overhead beams and cables and the sides of the fuselage and splash through the airplane.

The thunder within the great hold echoes and resounds back and forth like reverberations booming through a thousand deep wells. There are blowers and turbines and all manner of equipment exposed to the ear rather than being ensconced behind thick insulation as in the Hercules' commercial cousin, the Electra. There is no other way to say it—it is a hell of a din.

And the most amazing thing about this sonic onslaught is that the airmen passengers ignore the noise with the classically stoic patience of the GI who dismisses it as simply a temporary disturbance of his military life. They are sprawled in bone-twisting positions which by some strange process they find comfortable; men wind themselves into these positions and sleep like babes. Others read . . . or eat, or write letters, or argue with one another. Some engage in animated gestures and conversation to spark a poker game. Still others just—rest. And there are three young GI's hard at work, studying advanced technical correspondence courses.

Moving forward into the flight deck through a doorway, one passes into another world. By nothing more than several quick steps up a ladder into the spacious compartment is this journey made. It is a meaningful transition, for here is the business end of flight. The harsh necessities of the logistics mission of this airplane are dismissed with an unkind finality. The world of flight takes command, and the thunder is banished; the naked walls and open cabling and conduits are gone, concealed behind deep instrument panels and thick insulation.

I have flown in many, many airplanes, of all sizes and types, and across most parts of this world. But here, within the nerve center of the Hercules, there is a definable difference from past experience. For one thing, there is all that space, superbly designed by technicians skilled in anthropometric engineering for freedom of movement. The spaciousness is enhanced by skillful selection of lights and colors, of equipment and panel shapes. Science and technology have tailored this flight deck to humans, and it is a radical departure from other aircraft. The freedom from the pressing closeness of other transports—bigger machines—is marvelous.

The flight deck is a muted symphony of varied hues, lights gentle to the eye with the glaring overtones stripped away. For the most part it is red light. The human eye can be bathed in red light, can resolve instruments and controls and figures, and lose not at all the vital ability of night vision. There is red above, to the sides, ahead, below, all around us, a microscopic universe of red in stars and comets, in jagged streaks and pinwheels. The instruments swim in redness with tiny sparkles of green and sometimes amber, but it is a red universe. Sometimes there is a soundless mushrooming of greater redness; it is a red beam in the hands of our copilot—McReynolds is providing additional illumination for the scrutiny of a dial or control.

Bowman in his navigator's cubicle is the center of a vast but invisible interplay of forces; the taming of the atom and the control of electrons give him the equipment with which to pierce space and time and link us to places and men distant from our constantly changing position. With this magic wand of electronics at his fingertips, he is free to weave his own strands of contact with the outside world with the aid of compass and protractor, pencil and slide rules, computers and charts. Above and behind Bowman there

The navigator of our Hercules, Captain Alfred C. Bowman, Jr., glances away from his radar scope to check the position of the airplane. (*Photo by Henry A. Curth*)

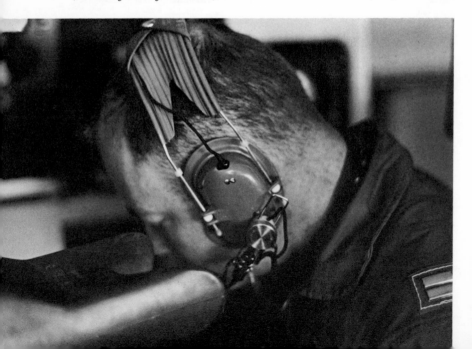

floats beneath its hook an elaborate sextant with which to scan the heavens with precise computation and orderliness. From the random pattern of the celestial vaults, he extracts the mathematical bits and pieces of information needed to arrive at his coordinates of longitude and latitude.

Our invisible world is alive and filled to Bowman. To him the earth is neatly intersected and sliced into convenient patterns; from these he deduces positions that relate constantly to the swing and the tilt of the ponderous world. He mates these things with the atomic furnaces burning in the heavens, the stars all about us. It is fascinating and very wonderful, and it will always be veiled behind a blur of awe, even to those of us who partake of this science of flight.

To take a long look through the flight deck to the outside is to be overwhelmed with the sight before the eyes. Below the wings the clouds still ride the ocean, but these are atmospheric denizens that assume different shapes and forms under the touch of night. Now, as the nocturnal guardians of the darkened seas, they growl their presence and bristle angrily at us with warnings of electrical energy. Jagged tongues of electrical force flash freely from their battlements; lightning gleams and reflects weirdly in the bottomless gloom.

It is as though we were children subjected to the sudden appearances of flickering goblins, casting a spectral gleam all through and beneath us. How deep is the abyss falling away beneath our wings? Impossible to tell, but it is real and it is alive with creatures that we can only imagine—not merely the interplay and reaction of negative and positive electrical forces. Never could it be so mundane as that!

It is never mundane, and it is always respected, because of the things that these airplanes have suffered from the stabbing rivers of energy, when they run amuck and churn the ocean of air into a spitting, howling frenzy. Every man who flies a Hercules through Europe knows the story of two of these transports that once fought their way toward the American air base at Incirlik, Turkey. . . .

Line after line of storms marched before the two Hercules: storms that burst all their bonds and towered to 60,000 and 70,000 feet above the earth; storms that swallowed the airplanes, smashed at them with rain and hail, with turbulence that injured the crews and tore equipment free and that literally bent metal within the machines. The airplanes plunged wildly through a raging sea of lightning, an ocean of liquid, screaming fire.

The navigators in those airplanes worked frantically to aid their pilots, to guide them by radar through the worst of the storms;

for the worst is more than enough to tear the wings from *any* airplane, to rip its sides and pluck its entrails of human passengers and fling them crazily into space.

The sky erupts suddenly about the lead airplane. A searing bolt of savage lightning appears magically in front of the Hercules' nose. Through the thick glass and the metal, through the sealed and pressurized hull, over the howl of the wind and the roar of the engines, there comes an unbelievable smash of thunder; it is an explosive cry that spears the machine and strikes the men with a physical force. Several of them cry out involuntarily with the terrible impact; the blinding light and the terrifying blast are simultaneous.

The pilot stares in horrified awe. He sees a great river of electrical fire; he sees clearly its dazzling and ragged edges. The lightning bolt extends from the front of the airplane far into space; then it sweeps around in a huge arc of blazing hell until it curves around itself and vanishes. But long after it is gone the men still see that terrible bolt, each man retaining on his retina the white-hot image.

Minutes later, descending in the unabating violence toward the air base, the scanner reports quietly to his pilot that the number-four engine is flaming. It is a gross understatement; a huge blowtorch of flame three feet in diameter extends backward for more than *80 feet!* The howling flame turns the cavity of the storm into a constant bright orange glow, flickering like some impossibly huge torch.

The engine instruments show no sign of fire, but the crew hits the necessary switches and feathers the propeller into knife-edged rigidity. The great airplane wheels earthward, gear and flaps down, rushing toward the haven of the runway. A lifetime of seconds later the tires screech on the wet pavement, the pilot decelerates carefully, and the men pour out of the airplane at the same moment that the flame disappears.

With amazement the crew learns that fortune had indeed smiled on them—and that the engine was in perfect order. It was impossible to tell from the interior of the airplane that the lightning bolt had smashed into the big fuel tank suspended beneath the wing, cut the rear of the tank away as cleanly as a knife, and ignited the fuel within. The sight was terrifying, but in reality the fire streamed back well beneath the wing and the right horizontal stabilizer.

The crew waited to tell their friends in the second airplane of their experience. The trailing Hercules landed and rolled slowly off the runway, grinding to a stop. The men gathered in front of

the second Hercules and stared—speechless. The entire front of the airplane was a shattered, mangled mess.

Lightning works in strange ways. A great bolt had smashed into the bulbous black radome of the second C-130, torn apart the metal and plastic, and left it a gnarled mass of wreckage. But the bolt was not yet through . . . it raced through metal into the navigation and communications equipment. Fingers of savage, crackling light erupted from the navigator's console, flashed wildly through the flight deck. The bolt seemed to pause for an instant, gathering strength and howling; then it burst rearward into the great cargo hold, roaring with a thunder that rattled the entire airplane. It flung itself up and outward through the vertical fin—leaving behind it a cargo loadmaster with mouth frozen open and eyes staring in total disbelief.

So it is not without profound respect for the energy contained in those distant bolts that we study the flickering amidst the clouds well below us. . . .

Our vantage far above the murkiness of earth's lower atmosphere presents to us one of the most remarkable and impressive sights of this world. The air is thin and bitterly cold at our height; it is also air with unbelievable clarity. For long minutes I find it impossible to tear my gaze away from the sight to the side and above the airplane.

We are suspended in the midst of some incomprehensible bowl of stars. They blaze in such profusion that belief in the sight is almost impossible. And the strange nature of the earth's atmospheric horizon—a band of darkness lying just above the curvature of the physical planet—creates an effect eerie and misleading. The stars spill down to the horizon and vanish—and reappear again beneath the blackness at the edge of the world. If you are not careful and are unaware of this strange behavior on the celestial stage, all conception of up or down vanishes. The lights in front of and below the airplane, which sometimes appear as ships, or even the lights of a distant shore, are in reality the stars. . . .

A new light appears in the flight deck. Wallick has leaned forward, flicked a switch, and by the movement of just one finger has brought marvelous forces within his control. At the very fore of our winged giant there is a curving black mass, a great radome. Within that compartment, shielded against the hammering blows of air, is an intricate electronic assembly. Technically it is the Sperry APN/59 Radar System, a matter-of-fact designation for a modern-day miracle.

A spherical dish 30 inches in diameter on a rugged but sensitive mount is swung back and forth and up and down through a cycle of 360 degrees. The dish—a paraboloid—emits two powerful beams of energy, which rush unseen from the Hercules with the velocity of light. Measured in the terrestrial terms of flight this would be 676,000,000 miles per hour, a figure utterly meaningless to the mind. Suffice to say that the outward rush of the beams and their return is, in human terms, quite instantaneous.

The first beam is precise and pencil-thin; it reflects off specific targets and returns information as to these targets (mountains, hills, ships, and so on) to the airplane. The other flash of energy is a cosecant square beam for observing a number of objects in a given area. Together they create an all-seeing navigational eye. They provide running information on land, ships, aircraft, storms, rainfall . . . and linked to a compact electronic brain which clearly distinguishes between a thunderhead and a mountain peak, they aid the pilots and the navigator in safe flying and computing the drift effects of crosswinds.

The electronic beams are off in the wings of this particular stage; none of their intricate operation is visible to the eye—only the results. And they add a fairyland touch to that universe of red that is our flight deck.

Atop the instrument panel is a glowing amber scope five inches in diameter. On the surface of that scope are brightly luminescent grid lines and a single pencil beam of light sweeping around and around. Following the sweeping line are brightly glowing blobs; like fireflies in amber, they pulsate brilliantly and fade almost at once.

The two pilots, the navigator, and the flight engineer are skilled in deciphering the shapes, intensities, and patterns of the blobs. Thus it is possible for this great machine, in thick fog or the blackest night, to traverse a safe path through storms, and to "see" clearly islands, coastlines, and other terrain. And there is that wonder of wonders: the ability of the computer built into the system to separate clearly the massive thunderhead from the immovable mountain.

The Hercules is able to ride upon the interpretation of this constant electronic pulsation. We feel the effects of the air sliding and heaving through the night; but the machine is in its element and the feeling is one of comfort and solidity to a pilot.

We have many devices to link us through our senses of touch, sight, and balance with the outside world; one such is a bowl of red-glowing magic sealed within a glass cage. Behind that transparent shield there floats the curving half of a sphere sectioned off by vertical and horizontal lines. The floating evidences our capture of gyroscopic forces; we have taken the same order and energy of balance in the solar system itself and sealed it within that glowing red bowl. The upper half is red, the lower blackened. By reference to the grids and lines as the spherical face moves, the pilot actually gains the effect of being an observer *outside* his aircraft. . . . In the truest sense of the word, he is able to interpret constantly the relationship of our wings and the nose of the airplane to the horizon and to the downward pull of gravity.

It is thus we fly: one moment, one airplane; a small group of men out of thousands who at this very moment, and every hour of the day and night around the world, sail the upper skies in fulfillment of the needs and missions of their country.

And that is a thought that persists, that allows the mind to envision the swarming of the winged fish through the aerial oceans of the entire planet. Sitting now in the copilot's seat of the Hercules, secure in the feel and strength of the machine, gratefully comfortable, I remember what it is like to be squeezed into the cockpit of one of the single-seat jet fighters that also, by the hundreds, must leap these vast stretches of water far beneath us.

There are Air Commandos and Special Warfare troopers . . . paratroopers and Rangers and other men with a blending of many outstanding skills at their tasks. These are the new breed of our fighting men, but we have not brought into focus perhaps the most skillful of the modern warriors, men who display the greatest versatility and stamina. These are the pilots of TAC who fly the oceans for hours that become agonizing physical discomfort, at times so acute that the pilots land with their teeth clamped together to ignore the pain as they settle their sensitive razor-winged machines safely to earth.

Without question it may be said that these transoceanic flights in the single-seat fighters are a singularly sadistic form of torture. The public concept of the dashing young hero who leaps on a torrent of blazing gases through the sky is valid from the outside looking in . . . but not from within the rack framed by metal and plexiglas. These missions are not simply exhausting; mercilessly they flog the pilot of his energy and strive to drain his mind of active thought. Since both are needed to remain master of the modern fighter, it is a constant struggle on the part of the pilot to retain his keys to survival.

Nine to 14 hours in formation, by day and by night, in calm air and in clear-air turbulence, in storms and rain, in weather foul and vicious that can flip a 14-ton fighter crazily through the sky . . . this is the domain of these men. The pilot is sealed into a strait jacket with multiple layers and steel-cord binding. He wears thermal underwear, g-suit, flying suit, survival suit, boots, gloves, parachute, mae west, survival kit, oxygen mask, helmet, knife, gun, and so on *ad infinitum*. And there are straps *everywhere* with sharp buckles to jab and knead and create spots of white pain. . . .

The engineering systems in these single-seat fighters dazzle the eye and overwhelm the newcomer in their almost unbelievable complexity. There are as many controls and switches, perhaps even more, in this one-man machine as are to be found in the cockpit of a modern jet airliner.

There is only that single engine, whirling at revolution speeds of hundreds of times per second. *All* the dials, gauges, lights, switches, toggles, meters, and other paraphernalia of the cockpit must be watched and distrusted, for failure within the systems of the modern jet fighter is always pregnant with catastrophe. The life-support system also demands its attention, for often the fighters skim the very bottom of an environment that is physiologically the equivalent of space. At their speeds the air just beyond the plexiglas is as hard as steel and as thin and cold as the surface of a dead planet.

There must be absolute adherence to the demands of man, machine, and the intricacy of systems that fuse the two into a single entity: electrical, hydraulic, pneumatic, electronic, mechanical and human systems, all rolled up into a single package of sensitivity. And the pilot must attend to the requirements of flight in relationship to gravity and the horizon, to the rate with which he consumes his precious fuel, to the angle at which his wings slide through the air. Balance is not merely important; it is indispensable. And there is always that terrible and grim danger of a moment's lapse at the controls, of only a brief yielding to weariness—when two fighters may lock wings, embrace in twisted metal and mushrooming flames, and close the books on two lives.

From one mission across the Atlantic some years ago, four powerful fighters . . . disappeared. Why, where, or how no one knows or ever will know. It was as though they never had been.

Even the little things can drive a man wild. A pilot learns by sad experience that his oxygen mask will rub the bridge of his nose to raw flesh, from which the blood seeps slowly, and there isn't a damn thing he can do about it. So bandaids across the nose are a requisite for the long missions. And if a man has even a slight cold, rapid letdowns from high altitude to the dense air far below can explode his head into a fury of pain. To clear the sinuses the book recommends nosedrops (that's a laugh all by itself in one of these machines), but nasal inhalers have to do.

Sometimes the body simply hasn't any more to give; some pilots grab for the "go pills" supplied them by the medics. The world swims before a man's eyes and he drowns in weariness and he is in deep trouble. The "go pills" aren't retroactive; they should be taken 90 minutes before they're needed. Easier said than done, so the pilot breaks the capsule and dumps the contents onto his tongue and swallows it. It tastes like the grease rag his mechanic has used for the last six years, but it gives him a walloping kick where he needs it and snaps him out of his dangerous funk. There are other pilots who grimly stick it out on their own.

Then there's that great gadget called the relief tube. Ever sit in a theater through one of those interminable shows that runs for four hours? Or maybe even five hours? *Without* an intermission? Try it sometime for nine, or perhaps even 12 hours, almost rigid in your seat, cold, clamped by your equipment, and you'll know the demands for relieving the bladder. The jet pilots at least have a tradition to ease their discomfort; they recall the Mustang pilots, some of whom are flying the jets today, who flew six- and seven-hour missions in 1944 to Berlin and back. No pressurization then, no heating; just bitter cold, and relief tubes that jammed up. They had no choice; and they came home with their clothes frozen stiff from their urine in cockpit temperatures down to 30 and 40 below zero. That's one of the unpublicized "glories" of being a Tiger. . . .

Refueling, especially at night or in stormy weather, is a murderous bitch. Here electronic aids are vital, with radio homers and radar coming into play, for over the vast oceans the airplanes are the smallest dots in the world.

TAC's KB-50J tankers are overmodified ships based on the B-29 of World War II; TAC hasn't received the jets yet, although the Marines sigh with relief at the performance of their Hercules aerial tankers. The KB-50Js at night are mad whorls of glaring light, so they may be seen from miles away. Brilliant lights spray on the long hoses snaking back; more lights splash the fueling pods into stark relief. There are rotating beacons and flashers, white lights and navigation lights, and blinking green and amber signal lights, all coded to tell a pilot when he is ready to suck into his tanks that precious, wonderful, smelly kerosene, the blood of jet life.

The hoses are long and black. They trail behind the tankers, ending in a drogue that's a wire basket with steel ribs spreading into a funnel shape.

"The trick is to come in with your probe, jab it right into the drogue, and make a positive contact. But it's not that simple in practice," Gayle Williams recounted in bone-sagging weariness after a transpacific mission. "We got turbulence at 20,000, and things got sticky. You're supposed to slap in the probe at 60 feet and creep up on the pod for another 30. The tanker is only 30 feet away and it just fills the whole damned sky.

"There's wash coming off the tanker's wing, and there's turbulence from the props, you're so slow you're fighting the edge of a stall, and the whole blasted mess just doesn't make for any relaxed flying, *that's* for sure!"

The writer will not easily forget one training mission—over nice, safe land—when turbulence became rough; the drogue bounced like a wild and gibbering creature that defied contact. The actual flying drains one's energy away. There are the rudder pedals to work with nimbleness, the stick, the ailerons and the big slab tail, the throttle and the radio, and watching the instruments and trying to keep from stalling out because the tanker's top speed is far below safe speed for the fighter.

"If you miss the drogue," explained Captain Herman Griffin of TAC, today flying the F-105 in Okinawa after several years in the shovel-nosed Super Sabres, "you're either under or over or short, or maybe even two of them. Your hands and feet seem disembodied, working by themselves. You correct the sight picture constantly. You never look at the drogue but at the guidelines on the windscreen, because if you do try to stab the probe in, you end up chasing the thing all over the sky, and that is no way to fly an airplane that is one shake away from stalling."

During one refueling hookup in "brutal" turbulence, Griffin moved in to his tanker and, like slipping a key into its groove, slid his probe into the drogue. The air was too rough; without warning "the hose came off the tanker, ripped clean away, and tumbled down into the Pacific 20,000 feet below." Griffin slid in to another hose and drew his fuel.

Gayle Williams again: "Flying formation was brutal. We were all over the sky. It was the hardest flying I ever had to do, and I don't expect it ever to be any worse. To keep that hose lined up and level with the tanker, keep it from getting twisted, worrying about whether or not the entire boom might tear off—it took everything I had to give. I had a tiger by the tail, and I was afraid to let go, because I *had* to hang on. Not only me, but the rest of the boys, of course. It was murder up there. . . ."

And there are hours and hours of flying after these hookups. . . .

Ask the fighter pilots sometime about the tanker crews, and watch respect come into their eyes. For these men *must* take off no matter what the weather, to keep the fighters going, even though the tanker itself may run short of fuel, or be forced to land in a screaming gale with zero-zero weather conditions on the slick runway. The tankers operating out of the Azores sometimes fight crosswinds so severe that the engines on one side of the airplane are running at maximum power, and on the other side the props are *reversed!*

But they get the job done, again and again, no matter what the odds. And there are times, too, when the tankers don't come home, when their job of fueling the fighters drains their own tanks, and they can't make it back, and the sea claims some more victims that rarely, if ever, are known to our people as men who gave their lives for their country.

Early in 1962 the Marines were fully operational with their new GV-1 (now, KC-130F) Hercules tankers, and they shifted from slow surface movement of their fighters to overseas bases to "by air all the way." On the first mission 18 big Crusader jet fighters departed California in Operation Pine Needles. Thirteen Hercules tankers during the Pacific-spanning flight of 7,100 miles completed 108 hookups and fuel-transfer operations in a mission unprecedented for the Marines.

Shortly afterward the Hercules were back in the air to change innovation to routine, shepherding 18 Skyhawk attack bombers along the same route.

And then there was the night of April 2, 1962, when an airplane crashed on the runway of Iwakuni air base in Japan . . . with the weather stinking and right down to the bottom as far as landing

Hercules tanker and Crusader fighters—gas station over the Pacific

minimums were concerned. Four big Crusader fighters were low on fuel, so low that the radar controllers brought them down through the storm not singly, as is usual, but in pairs—until they were approaching the field . . . and received emergency instructions to climb back out again because of the airplane blocking the runway.

That sort of wrapped it up for the Crusaders. The Marines couldn't get in to Iwakuni; they lacked the fuel to fly to Atsugi or even the nearest emergency field big enough to take the heavy supersonic fighters. The pilots had no choice: head out to sea and, at night and in a storm, eject from the planes. And then hope and pray that the seats would work, the parachutes would work, that they wouldn't drown after getting into the water, and that they could be found on the surface of a black and stormy sea.

Four Marine Hercules were at that same moment in the air. A frantic emergency radio call brought all four GV-1s wheeling around and at maximum speed racing for a rendezvous with the fighters. Jubilation on the ground in Operations choked off abruptly when word came in that the GV-1s were *not* carrying their refueling tanks, but were instead loaded with cargo for an airlift mission.

And right then and there four Marine fighter pilots and a great many other people found good cause to cheer for a quality often mentioned but seldom understood—versatility. The Hercules' flight engineers twisted fuel valve controls, deployed the drogues, and told the Marines to "come on in and fill 'em up." For the GV-1 has a system built into the airplane whereby the fuel from the

In a setting of great majesty, miles above the sea and the earth, a Hercules of the U.S. Marine Corps provides the sustenance of flight to four deadly Crusader fighters. The coastline of Japan is etched against the sea. (*U.S. Marine Corps*)

Hercules' own wing tanks can be fed into the refueling system—something that's been needed very badly for a long time.

That's why four pilots received enough fuel to fly on to Atsugi for safe landings, and why four Hercules transports "failed to complete" their airlift mission that night, because they were low on fuel.

Somewhat irked at this blot on their record, the Marines decided to make up for it on their way back to the States. After refueling at Barbers Point, Hawaii, the Hercules set course for Cherry Point, North Carolina. A little less than 14 hours later, they landed at Cherry Point, with a neat record for the airplanes of 4,596 miles nonstop in formation.

These thoughts, and others, come to mind here in the quiet spaciousness of Hercules Number 297 as we sail the aerial seas for Spain. The moon splashes silver on the ocean far below us. We watch clouds casting dark and ghostly shadows on that surface.

Almost directly overhead I look at a shining red marble in the heavens—the planet Mars, clearer than I have ever seen that world before. And then there are more lights; there is the shoreline of Portugal like a relief map in shadow, sprinkled with the glow of towns and lighthouses. A wide and curving sweep through the heavens, a long slide down from the skies, blinking lights atop a tower and flashes before a runway, and there is our destination.

Wallick, McReynolds, Bowman, and Quinn shift imperceptibly but significantly. Fuel flow changes, pressures surge in their lines. The great propellers thrum with changing pitch, the gear rumbles down and the belly of the airplane quivers. Flaps and the flatter pitch of the prop blades provide rapid deceleration.

The lights rush at us as Wallick eases the giant out of the air. There is a faint squeal as rubber skims beautifully onto concrete —Wallick has painted her on the runway in a perfect landing—and this leg of this mission is over.

CHAPTER XVI

Angels with Steel Wings   THE 29TH OF
February comes around only once every four years. It is a date
that upon occasion burns itself into the history of a people—as it
did on February 29, 1960. On that "once in every four years" date,
the earth beneath the Moroccan city of Agadir went berserk. It
lifted upward, heaved mightily to one side, and crashed down
again. The brief terrestrial spasm tumbled walls, shattered homes,
and terrified the 40,000 inhabitants of Agadir.

It lasted only for a moment. Yet before the dust settled back to
the now quiescent planet, one fifth of all the people in Agadir had
departed the living. Many thousands were badly injured. Almost
all were homeless. And then the plague rose on the scene like a
huge and terribly real nightmare.

The thread of this book has been that of the Hercules, an instrument of our national policy. Yet it would be greatly in error
if there were to remain the impression that the sole function of
this unique winged machine has been and is its role as a carrier
of weapons and armed men.

That is certainly the philosophy of its design, and the hard foundation for its existence. But there is another, even more shining
page in the history of this aircraft that still is in its writing.

Perhaps it can best be placed in perspective by noting that if
the Hercules did not, and had not, fulfilled even a single military
mission . . . it would still be worth its cost to the United States, in
money, time, and effort, a thousand times over.

As a cargo, troop, and assault transport the Hercules has been
the cutting sword of the long arm of America.

As an angel of mercy with steel wings, it is the helping hand to
much of the world's population.

It has flown the overwhelming majority of its missions not with
weapons and not with troops, but with other cargoes and passengers
in its capacious hold—cargoes such as food, medicine, hospitals,
construction equipment, and passengers such as doctors, the sick
and injured, and refugees by the tens of thousands. . . .

The life of a nation is closely conditioned by the daily, consistent communications and transportation of that nation. This is a fact of life that escapes the attention of our news media, for it is not exciting or dramatic or exotic. The Hercules has become vital in our international transportation; and the role is to expand in importance. But it does not make headlines, and its crucial part in our national activities is known to few, and even less generally understood.

Yet the squat and rugged air transport has done all these things, including the making of important contributions to the opening of a continent that permitted only fleeting penetration until the Hercules arrived on the scene. Its performance has given us access to all of Antarctica on a scale hitherto unknown.

But of all the things that the Hercules can do, and has done, none is so deeply cherished as its role in aiding the stricken . . . as in the shattered city of Agadir in the winter of 1960.

A piercing cry for help burst from the Moroccan people. This nation responded with aid from our Naval Mediterranean forces and from the bases of the Strategic Air Command in Africa. But this was a reaction severely limited in scope, and the helping hand opened to the full only when the 322nd Air Division from France responded with a massive airlift by 52 transports. Of these, four out of five were the high-winged Hercules of the 322nd, which because of their high speed and long range formed the vanguard of the aerial bridge to Agadir.

Nearly 600 tons of critically needed supplies and almost 500 skilled engineers, doctors, and technicians rode the aerial bridge into the shattered city. The powerful *military* force fought a battle by the United States for those devastated people. It was not a dramatic battle, and there were no medals, and there weren't even any heroes, really. But there were Americans in Air Force, Army, and Navy uniforms whose hands were cut and bleeding and whose clothes were ripped and torn because they worked alongside the Moroccans in digging in the rubble to rescue the living and to extricate the dead. They cleared rubble and attended to thousands of injured; they set up great temporary living areas and fed and clothed some 30,000 helpless human beings. Bulldozers rolled off the ramps of the Hercules transports so that the Army engineers could clear the blocked streets, and the airplanes trembled slightly to the tread of men carrying hundreds of critically injured adults and children who were to be rushed to hospital facilities many miles away.

Rats swarmed from the rubble through the city; the rodents grew fat on the bodies and became bolder in their attacks. The authorities could not put out poison because they were still finding children wandering around, dazed and shocked because their entire families were dead. As fast as they were found they were brought to the housing areas.

Housing is not the word. The quarters were tents—hundreds and hundreds of tents that would adequately care for a family or a group, and that in many cases were superior to the homes that had tumbled in the tremors. The floors were of solid wood and raised from the ground. Beds and cots, blankets, clothing, refrigerators, whatever was needed poured in over the aerial bridges.

The crews of the planes, when they went into the area of devastation, carried sidearms with them, because of the rats; the idea was to shoot them at every opportunity and to stave off the threatening plague.

Those were the only guns that fired in Agadir's struggle for survival. . . . It was a very successful "war."

Four months after the Agadir operation, violence exploded in the Congo. Dag Hammarskjöld's response to the erupting violence was the commitment of powerful United Nations military forces to the area. To the 322nd Air Division especially this meant the greatest air-support operation since the Berlin airlift of 1948-49.

Few people know of the predominant role played by the Hercules in this massive aerial bridge, for on July 14, 1960, the 322nd received its orders to provide complete logistics and troop-carrying support to the U.N. forces. From July 15th to 25th the Hercules were in the air almost constantly, their speed and range a critical factor in the long-distance flights that grounded other transports. In the initial airlift operation lasting ten days—despite the fact that four of the C-130 aircraft were undergoing modification at the time—the Hercules force "moved out." They flew 5,000 armed and fully equipped troops and a million pounds of food to Leopoldville.

That was only the beginning. Aboard the Hercules in the ensuing constant aerial convoys were fighting men from Tunisia, Morocco, Ghana, Sweden, Guinea, Ethiopia, Liberia, Ireland, Mali, the Sudan, India, the United Arab Republic, Canada, Pakistan, Nigeria, and Austria. In the first five months of the airlift the 322nd, with MATS airplanes assisting, moved 16,000 soldiers and more than five and a half million pounds of supplies into the Congo. This was a one-way operation; returning aircraft carried thousands of refugees out of the Congo, and kept pushing back into the area with separate airlifts, each of which brought from a hundred tons and upward of food to separate areas.

The 322nd Air Division's force of Hercules transports turned in one of the most astounding records in the history of aviation.

In more than 600 flights to and from the Congo, with missions running to 3,500 miles, and many stops in between at grass and dirt fields, the crews flew their Hercules with a *perfect* safety record. Not a single airplane was involved in even a minor accident.

It was a record of which the 322nd could be justifiably proud, and this hard-flying organization went on to confound the experts and defy all the odds of flying through storms and over uncharted areas, often with primitive facilities—while sustaining that brilliant performance. By July 1962, two years after commencing the airlift, the logbooks of the 322nd Air Division and MATS bulged with the statistics of the continuing mission. In nearly 1,300 separate mission flights, the transports carried 57,714 United Nations troops and passengers, as well as 8,665 tons of cargo.

This amounted to a total of 33,000 hours of flying—*without a single flying accident.*

It is impossible to exaggerate the conditions under which the Hercules were forced to operate. The route to Leopoldville covers some of the most formidable and inaccessible terrain on earth. Navigation facilities were nonexistent, and everyone scrabbled for information and assembled it at Evreux-Fauville Air Base to create some semblance of operational pattern to aid the crews.

Maintenance operations resembled that of a remote outfit in World War II, working with isolated and primitive facilities in combat. The mechanics and engineers of the C-130s, aided by their navigators and pilots, performed feats of near legerdemain to keep the airplanes running. In one instance, an ingenious flight engineer who refused to accept an "impossible" situation roared into a small town by jeep, rented an auto wrecker for five dollars, and raced it back to his airplane. The crew used the ancient wrecker as a hoist and sling to change an engine on the Hercules.

At Evreux-Fauville, every man—officer, airman, and civilian—worked day and night. The maintenance personnel worked straight through, without a stop, for the first 48 hours of the airlift, and then went on an "easier" shift of 12 hours on and 12 hours off, seven days a week, for wearying months.

A maintenance team of Air Force and Lockheed field representatives and technicians moved along with the operation in the Congo and at connecting bases. Jack Pruett of Lockheed was in the thick of activities from the first hour of the missions. He explains that as violence spread and the dissidents took over control in the Congo, they "decided to run all the whites out of that area, and all of a sudden we had a full-scale emergency to get those people out before they were killed. The night of July 15 we were at a staging base in France, picking up a heavy load of food supplies.

Food was almost unavailable, since almost everything was at a standstill in the Congo—and very quickly those people would be going for days without anything to eat.

"We moved out—the entire C-130 force—with just about everything there was to get into the Congo in a hurry. We soon had 48 Hercules in operation, and in-service commission rates became matters of life-or-death. The reliability of the old bird was real good when the heat was on. . . ."

An Air Force maintenance officer explained that "under this kind of emergency situation, there isn't a chance to fall back on established procedures, or supply lines, or the kind of maintenance you give to airliners. You just couldn't do it—period. You never saw so many crews who came back telling us, 'Thank God for those backup systems. . . .' The birds would be out in the middle of the African boondocks, they'd be landing on dirt and grass strips, flying through storms, loaded to max gross, and sooner or later *something* has got to give.

The crew of a Hercules from the 322nd Air Division in the Congo, cooking over a small fire and grabbing a meal "on the run." (*Lockheed-Georgia*)

"We had plenty of systems failures in the '130 in that operation. But we had less in the '130 than we did in the other cargo planes, and there was a hell of a difference in the outcome. When the other ships had a system failure—that was it. They had to wait on parts and mechanics to get moving.

"But we *never* put a Hercules out of commission out there in the bush when something failed. That machine has so many backup systems that when something went haywire, the crew just shut it down and kicked in the backup, and continued right along just as pretty as you please.

"They were beating up those airplanes so badly without a worry in the world that we finally ordered a restriction in the operation. We said that if a system failure compromised the safety of flight of the airplane, we wanted it checked out thoroughly. Only then would we stop the birds.

"The air-conditioning systems gave us more trouble than we expected. The temperature was a killer down there, but that never interfered with the airplane. The people were too hot; maybe the old bird had spoiled them with air conditioning. But we hauled in the food, and we hauled out the refugees, and the Hercules just pounded along right through the worst of it."

The biggest problem in operations wasn't the airplane—it was the crews. In the initial stages of the Congo airlift and evacuation, the pilots and their crew members were flying 20, 30, and even more hours in a single stretch without a break. Sometimes a man would grab forty winks on a stack of cargo, but all too often even this wasn't possible. Finally the commander of the 322nd Air Division flew down from Evreux.

When he saw many of his men with circles under their eyes and some of them so tired they were even shaking a bit, he told the crews they did *not* have to fly so many consecutive hours.

They kept flying.

Then he told them he didn't even think it was very smart for them to continue in a manner that was certain to guarantee physical exhaustion.

They kept flying.

He blew his top and *ordered* the crews out of the area and limited to a maximum of 18 hours' operation at any one time.

"Our normal route for the refugee evacuation," said Jack Pruett, "ran from Leopoldville to Kano, Nigeria, and then to Wheelus, Libya. From there we went straight on to Brussels, Belgium, which was the terminus for the refugees.

"Many of these people had been born and reared in Africa,

and they knew nothing else of the world except the Congo. They were literally white Africans. And in many ways this was a really pathetic operation.

"Many of the women had been beaten and raped. The children were beaten and abused, and we saw plenty of kids that had been maimed at the hands of the Congolese. When those Air Force crews saw things like that, they wouldn't stop working because someone had written a regulation. They flew day and night, until they were ready to drop in their tracks."

No one has yet written about the pilots and crewmen, with tears running down their faces, carrying children whose bodies had been slashed and battered mercilessly, many of whom would never walk or never see again.

Boeing's giant 707 jet airliner performed fantastic feats of passenger evacuation. "They were carrying really tremendous loads," Pruett said. "I don't think anyone even thought about weight—because the 707 can carry almost anything you can cram into the fuselage. At Leopoldville and one other city, they have two beautiful runways. Each is 15,000 feet long and 300 feet wide; they're practically at sea level. As an idea of what they were pushing into those Boeings, they normally get off the ground at sea level in about 7,000 feet of run. But they had to use just about every one of those 15,000 feet to get airborne. . . ."

No one could have anticipated that the Hercules would gain an extraordinary and singular distinction with the Africans. When the first force of Hercules roared in from Europe, they were carrying food for both the refugees and the African natives. "The natives were so glad to see that food," Pruett said, "that without asking hundreds of them came down to the fields to pitch right in and work, and get the airplane unloaded and ready for turnaround."

The distinctive appearance of the Hercules might well have proven a lifesaver for several of the Air Force crews. Emotions ran wild in the Congo, and the fact that many of our airplanes were flying in U.N. troops did not sit at all well with the Africans.

An example is provided in the case of one crew from a huge C-124 Globemaster. As the airplane rolled to a stop sullen natives crowded around. That crew never took off in their own airplane, and they didn't fly for a long time afterward. Screaming natives attacked them with knives, sticks, and rocks; they were beaten so severely that most of them were removed on stretchers and spent many weeks bedridden in a hospital.

But never did a C-130 crew receive so much as a touch from the natives, who associated the airplane with food and other

(*Above*) Natives of the strife-torn Congo unload sacks of flour from a 322nd Air Division Hercules at the Leopoldville Airport. (*Below*) United Nations personnel help a battered U.S. pilot to a hospital plane. As the crew of an Air Force C-124 landed in the Congo and climbed out of their unarmed transport, "screaming natives attacked them with knives, sticks, and rocks. . . . Most of them were removed on stretchers. . . ." (*Upper photo: U.S. Army; lower photo: Air Force*)

supplies to help the natives. Although one crew did exercise prudence. . . .

The Hercules (with Jack Pruett aboard) landed at night on a field despite a lack of response from the control tower. The pilot didn't like the situation: the seeming lack of activity, the silence of the tower, or anything else. But their cargo was needed here; he came down in a long approach, rolled swiftly along the runway, spun the Hercules around, and then stopped.

The tower remained silent. No one appeared on the field or approached the airplane. Sometimes you can just sense trouble coming, and this pilot believed in a sixth sense. He rammed the throttles forward and went hell-for-leather down the runway into the air. As it turned out his hunch could not have been more accurate; rioting troops had swept the area and were even then on a rampage toward the airport.

"My airplane stank for a month after being down there," one pilot said unhappily, "as did five other birds. You ever smell an airplane that's loaded with 28,000 pounds of *fish?* All that fish and it's 135 degrees in the shade, and *we* get stuck in a place where there's no provisions to offload the Herc'. My God, it stank to high heaven and back again. When the lift was over, you could walk blindfolded down the flight line and you couldn't miss the six birds we used hauling fish down from Norway—your nose gave you perfect identification."

The impression of the crews who flew the Congo operation wasn't one to make them sanguine about the immediate years to come. The Hercules crews who brought in millions of pounds of food to counter a famine among the natives were received with jubilation and gratitude. But the crews were unanimous on the point that the local "people just didn't know what to do. It was like turning our country over to our second- or third-grade schoolchildren. Most of the people were anxious to return to their ancestral ways. They just wanted to live their own lives as they saw fit; they didn't want any part of the white man's world. But wherever we went, the Hercules was a sign from the outside world that appealed to them. We brought them food or other supplies they needed badly, and we didn't come with any tricks up our sleeves.

"The '130 looks like nothing else that flew through Africa then . . . and word in that jungle travels faster than we think it does. Their communications may mystify us, but they get the word around *fast.* We went into fields in the Hercules where they had never heard of us—and where a lot of people were getting cut to pieces—and not one of our men, ever, was molested or even threatened. The Hercules soon became the talisman for a safe flight throughout the troubled areas. . . ."

The record of the Hercules isn't one splashed in bright red letters so that it is easy to find, nor has a chart ever been designed that can translate "incidents" into the feelings and deeds of human beings. All over the world, there are hundreds of isolated flights known as "Helping Hand Missions" in the logbook of the Hercules that don't make headlines or even front-page news items. A boy is critically ill and must have attention in a distant hospital; a Hercules carries out the mission. An iron lung victim is dying; transfer must be made to a hospital, but within the iron lung. Parents watch in awe as the iron lung is rolled into a Hercules, hooked up to the permanent installation for just such an occasion, and the trip is made in complete safety—toward ultimate success for the patient. Flight after flight: individual flights, flights in twos and fours, to carry food, medicine, clothing, emergency supplies. There is a long and varied list of services that, while almost unknown here in the United States, *are* known to the people of the many countries the Hercules has visited.

Jungle airstrips . . . dirt strips hacked out of the ground near remote villages . . . or just open fields—all these are "home" to the Hercules transports flying "Helping Hand Missions." A C-130 roars low over a village in Asia after taking off from a grass field. (*Air Force*)

And there are always those tragic mass disasters. . . .

In October 1960 two cyclones smashed at East Pakistan; as the country reeled from the blows, giant tidal waves thundered ashore. When the dazed nation took stock of what had happened to them they could hardly believe the reality of the disaster: 12,000 dead, thousands missing, at least 100,000 homeless.

Six Hercules of the 322nd Air Division flew what was then the longest one-way mercy mission in the history of this division. The airplanes sped more than 6,000 miles carrying 100,000 pounds of blankets, 6,250 pounds of sulfa drugs, 200 pounds of anti-malaria tablets, 6,486 pounds of multivitamin tablets, and another 42,000 pounds of critical supplies.

Cost to the Tactical Air Command for the operation—$125,564. The United States issued an immediate grant of five million dollars to East Pakistan, but it was the airlift that received greatest prominence in the East Pakistan press and among the people . . . especially when all the airfields in the disaster area were closed because of silt six to 12 inches deep—closed, that is, to everything but those six Hercules.

Hercules transports in November 1961 brought desperately needed supplies to flood-stricken areas of Kenya and Somalia. Three months later 15 Hercules roared into the flood-devastated north German coastal region around Hamburg with more than 230,000 pounds of clothing and blankets. Time required to respond to the appeal of the German Red Cross for assistance: exactly two hours before the first group of Hercules transports started rolling down the runway in France.

Rushing to the assistance of people stricken by disasters became one of the major roles of the Hercules, and the area covered by the airplanes seemed to abound in natural catastrophes. The violent earthquake of September 1962 that shattered northwestern Iran and killed 10,000 people outright was termed by that country as "the greatest calamity in the history of Iran." An area as great as Massachusetts and Connecticut combined counted its dead, plus another 10,000 injured and 25,000 homeless. Food supplies were lost and underground water stocks destroyed, and medical care was almost completely nonexistent.

The 322nd Air Division committed 28 Hercules to throw up an air bridge 2,500 miles long to Iran. In the first 68 hours of that mercy airlift the force of 28 Hercules flew in more than a million pounds of supplies desperately needed by the earthquake victims. In the great holds of the airplanes came 1,000 tents, 10,000 blankets, a complete U.S. Army field hospital with 128 beds, 200 doctors, nurses, and medical specialists, and many tons of food. Several crews made two 5,000-mile round trips within this time; the airplanes logged an aggregate in less than three days of 1,200 flying hours.

All operations weren't "normal." "We'd get some strange messages from the control tower before landing," recounted one C-130A pilot. "The tower operator would say to us: 'Extend your landing pattern; we're having ground tremors here.' I never thought I'd be landing between earthquakes. . . ."

Before the Hercules went into operation in Europe, of course, there had been many mercy air missions flown. By the close of 1962 United States Air Forces Europe (USAFE), just one of many commands throughout the world performing the same humanitarian service with our military aircraft, looked back on a decade of emergency mercy missions that covered 25 disasters in 20 countries. The roll call of catastrophe included 12 floods, seven earthquakes, two emergencies caused by raging storms and blizzards, an avalanche, a terrifying holocaust, a cyclone, and a wall of death-dealing water that burst from a ruptured dam.

What price tag on this picture of the United States? Where is the "Ugly American" in this scene? How do you estimate the deep gratitude and good will of millions of people as a result of these operations? Such emotions are indeed beyond estimation—but never beyond doubt.

Just *one* organization—the 322nd Air Division—transports 100,000,000 pounds of cargo and more than 100,000 passengers annually. Today the bulk of the 322nd's operations are flown in the C-130 Hercules; and *all* the "rough assignments" go to the Hercules because of its unmatched performance and unprecedented reliability. That is quite an order considering that the 322nd operates in an area five times greater than the entire United States.

"It Ain't Easy . . ."

Operations on so vast a scale as those of the 322nd Air Division (which has its counterpart in the 315th Air Division, assigned with its Hercules transports to the Far East) prevent us from being able to "walk in the shoes" of the men who fly these manifold missions. The smaller, more compact unit, however, permits a more personal understanding of what is required from the men who attend and control the big turboprop transports.

The writer spent many weeks with crews of the 839th Air Division stationed in Tennessee—not at that air base for long, but "on the road" in mission assignments. To keep its crews completely aware of the "feel" of operations in many lands on several continents, the 314th Troop Carrier Wing of the 839th maintains, as we have seen, a small force of 16 aircraft, 16 complete crews, and about 130 maintenance men on duty with the 322nd Air Division in France.

This rotational duty with the 322nd runs for a period of at least three months, and each crew of the 314th Wing departs from Tennessee twice a year for this tour. There are three squadrons (16 Hercules make one squadron) in each wing, and two wings to each division—or six squadrons of 16 Hercules to the division.

One sixth of the strength of the 839th Air Division, then, is always on overseas duty on a rotational basis. Colonel William G. Moore, Commander of the 314th Wing, has perhaps the most interrupted schedule of all, since his leadership of the wing demands his appearance almost "anywhere," and sometimes the need or demand for that appearance assumes the characteristics of a tug-of-war, to be solved only if the colonel could find the secret of being in two places at the same time. I spent some time with Colonel Moore at Fort Campbell, Kentucky, saw him next in Tennessee, and greeted him on the third occasion in France. We didn't meet in the Far East, but the colonel is sometimes there as well.

The workload of each rotational group in France the writer can describe only as unprecedented for troop/cargo-carrier aircraft in peacetime—and it rivals and sometimes exceeds the demands placed on wartime transport outfits. This is what this one squadron of 16 planes did in the ten-week period from January 1 through March 15, 1963, operating out of Evreux-Fauville:

Flew 212 major missions which involved a total of 877 separate flights of short and maximum range; covered a distance of 422,644 miles; carried 4,107 passengers; and hauled four and a half million pounds of cargo. This is a *quiet* and normal schedule. . . .

During their stay in France, at least half of the crew time is spent on missions away from the base; on the average, six to nine aircraft are *always* absent from Evreux-Fauville on long mission assignments. To sustain this almost constant operations schedule, the squadron (fiercely proud of its record) attends to all its major maintenance at the home station of Sewart Air Force Base in Tennessee. In this manner the maintenance requirements while overseas are kept to their absolute minimum—and from the maintenance standpoint the rotational squadrons of the 839th in France are the shining lights of the Air Force.

By now the notion that life in the troop-carrier squadrons is "soft" as compared to fighter or bomber outfits is somewhat shredded at the seams. The crews from the squadrons are on overseas duty rotational assignments four months out of each year. As for the remaining eight months operating from the home station in the

United States, at least half of this time is spent on missions far removed from Tennessee.

That means that these crews are separated from their homes and families *at least* seven out of every 12 months. This creates, as may be readily believed, serious and sometimes monumental problems in their family lives. When you ask a man how he manages to solve the problem that never goes away, often you will receive a tired sigh and a weary: "It ain't easy; it ain't easy at all. . . ."

It "ain't easy" from the financial side of things as well as the emotional. Take the case of a typical officer. . . .

When he is overseas he must maintain *two* homes—one for his family, and the essentials for his own living. He does *not* receive any additional funds to help with what is often a telling financial burden. The austerity program of the Department of Defense restricts an officer on TDY (temporary duty) assignment to a maximum allowance of $5.15 per day, plus his room in the officers' quarters. This lordly $5.15 daily must pay for all his food, toilet

Big C-130A Hercules of the 322nd Air Division, with long-range tanks, lined up and "ready to go" for a mass-effort airlift operation in Europe. (*Air Force*)

articles, laundry and dry cleaning, cigarettes and personal goods, clothing, and the dozens of small but necessary items which individually are minor, but collectively far exceed this allowance.

That is why one of the greatest problems faced by the officers and airmen has little to do with their demanding workload. It is the problem of knowing that their families are being denied financially.

One wife summed it up for the writer. "If I could talk my husband into quitting the Air Force," she said, "I would do exactly that. There's nothing he wants more to do than to serve his country as a pilot, no matter how hard or how much work is involved. He doesn't appreciate my saying things like this, but I think it's a sorry mess when a man with outstanding skills and abilities—who is being *offered* jobs at twice his annual pay—must accept a financial sacrifice in order to serve his country. . . ."

She asked me if I could possibly explain to her why this should be so. She said that good men, men with extraordinary talent in their work, were leaving the Air Force because they felt that no other choice was open to them. And then—with a touch of bitterness and sarcasm combined—she referred to such things as a 20-*billion*-dollar program that would permit two men to walk on the surface of the moon for several hours.

"How can we have money for things like that—as important as they are—and not have money for people like these, with all they do, working day and night, and the things they do to stop these wars around the world, the help they bring to people. . . ? Why should it be like this?"

I'll be damned if I know the answer. . . .

CHAPTER XVII

Assignment: Anywhere   Including even Moscow . . .
The mission assignment for the 322nd Air Division was not only unique; it stopped even the hardened dispatchers in their tracks. Men accustomed to sending airplanes from the Himalayas to the African deserts find few geographical corners of this world to be unusual. Except that this time the division was to send a Hercules to Moscow—the same Moscow in the U.S.S.R. where . . .

The men looked at each other, shrugged, agreed that "there's always got to be a first time," and stuck a pin alongside the pilot's name on the operations board.

Ambassador Llewellyn E. Thompson, Jr., was to be picked up at Moscow's Tsushino Airport, along with his family, a number of United States government officials, and all the personal furniture and belongings of the ambassador, plus other heavy but as yet unspecified cargo. It was a mission to be executed in a completely military manner, and one that would be carried out with a regular operational aircraft of the Air Force, on permanent assignment to Europe.

The government pointed its official finger at one of the Hercules transports lined up on the ramp at Evreux-Fauville. . . . The fact that the finger pointed directly to one of the C-130B Hercules of the 839th Air Division on rotational duty in France "delighted the absolute hell out of us," in the words of one officer.

The Hercules flew into Copenhagen from France and remained overnight. Here the crew went carefully through the airplane; the checklist, as might be expected, received rather strict scrutiny. The engineer ordered a maximum fuel load into the wings.

The next morning a Russian Air Force pilot-navigator and a radioman met the Hercules crew in the operations office. The Soviets would attend to all flight clearances, communicate with the officials and authorities on the ground controlling the flight, and— the crew liked *this*—monitor the ground and air defense systems through and over which the Hercules must fly.

The Americans were more than "mildly surprised" to note that the Russians were completely and *immediately* familiar with the communications equipment aboard the C-130B—familiar not in that they recognized the instruments and controls, but that they *knew* every part and were clearly expert in the operation of these devices.

The route from Copenhagen covered a little more than 800 miles, which the airplane flew in just under two and a half hours, cruising at 23,000 feet.

Once parked on the ramp at the Moscow airport, the Americans were anxious to see the reactions of the Russians to their airplane. Russian flight crews looked at the Hercules with the same interest with which pilots and crewmen look at any new airplane, but that was all. The Hercules is not even in the competition for airplanes with graceful or sweeping lines, and parked about the airport were sleek Russian jetliners and a number of Ilyushin IL-18 turboprop airliners. To the Russians, then, the Hercules was simply another cargo airplane, not unlike their own Anatov AN-10, which also has four turboprop engines. But it does *not* have certain characteristics of the Hercules. . . .

Several trucks rolled up to the rear ramp of the C-130B with the ambassador's furniture and other cargo. Immediately behind the trucks was a bus with two dozen men, assigned to assist the Americans in wrestling the bulky and heavy crates into the Hercules.

The loadmaster and scanner from the '130B walked back along the ramp to meet the Russian work crew. "Where are the rest of your people to load the cargo?" the leader of the Russian group asked.

The American sergeant leaned against the side of the airplane and replied casually, "Oh—well, you see, there aren't any more. Just us two."

The look of scorn for inadequate preparations by the Americans was plain on the Russian's face. "All right, these men help," he said, pointing to his crew.

"Well, now—thanks, friend, but that won't be necessary," replied the sergeant. "We'll handle it all by ourselves. Now, if you'll just back those trucks up here . . ." He reached up, pulled a switch; motors whined and the loading ramp eased to the height of the truckbed.

"Very funny. You make nice joke. But now we work, all right? We help you now."

The sergeant's smile almost dripped. "It's like I said," he answered. "We sure appreciate the offer, but we don't need any help."

The Russian sneered. More Russians came walking up, attracted by the lengthening conversation. The leader of the group turned to several officials who came up to the airplane. There was animated conversation, and a derisive arm was pointed at the Hercules' load-master. The latter looked at the scanner, and both men grinned broadly.

And the Russians gaped. The two Air Force sergeants quickly brought their towbar into play. In the Hercules was that overhead, cable-attached system run from the airplane's own power source. The two sergeants ran the towbar to the rear of the airplane, snapped the hook onto a huge crate, and pulled the switch.

Several dozen Russian jaws fell—and remained open as the crate slid smoothly and effortlessly into the airplane and disappeared down the far end of the cavernous hold. The crewmen sauntered back, hooked their towbar to a second crate, and repeated the loading process.

In less than 15 minutes the two sergeants accomplished what the Russian work crew of two dozen men would have taken an hour and a half or two hours to do. The pilots shook their heads and laughed. The airplane didn't mean a thing to the Russians—but that loading system had them agog.

The fun wasn't over yet. A Russian officer asked the pilot: "How much oil will you need, please?"

"None, thank you."

"*No* oil?"

"No."

Much conversation among the Russians; some hastily scribbled notes, and the return of the officer.

"Our fuel trucks are ready for you. How much fuel will you require?"

"None, thank you."

"No *fuel?*"

"Nope, but thanks anyway. Awful nice of you to offer."

"But you have flown all the way from Copenhagen, and you have a full load to carry back! You must be mistaken. How much fuel will you need?"

"Don't need any; thanks."

The Russians walked away with much head-shaking and backward glances at the ridiculous pilot who, perhaps, *liked* running out of fuel in the air. . . .

The Hercules fired up, taxied out to the end of the Tsushino Airport runway. The crew looked down the 7,000 feet of concrete, where they'd seen Russian jets and turboprops beating along, taking almost the full runway before breaking ground.

Now, was this or wasn't this a golden opportunity. . . ?

There came a hurried consultation between the pilot and Ambassador Thompson. Would the ambassador mind if the crew took this opportunity to "sort of demonstrate the takeoff of the airplane?" Ambassador Thompson smiled and nodded; wisely, he pulled his seat belt a little tighter.

No one told the two Russians in the flight deck about an assault takeoff. Or the tower, for that matter.

The pilot clamped on the brakes, ran the power levers all the way forward to maximum thrust from the props, winked at the copilot— and "shot the bolt."

With a cry of energy the Hercules crashed forward, accelerating like a boulder falling over a cliff. The Russians looked at one another in astonishment; the sudden burst forward had thrown them roughly back in their seats. The gear pounded on the runway as the pilot "let her wind up." One thousand feet and the Hercules had more than enough speed to soar away from the earth. Still the pilot kept the nose down. At 1,700 feet from starting the roll, he hauled back on the control yoke.

There was a sudden excited shout in Russian as the nose came up—and up, and then up some more. The Hercules clawed her way at an almost impossible angle into the air, rushing upward in a steep maximum climb. As the airplane crossed the end of the Tsushino runway, the Hercules was already passing an altitude of 5,000 feet and boring steadily upward.

The crew couldn't help watching the Russians in the flight deck with them. The Russians didn't say a word, but their expressions were wonderfully eloquent. They kept looking at the altimeter, then leaned over to gaze down at the airfield far below. One closed his mouth with a visible effort. . . .

And it seemed almost in the cards that on the return flight . . . the number-four engine quit. Just like that; no fire in the barrel. The flight engineer killed the engine and feathered the propeller.

The Russians reacted with excitement, because the altitude, speed, and time hacks from one defense radar checkpoint to the other were scheduled rigidly. Immediately the Russians reported the engine failure to the ground; the controller came back with a request for what lower altitude the airplane would need.

The pilot told the Russian radioman: "No sweat. We'll stay up here at 23,000 feet."

"But you have lost an engine!" shouted the Russian.

"No sweat, friend. Two-three thousand is just fine."

This required several rapid exchanges of conversation between the ground controller and the radioman; finally the Russians accepted the American as "mad," and waited for the Hercules to descend. It didn't.

The Russians stared at the True Air Speed Indicator dial; the airplane had slowed its speed by 20 knots. The American navigator whirled his computer a few times, jotted some figures down, and asked to have the flight-plan time for leaving Russian airspace extended by several minutes. No change was necessary, the Russian replied wearily, as the airplane sped on, still at 23,000 feet. . . .

The Frozen Northland

A veteran newsman of many years, hardened to the unusual and unimpressed by the bizarre, apparently was overcome by the raw wastelands of the Far North and the manner in which a new machine on wings had conquered those same wastelands. The newsman's home office was stunned when it received a report from the Greenland icecap that began:

> An heroic airlift drama pitting raw courage and faith in a new airplane against ruthless peril has been enacted quietly atop Greenland's forbidding 10,000-foot high inland ice cap— an endless plateau of ice and rock. The job was to forge the vital new radar links in our arctic DEW [Distant Early Warning] line chain, and it had to be completed in record time before the violence of full winter set in. The star of the drama is a newcomer to the frozen northland—a giant transport with huge skis and tremendous power. It is called the Hercules. . . .

After extensive tests on frozen Minnesota lakes in 1957, the Air Force deemed the Hercules ready for its most grueling task to date —to wrap up the delivery of needed construction material for the DEW line as quickly as possible. The first series of tests in Minnesota with a C-130A modified for giant skis held great promise for a logistics breakthrough in the frozen northland. In 1957 the airplane was tested with a weight of 90,000 pounds. Despite the penalty of drag imposed by the huge skis, it set an average for the takeoff roll of only 985 feet, and after touching down on landing, slid only 1,425 feet before careful braking action and full reverse thrust brought the Hercules to a complete stop.

By February 1958 the Hercules was up to 124,000 pounds for operation from snow fields, and experienced arctic explorers were staring in disbelief at the airplane as it lifted into the air at this weight after only 2,100 feet of takeoff run. Improved techniques and modified equipment brought a dramatic reduction in landing distance. Despite the additional weight of 34,000 pounds, the pilots squealed to a stop on snow fields in a distance of only 1,200 feet.

The final test came with rocket-assisted takeoffs. With the weight at 124,000 pounds and the drag of the skis, how quickly could the Hercules become airborne? When the airplane, in repeated take-offs, averaged only 1,425 feet before bursting into the air, the Air Force nodded happily, christened the ski model the C-130D, and told the 314th Troop Carrier Wing of the 839th Air Division to get plenty of long, warm, woolen underwear.

Twelve Hercules with 314th crews moved en masse to Sondes-trom air base in southern Greenland, where they operated on an almost continuous schedule for the next six months, carrying sup-plies for radar sites under construction. As many as ten airplanes were airborne at one time, flying to different points on the danger-ous icecap; the men started their flying at four o'clock in the morn-ing and worked straight through for the next 18 hours. The long hours of available daylight and the critical demand for equipment dictated the rugged schedules.

During the initial six months of "almost constant" operations, the 12 C-130D airplanes landed and took off from the icecap more than 2,500 times. Many times the pilots simply didn't know what they would run into when they touched down. First, they were operating on the top of the icecap at an elevation of 10,000 feet, and this by itself was a tremendous hurdle to overcome. The com-bination of the weight of the airplanes, 62 tons, the drag of the skis, and the icecap altitude of two miles was considered by many people as beyond the capabilities of any existing airplane. As events turned out, the Hercules experienced no problems in performing as required—except for the totally unexpected.

The depth of drifting snow varied from four to ten feet; it was impossible to judge from the air. More than one Hercules sent tre-mendous white plumes flying in all directions as it plunged head-long through the blinding white. Temperatures ranged down to 40 degrees below zero; this didn't help the crews to handle cargo that included large and heavy steel beams and tractors that indi-vidually weighed more than 28,000 pounds.

One of the most critical questions to be answered centered about the engines. How would the Allisons perform after they had been on the icecap for 30 minutes, at heights of from 8,000 to 10,000 feet, with the temperature far below zero and bitter winds blowing against the airplane? Once again the turboprops came through with flying colors. As a safety precaution, the crews at the remote sites always kept one engine running while the men offloaded the cargo. This provided a guarantee of starting both that engine and the self-contained turbine in the wheel well.

There was yet a third safety factor, which already had been proven in operations around the world. With only one engine run-

(*Above*) Flame spurting from its rocket bottles, a Hercules in gross weight tests—124,000 pounds—booms upward from its ski tracks. Average takeoff distance with the skis at 62-ton weight: 1,425 feet. (*Below*) Cargo in foreground has just been dumped from this Hercules that has landed on skis on an unprepared snowfield in Greenland, lifting vital supplies to remote radar installations. (*Lockheed-Georgia*)

ning the Hercules could build up a fast speed run over the ice. This provided enough wind effect to start a propeller windmilling and spinning rapidly, thus achieving an "airstart" while still on the ground. (Two Hercules crews on another operation found an ingenious solution to starting one airplane when all the starter mechanisms froze, making the ground compressor turbine helpless to rotate the props. The second Hercules moved up in front of the balky airplane, aligned itself carefully; the pilot reversed his propellers and *backed up* to the other airplane. He returned to normal propeller-blade pitch, locked the brakes, and went to full power with his engines. The tremendous blast of air from the propellers started the props of the second aircraft windmilling—and in a few minutes all four engines were running!)

Every day that the weather permitted (blizzards *did* ground the airplanes) the crews were in the air. Ice storms were worst of all, for they could impose on an airplane many tons of ice that overloaded the Hercules and destroyed the smooth lift of the wings. There were storms that couldn't be seen—magnetic and solar storms that raged in space and completely disrupted all electronic communications. On such occasions the airplanes were forced to remain bound to their snow runways, their instruments and radio equipment useless.

"The whiteouts were really wild," explained Jack Burdick, Lockheed engineer assigned to the airlift project. "There simply did not exist any ground reference of any kind. Everything was white; up and down, left and right. Just white. It was like flying around in the inside of a milk bottle. When that happened, you were cut off completely from the world. You flew your instruments, and you even landed by instruments. . . ."

One Hercules caught in a whiteout had to land; low on fuel, with night coming on, there wasn't any choice. The powerful radar in the nose of the airplane picked up a long line of empty oil drums marking off a "highway" in the midst of the ice. The crew sighted on the drums and landed blind—perfectly. Then, still guided by their radar, they had to taxi *eight miles* in the "inside of the milk bottle" to their station!

Experience proved, however, that the greatest danger to the Hercules lay in the hidden ice cracks and the sastrugi (hard ice ridges) concealed by thin snow. An airplane racing over the snow-covered icecap could rip into sastrugi with the same effect as running into a low concrete wall.

"You study the terrain from the air," Burdick recounts, "and it looks real good, and so you drop on down. You go along for a little while, everything is fine, and then all of a sudden there's an ice ridge smack in front of the airplane and—*WHAM!* We had two airplanes inside of two hours that crippled their skis. If we had been on a hard runway, we could have changed the skis in just about four hours. But on the icecap it was a maddening job. . . ."

For several days and nights the men of these two Hercules lived on the icecap in temperatures down to 30 degrees below zero with the wind shrieking at them. Intensive training in military survival schools now proved their worth as the crews labored to repair the airplanes. Except for food airdropped to them by a third Hercules, they lived under raw survival conditions, trying to replace the big right skis of each crippled transport.

"We were working against the bitter cold, the winds, the thin air of altitude," continued Burdick, "and we had to jury-rig almost everything. Remember—those damn skis weigh about a ton each. We had no equipment to haul them around. But the worst problem was that ice and snow. The more the sun shone, the faster things sink into that compacted snow. If you put anything black on the snow, the way it absorbs heat, why—it melts right down into the surface no matter how cold the outside temperature might be. I put down a wrench for a few moments and the damn thing just disappeared. . . ."

At the close of the six months' mission, the Hercules crews sat back exhausted—and manfully proud. Three thousand flying hours lay behind them, and so did a record of 26 million pounds of cargo moved to all radar sites. For icing on the record (no pun intended) the Hercules completed the unprecedented mission nine days ahead of schedule.

The next year—1960—the Hercules came back and finished the two-year job by airlifting an additional 23 million pounds of equipment as well as some 5,000 passengers. The United States Navy took a long look at the outstanding record. They counted up a total of nearly 25,000 tons of supplies, thousands of passengers, the incredible durability of the aircraft, and the completion of the missions ahead of schedule.

The Navy promptly ordered its own series of ski-equipped Hercules from Lockheed. These were to be modifications of the C-130B model, which the Navy christened C-130BL (now the LC-130F).

Until delivery was made, could the United States Navy "borrow" some Air Force ski-Hercules and their crews for Operation Deep Freeze (1960) in the Antarctic?

The Hercules transports wheeled around and headed for the other side—this time the *bottom*—of the world.

But the frozen northland hadn't seen the last of the Hercules; this time, however, the airplanes carried the insignia of the Royal

Powerful tractors push snow sleds up to open cargo ramp of C-130D ski-fitted Hercules in Greenland; crews roll heavy loads out, are ready for takeoff again in less than four minutes. (*Lockheed-Georgia*)

Canadian Air Force and flew *without* skis. The RCAF C-130Bs quickly broke every record in the Canadian books. . . .

The prime mission for the four new airplanes was supplying Arctic weather and radar stations with cargo, mail, and replacement personnel—a mission conducted each spring. For several years the RCAF had flown these supply trips with twin-engine C-119 Packets, which were a generation removed in performance from the new Hercules. Now, operating with conventional gear systems, the RCAF C-130Bs landed on ice, snow, and shale rock strips, the longest of which was about 3,400 feet.

During the 1961 spring supply missions the RCAF assigned to this work two of their Hercules (with five crews because of the almost nonstop operations). "Normally we work 12 hours on and 12 hours off, and get in as many flights as possible," reported an RCAF Hercules pilot. "While one crew sleeps, the others are out in the airplane—which doesn't get any rest at all. Working around the clock like this has let us do jobs that we never believed possible.

"For example, we've moved into areas where we used Dakotas [C-47s] and Packets for our supply tasks, and the job took anywhere from three to six months. With the Hercules we can do the very same job in just two weeks. It's an incredible machine, and we're very glad to have it."

In one airlift, two Hercules operating day and night swung back and forth in a constant shuttle—and completed the job of moving 850 tons of supplies in just eight days.

Troops move out quickly and crewmen prepare to pull heavy cargo pallets from Hercules of Royal Canadian Air Force somewhere in Far North. Engines are kept running for takeoff immediately after cargo is free. (*Lockheed-Georgia*)

"We did this with those two airplanes despite some terrible winds and drifting snow," continued the RCAF officer. "Sometimes the snow was so bad we couldn't even get on the ground for fear of hitting snow walls 20 and 30 feet high. We solved this neatly by picking areas clear of snow and simply dumping the cargo off the rear ramp. We'd come in at about 50 feet—no 'chutes, of course—and just heave the bloody stuff out.

"Of course, it was better if we could get down. We had fun at times in trying to beat out a storm that would be sailing down into the area, and we had just a few minutes to get a heavy load out of the machine. We finally developed some rather good fast turnaround techniques. We'd come off the runway to the unloading area, and the people in the back of the airplane could unload 32,000 pounds of cargo in big drums—the size of 55-gallon oil drums—in only a few minutes' time.

"In fact, headquarters flat didn't believe us until we started making official time records of it. The next time around in my aircraft, I hit my stopwatch the moment the wheels touched down. We turned off to the unloading area, engines still running, of course, and I told the loadmasters to get with it. They rolled out 73 of these big drums, our entire load of 32,000 pounds, very quickly. We came about smartly, pulling up the ramp as we taxied back to the end of the runway.

"The moment the wheels were off the ice, I hit the stopwatch again. The entire time for the operation—from the second the wheels touched down, through unloading, and back to the wheels in the air again—was *exactly* six minutes, and not one second more. That is really a spirited aircraft, all right."

And on the Bottom of the World . . .

The end of the world is many things to many people. Those of us accustomed to accepting the world as it is pictured by a desk globe find it difficult to accept the viewpoint of the man in Antarctica who looks up into a "deep, almost black-purple sky, a darkness such as you'll never see anywhere else on this planet." This man feels that he is not only on top of the world, but that he's closer to space than anywhere else that man can walk on his own two feet.

And he's right. . . . Standing at the South Pole a man is already some two miles above sea level. There are very few dust or smoke particles to turn the air into the murky substance with which we

Racing at high speed through stratosphere over Antarctica, a C-130BL of the Navy's Deep Freeze 61 Task Force pushes toward the South Pole, trailing four white contrails. (*Lockheed-Georgia*)

are sadly familiar. The air is bitterly cold; it is much more dense than the air in warmer climates, and so it presses down heavily on the Antarctic continent. The stratosphere begins only some five miles above sea level; thus the man standing at the South Pole is only three miles from the beginning of the cruelly thin stratosphere.

The stars "are at least twice as bright as those you see from the United States. The fact that many of them don't even twinkle is startling. It is really and truly like looking upon a vast field of distant suns; you get the feeling of *suns* rather than the old and familiar concept of 'stars.' It shakes the hell out of you sometimes. . . ."

There are other things to see in the skies above the bottom of "our" world. To Lockheed engineer Bill Smith the great auroras of the southern polar skies are "weird, to say the least. They're also incredibly beautiful. In front and to the side of the airplane there soared great shimmering curtains. There were all sorts of colors— orange, yellow, red, a whole spectrum of color. It was like a pulsating, snaking gossamer curtain that dances and moves and heaves throughout its length.

"They *danced*, like filmy drapes moved by the wind. They danced and moved and all of a sudden it seemed as though the Hercules was going to fly straight into these great sheets of color; the next minute they had vanished and were far to the side of us. The night sky then . . . well, it sort of shimmered, and it would be back in front of us. Then there came a silent, swift expansion and there was light flowing in the sky, shifting and dancing, extending far to the left and far to the right, as far as you could see. It was fantastic. . . ."

And what of the ice world itself? Here again the first impressions are as varied as the minds that study and judge what they see from the wide windows of the Hercules. "You can't *really* put into words what this place does to you," Hank Dees said quietly. "Immediately upon coming into sight of Antarctica—we were at 30,000 feet—I had a deep impression of whiteness and vastness. It's a . . . it's *vast*. You just do not realize—I know I didn't—just how incredibly white and big it is.

"You sit back and take a really good look at Antarctica as the miles flow beneath you, and it seems that you have entered a completely different world than the one you know.

"It's *hostile*—white and vast and hostile. And then, later, the longer you stay there and the better you come to know it, you begin to develop entirely different feelings. There's sort of a kindred spirit—an adventuresome spirit, and you get a craving to see

Navy LC-130 (formerly C-130BL) Hercules of Squadron VX-6 is un-loaded at field site of scientific party in the Pensacola Mountains in Antarctica. (*U.S. Navy Photo by M. W. Huntley*)

more. You want to keep moving, to actually explore and penetrate where other men have never been.

"I can't explain it. Right now I want to go back. . . ."

Or, as seen from 25,000 feet by Doug Chambley: "It looks like a great fingerpaint mural from the air; you know . . . streaks and eddies and curving lines. Everything is black and white. The black is lava ash and the white is the snow, and you get some of the most beautiful patterns you ever saw. You see glaciers here and there—they're all over the place. And there's not a living thing in sight. You get back from the coast just a couple of miles, and you're on a dead and frozen planet. . . ."

Rear Admiral David M. Tyree, then Commander of the U.S. Naval Support Force for Antarctica, sees the continent in several different ways. "Antarctica is the coldest, highest, windiest continent on earth," he states. "At the same time, it is dramatically and fantastically one of the most beautiful. Mountain ranges rising high along the coast show constantly changing colors in the summer sun. The interior of the continent is a great ice plateau which rises as high as 14,000 feet. Rivers of ice flow down the valleys leading to the coast, producing innumerable glaciers. Temperatures range from a record winter low of minus 110 degrees at the Pole Station to a few degrees above freezing occasionally at McMurdo and more

Without stopping on frozen snow, Navy Hercules' crew pushes cargo
load from the airplane as it swings in a wide circle (*above*): the airplane
is into the air again without even coming to a complete stop. A single
cargo package of 23,000 pounds (*below*) is unloaded from a VX-6
Hercules at the South Pole Station, Antarctica. (*Upper photo: U.S. Navy
Photo; lower photo: U.S. Navy Photo by L. R. Mathis*)

frequently at Hallett in the summer. Vicious Antarctic blizzards rise with sudden fury. . . .

"It is also the unforgiving continent. Usually, the Antarctic lets you have only one mistake—this can be your last."

Admiral Tyree refers to the seasonal struggles to resupply Antarctic stations as "long and difficult," and a "battle from start to finish . . . a battle against bitter cold, against blinding storms, against pounding frozen seas. . . ."

This is Antarctica, a slice of the continent of ice as it is seen and interpreted by different men. But all agree that it is a vast and howling frontier the like of which exists nowhere else on this planet, a land of winds that screech at 200 miles per hour and more, where temperatures of 60 degrees below zero are not only commonplace, but "warm" compared to the areas where 80 and 90 and 100 below also are not unusual.

At the South Pole itself there exists in this white oblivion a tiny spark of human life—the scientific station of the National Science Foundation and the U.S. Navy's Operation Deep Freeze. Here in the midst of more than five million treacherous and brutal square miles is the spirit of scientific curiosity, of men using the tools of science to chip patiently away at the natural secrets of our planet that are imprisoned in the ice shelf of Antarctica.

For centuries Antarctica remained an unknown. With the outward spread of man around his spherical ship of life, men from the early nineteenth century on knew fleetingly of the ice continent, and then dismissed it from their daily affairs as a vast and inhospitable plateau of frozen hell.

But curiosity is an impelling force; with new transportation and scientific tools curiosity burgeoned in an overwhelming drive. Especially since the International Geophysical Year of 1957 have American scientists struggled to fathom the secrets and plumb the depths of Antarctica. In the next several years they charted thousands of square miles and studied carefully the relation of the ice-covered continent to earth's past history, and its influence upon the rest of the world today. Much of the success there of our country—which makes no claims of ownership of Antarctic territory, nor does it recognize the claims of others—is owed to the brilliant performance of the U.S. Navy in its support of the scientific teams in Antarctica.

But the wealth of information extracted from the land at the bottom of the world has not been gained without staggering cost—cost determined by factors of hardship, sacrifice, matériel, and also of dollars.

To keep just one scientist at the South Pole for one year requires the expenditure of *one million dollars.* In time such a cost is prohibitive, and there must be found the means substantially to reduce this outpouring of dollars. Moves in this direction have been most significant; among them, the installation of a nuclear reactor at one major site has permitted an astounding slash in fuel supplies.

But beyond even this there has long stood the dream of every explorer since Byrd: an unrestricted supply line directly to the South Pole itself.

And to the Hercules went this demanding assignment, which no other aircraft had yet succeeded in mastering.

Rear Admiral David M. Tyree late in 1959 predicted that the Hercules would "cut in half the cost of operations" in Antarctica. To supply Deep Freeze 60, the Air Force moved seven of its modified C-130D Hercules transports to the South Pole. Lieutenant Colonel Wilbert Turk led the seven airplanes of the 61st Troop Carrier Squadron from Tennessee on a 13,850-mile flight to Antarctica to begin Operation Ice Flow, the Air Force's code name for supporting the Navy's operations at the bottom of the world.

Colonel Turk's Hercules were the first airplanes proudly to boast the motto "From Pole to Pole!"

The Antarctic didn't welcome them with open arms. As the airplanes roared into landings on the frozen runway near McMurdo Sound, the horizon vanished and an all-pervading whiteness replaced the normal world. The navigators stayed glued to their radar sets and called in the approach conditions to the pilots. The landings were "uneventful."

The Navy assigned the Hercules group their first mission with a request to "urgently expedite." The transports were to pick up 400 tons of supplies and equipment from the main base at McMurdo Sound and rush the cargoes to the outposts at the South Pole (850 miles) and in Marie Byrd Land (950 miles). And they were to do it quickly, before the long winter night set in and completely isolated the stations from the rest of the world.

Until the arrival of the Hercules, supplies for the Pole and Byrd Stations had arrived by parachute from giant C-124 Globemasters. The paradrop operation proved adequate for basic supplies such as food and heavy-duty equipment, but the scientists cursed the all too frequent consequences of the drops so far as their delicate instruments were concerned. Sometimes the parachutes simply drifted out of sight and the supplies were never found. Many times the instruments were broken or otherwise affected and rendered useless. Even when the drops were successful the scientists were forced to spend much time in calibrating and in checking every detail of instrument operation, a chore they could sorely afford in terms of time.

(*Above*) Unloading scientific instruments at the Pensacola Mountains. (*Below*) In biting winds and savage cold crew unloads cargo at South Pole Station, Antarctica. (*Upper photo: U.S. Navy Photo by M. W. Huntley; lower photo: U.S. Navy Photo by F. Kazukaitis*)

The waste in this type of supply operations was estimated by the Navy at approximately a million dollars per year. It took manpower and plenty of time to rig the chutes and pack the supplies in special containers. The bulkiness of the paradrop units and the weight of the chutes and rigging cost dearly in payload. And the chutes were not reusable.

The supply operations budget came to 13 million dollars per year. The arrival in Antarctica of the Hercules immediately sliced a million dollars off this figure, because of the ability of the airplane to land directly at both the Pole and Byrd Stations and while carrying heavy supply loads. No parachute drops were necessary.

The Air Force's seven ski-Hercules remained in the Arctic long enough to complete their mission—58 supply runs with precious cargo to the Pole and Byrd Stations. In 12 days the airplanes poured 400 tons of supplies into the scientific outposts—and completed the supply assignment *ten days ahead of schedule*.

Turk led the first mission to the Pole Station in his plane, *Frozen Assets*. With the Hercules crew was Admiral Tyree, carrying with him the same American flag which had accompanied Rear Admiral Richard Byrd in his historic first flights over both the North and South Poles.

Colonel Turk couldn't resist the opportunity to fly around the

First Navy Hercules to open 1962 supply missions taxis to parking area at McMurdo Sound. (*U.S. Navy Photo by Woods*)

bottom of the world—circumnavigating the planet—in four minutes. He circled the South Pole with his wingtip pointed directly at the station marker, and as he swung around he crossed every meridian of longitude, completely flying around the world.

The landings at the Pole Station were "rougher than anything we had ever experienced before," the pilots said. The Hercules ran into abrupt wind changes that screeched with sudden and explosive force across the icy runways. One pilot turned to the man at his right and muttered, "Hell, this isn't so bad, is it?" as his huge transport slid *sideways* down the ice.

As a precaution against that totally unpredictable weather the Navy ordered that no two planes were to be allowed on the ice at the Pole Station at the same time. So the Hercules had to unload its cargo, pick up returning cargo, if any, and be airborne within 15 minutes to make way for the next airplane which was already in sight. There were reasons for speed other than storms that might close in.

The temperature averaged 50 degrees below zero, and the Pole Station is at 9,200 feet. Here the air is cruelly thin, and under any prolonged exertion even the strongest of men feel a touch of fire in their chests and gasp for breath. The cargo-handling techniques and systems drew raves from the scientists and Navy crewmen. The loadmaster dropped the ramp to the height of huge cargo sleds; in moments the crews hauled the 15,000-pound cargo loads out of the airplane on pallets. A sled tractor was moving the sleds out of the way within seconds after the pallets slid onto them.

Some cargoes were offloaded in deep snow. The Hercules taxied slowly, the giant skis flattening out the snow into a firm surface. The men in the airplanes simply rolled the cargo off the ramp in a tight line onto snow packed tight only seconds before.

What had been a dangerous operation before, with only spotty success, became, with the arrival of the Hercules transports, a door-to-door delivery right at the South Pole itself. And before the airplanes swung around for departure from the ice continent, every man had become familiar with the bamboo pole planted in the ice at the exact bottom of the world, with a silvered dome that reflected the midnight sun to the incoming pilots of the Hercules.

"To those of us who rode to the Pole in the big, squat Lockheed Hercules," recounted Frederick G. Vosburgh of the National Geographic Society, "it was plain as the icicles on a polar scientist's beard that these jet-turbine, propeller-driven planes will lop years off the time required for the exploration and mapping of Antarctica. Before the end of this year the Navy expects to have its own Hercules propjets, and with these Ski-130s available for carrying aviation gasoline in bulk, Antarctic personnel can make the Pole a big fuel depot for trail support, rescue, and photomapping planes. By airlifting diesel oil and snow vehicles, they can also make it a jumping-off place for scientific traverse parties. Instead of a precarious outpost of science, Amundsen-Scott [the Pole Station] will have become a major advance base for exploration on the other side of the Pole."

The next year the Navy moved in with its spanking-new C-130BL Hercules which, in the words of a Navy operations officer, "were designed from the ground up as . . . ski-equipped aircraft and specifically for use by the Navy's Air Development Squadron Six (VX-6) for Antarctic operations. They were received by the Navy at an acceptance ceremony on the 4th of September 1960 at Quonset Point, Rhode Island. . . ."

Seven weeks later three of the Navy Hercules thundered into McMurdo Sound to open the logistical airbridge of Deep Freeze 61. Admiral Tyree ordered the three airplanes to fly 400 tons of cargo to the remote scientific stations.

Several weeks later the admiral looked at the record of his new airplanes in Antarctica, and officially evaluated their performance as "simply fantastic."

He added that from the beginning of Deep Freeze 61, "we have felt that the Lockheed C-130BLs would be a great asset in the resupplying of our inland Antarctic scientific stations. . . . The Hercules has more than lived up to our highest expectations."

Admiral Tyree ordered a fourfold increase in the logistics task for the Hercules for Deep Freeze 61, to 1,800 tons of supplies—which came to more than 60 percent of *all* the year's logistics requirements for the inland stations.

The VX-6 Squadron didn't just meet the new workload assigned to them—they *exceeded* their requirements. They started out with a no-stop operation that saw the three Hercules flying 20 missions in a period of four days, averaging more than 20,000 pounds of cargo per flight. On one mission the Hercules broke every record in the books by flying a round trip of 2,600 nautical miles, the longest logistical flight ever made in the Antarctic. The C-130BL raced across the entire continent at 24,000 feet, offloaded passengers and 10,000 pounds of cargo at a rough airstrip in the Walker Mountains, and returned. Time for the complete round-trip flight: 11 hours.

When the three Hercules of VX-6 were ordered back to the United States, they had behind them a record of no accidents, and not a single minute lost due to mechanical failures. They hauled 1,860 tons of supplies to inland bases, and left Navy statisticians

Lockheed-Georgia Hercules—Navy 148321—after completing in late 1960 the longest logistics flight in the history of the Antarctic continent up to that time. The flight to the Walker Mountain Range covered 2,600 miles and lasted 11 hours. (*U.S. Navy Photo by L. R. Mathis*)

pondering with delight the outlook for the coming year when all four C-130BLs would be on the job.

Early in 1961, the sudden illness of Russian scientist Leonid Kuperov opened wider the door to Antarctic supply. The frozen continent had been officially closed to all incoming air traffic for the regular period of seven months of the year when the Antarctic tucks itself in for total isolation. In fact, the last surface vessel had departed the Antarctic more than a month before, when the call for help was flashed to Navy headquarters at Christchurch, New Zealand. The word passed on to Washington, and orders went out at once to VX-6 at its home base in Rhode Island. The Hercules had left the Antarctic on February 11, not expecting to be sent back for seven more months.

But on April 9, 1961, Commander Lloyd E. Newcomer raced into the airstrip at McMurdo Sound. He remained briefly on the ice, and rushed at high speed onward to Byrd Station, where the crew picked up the scientist and began the trip back to New Zealand.

"The flight of Commander Newcomer and his intrepid crew . . . will always be one of the great flights of Antarctic exploration," declared Admiral Tyree. "This mercy flight, in the face of diminishing daylight and increasingly vicious and frequent winter storms, breached the curtain of winter isolation."

This proved to be the single most significant flight in the six years to date (by 1961) of Operation Deep Freeze. It proved that lack of daylight and even the effects of "vicious and frequent winter storms" could be overcome by the unique performance characteristics of the Hercules. Newcomer's mercy mission for the first time in history broke the rigid winter isolation of the Antarctic, bringing what one Navy pilot called "the first ray of sunshine ever to be seen in that long black night. Now that we *know* we can break the isolation, we might have the key to an entirely new approach to the Antarctic operation. We ought to give that Russian scientist a medal for getting sick. . . ."

For Deep Freeze 62, the year following, the Navy reported, its Hercules hauled 4,300 tons of cargo to the Pole and Byrd Stations, "including tremendous quantities of building materials for New Byrd Station, as well as establishing a unique field party some 1,400 miles from McMurdo at Ski-Hi."

On February 22, 1963, the Hercules demonstrated the seven-league snowboots it had donned for the Antarctic missions. Weighing 134,000 pounds, a Hercules roared into the air from McMurdo Sound on a nonstop flight that would cover more than 3,600 miles (a new all-time record for the frozen continent) over some of the most forbidding territory ever known. The VX-6 Hercules paralleled the track of Captain Robert Falcon Scott on his ill-fated expedition of 1911 over the Beardmore Glacier to the South Pole. From there the airplane went on to the Shackleton Mountains, into Queen Maud Land, southeastward to the "Pole of Inaccessibility," and then turned again toward McMurdo. After hundreds of miles of bleak, unbroken ice and snow surface, the crew sighted the Queen Elizabeth and Queen Alexandra Mountains near the edge of the Ross Ice Shelf. They flew just over the spectacular Byrd Glacier, took a bearing on Mount Erebus, and raced back to McMurdo.

The veterans of the Antarctic couldn't believe it—3,600 miles over known and never-before-seen territory—in comfort and within a span of ten hours and 40 minutes.

Lockheed engineer Bill Smith lived with VX-6 for 45 days during its first season at the bottom of the world, and for 135 days during his second time around. He recalls his arrival at McMurdo on September 27, 1961, "with the temperature already down to minus 55. And this is a Fahrenheit figure. At Byrd Station it went down to 65 below. At the Pole the needle stood at minus 70. And as we cruised from point to point at 30,000 feet the temperature plunged to 95 degrees below zero."

The first airplane ever to land at the South Pole was a Navy version (R4D) of the venerable twin-engine Gooney Bird. At an altitude of nearly two miles atop the ice shelf, the Gooney's engines were turning out only a fraction of their normal power. Veterans of the Pole Station described to the writer the harrowing takeoff of that airplane, which roared and thumped its way for *ten to 15 miles on the ice* before the wings could grab enough air and lift the airplane above the runway.

This didn't present too much of a problem, because "you can take off in any direction and go for hundreds of miles; it's as flat as the top of a table. The airplanes that came in here, even when they used rocket boost, had a hell of a time getting airborne. We thought they were going to run on the ice clear across the plateau."

The Hercules transports came into the Pole Station and operated off a semi-prepared skiway. The scientists and technicians gathered expecting to watch the unusual new high-winged airplane with the "monstrous skis" bang along the ice for ten or 15 miles, just like the other planes—especially since the Hercules did *not* have rocket-assist takeoff bottles on the airplane.

"We got off the skiway time and again as a standard operation in something between 2,000 and 2,500 feet," reported Bill Smith. "They just couldn't believe what they were seeing. . . ."

But no one can ever fly in the frozen continent without sooner or later running headlong into an emergency. The hazards inherent in the Antarctic environment—the savage cold, the terrible winds, the remoteness—all compound the factors of possible disaster. As witness one of the most unusual accidents in the thick logbook of Hercules experience . . .

Something that pilots and crews fear in the Antarctic is mechanical breakdown or failure, or even minor trouble, when they are anywhere but at a camp. An accident in the middle of nowhere, on the great expanse of the frozen plateau, can quickly mushroom into imminent death. There just aren't the rescue facilities, the people, or the navigational aids for help to arrive. And the storms explode so quickly that many times there isn't any warning at all before dead-calm air turns into the fury of a wind exceeding hurricane force—and at 50 to 60 degrees below zero.

The unexpected snared a Hercules at 27,000 feet, while the airplane cruised en route from McMurdo to Byrd Station. In the space of five minutes the startled crew lost power on three of their four engines. The flight engineer went frantic trying to discover the cause and effect a remedy, but one by one the engines just quit turning out power. One engine meant no trouble. Then the second quit, and things began to get sticky because of the heavy fuel and cargo load and the altitude.

The pilot started an immediate descent to denser air to keep the Hercules flying. Then the third engine quit and that airplane was in *deep* trouble. . . .

The pilot knew when he was getting into a mess well over his head. He ordered the engineer to open the cargo ramp and shouted at the crew to jettison the cargo—*everything*—and to get it the hell out of the airplane at once. Fighting the sluggish controls—with almost full weight on one engine—the pilot kept the Hercules in a steady descent, broken only by a pullup to help roll out the cargo.

With only one engine remaining—and with no assurance that the last Allison wouldn't quit at any moment—the pilot bored in for a landing in the midst of nowhere, while the copilot and navigator were frantically sending out distress signals and position reports. Everyone hung on grimly as the big airplane screamed low over the ice . . . and slid to a perfect landing.

Lockheed engineer Bill Smith picks up the story here:

"We sent out a field party in a Gooney Bird with special equipment and engine preheaters to find out what had caused three engines to quit just like that. I'd known of an Air Force bird that had to shut down three engines when hail beat up the airscoops, but we modified those years ago and it never happened again. I couldn't figure out what might have caused this trouble, and my hunch was that the engines were fine—but the fuel wasn't.

"Sure enough, the culprit turned out to be a very high concentration of water in the fuel. We had a bitch on our hands; the airplane actually had a contaminated fuel system. The filter screens were solid *ice*. The water must have been pumped into the aircraft with the supply from McMurdo, through the single-point system of the Hercules. That's the only possible way we could have gotten such a great slug of sea water in the airplane. All fuel is brought in by Navy tanker and in those rough seas you can't help but to ship water into the tanks. Well, the Hercules got a hell of a lot of that water."

Lockheed technician Doug Chambley went along in the Navy's Gooney Bird to troubleshoot the problem; Chambley says he would prefer to forget the five days that followed. The trouble wasn't to be solved by demanding technical work; it had to be solved by muscle-bending, back-breaking physical labor.

"We had to open the fuel tanks in the wings," Chambley recalls with a trace of a shudder. "Then we had to climb into the tanks. Next in the job was to heat the water—the ice—in the wings and then sponge out the water by *hand* before we dared to send the airplane back into the air.

"You see, we had to sponge out the tanks, but we didn't have any sponges. Where do you find sponges in the middle of Antarctica? We were 500 miles from McMurdo and 300 miles from Byrd Station—almost right smack in the middle. All they had there was ice and snow, no *sponges*.

"It's amazing what that airplane will endure. . . . We tore apart every seat cushion we could find in the Hercules. We tore them up and cut the sponge rubber out of the seats, and *those* were our sponges.

"It took more than three days in the middle of the Antarctic to open all the tanks, and physically crawl in and clean the water out of every damn one of them by hand.

"Well, it was interesting, anyway. We finally had the opportunity to put our survival-school training—which was worse than the Antarctic—to good use. We dug underground quarters, set up tents and shelters, and we ate hardtack. God, we ate hardtack by day and by night. We rigged up some old cans, made some fires with the jet fuel to melt water, and even managed to make something that passed for coffee. We lived strictly off our survival rations and equipment.

"We worked for four and a half days on that airplane until we had it ready to fly. On the fifth day we considered things safe enough for a takeoff, and the crew boomed out of there like there was no tomorrow.

"Apparently we hadn't cleaned out *all* the water, though. . . ."

On the flight back to McMurdo, the crew lost two engines. With the airplane light in weight, the crew said to hell with it, and went wide-open all the way back to the main station. The pilot said he would have kept on with only one engine and if he'd lost that one, too, he was determined to glide all the way back to McMurdo.

Safely on the ground again, the crew with the help of mechanics flushed the tanks and purged the systems of fuel and any sea water that remained. They pumped the tanks full again, ran a thorough check of the engines, and the next morning the Hercules was in the air with 20,000 pounds of cargo, headed for the South Pole.

Just as the admiral said: *"Simply fantastic."*

Operation X-Ray

About 80 miles southwest of Saigon is a short fighter airstrip that the Japanese threw together in World War II. In the midst of the South Vietnamese jungle, the strip is just about 2,900 feet long—but with no usable overrun. Just the 2,900 feet and not an inch more. The Japanese did a good job of construction, for the many years that had passed since the last Nakajima flew from the concrete had not obliterated this field as it had many others. The strip was old, the concrete deteriorated, but for a giant airplane with rugged landing gear—the Hercules—the pilots called the strip "comparatively smooth."

If you took off in one direction in a Hercules, about a thousand feet beyond the strip you'd find trees 80 or 90 feet in height staring you in the face. Not a pleasant takeoff, especially if the wind was on your tail. But if you took off the other way in the big Marine Hercules transports that pounded in and out of the old Japanese fighter strip, you had to cut sharply over a small town, and there were plenty of Communist guerrillas in the area itching to riddle the crew compartment and hole the tanks with some lead stitching —machine-gun style. And if the ship went down with a full load of fuel and clobbered the town, that wouldn't be very good either. So the Marines said to hell with the trees, and they took their GV-1s in that direction no matter what the wind. The treetops often swayed from the rush of air from the belly and props of the airplane, but "you soon didn't think about that any more."

South Viet Nam . . . the Hercules . . . how do these fit together? Until now there has never been a word linking the Hercules directly with the United States' support of our allies in South Viet Nam, but the absence of the words simply avoided any publicity until the need for secrecy finally abated.

Operation X-Ray was a hard-and-fast airlift by the Marines' GV-1 Hercules (five GV-1s flew in from the States to join a regular force of six planes based at Iwakuni, Japan), running from Cubi Point Naval Air Station in the Philippines to the old Japanese strip 80 miles from Saigon. There had already been one big push with the Marines into the combat zones—the Tulungan Backlift—and the effectiveness of the Hercules in its first combat role as an assault transport in a life-and-death situation was being described as "absolutely tremendous" in the official evaluations.

The Marine GV-1s roared out of the Philippines in steady succession, each airplane making at least one and, sometimes, two complete round trips a day. They hauled heavily armed fighting men as well as jeeps, trucks, ammunition, food, and other equipment. The Hercules took off from Cubi Point with little room left over either in their bellies or in their wings. They hauled 28,000 pounds of combat cargo and enough fuel (36,000 pounds) to leave the Philippines, climb to five miles, get into the strip, and return, without any refueling along the way. And to keep the combat airlift moving swiftly, each Hercules was allotted 15 minutes unloading time on the ground, and that was *all.*

"It was pretty wild," was the terse comment of one man aboard the lead airplane that began the airlift into the jungle strip. Colonel Robert White, USMC, reached the airstrip area before daylight, cruising at 26,000 feet. Then, with enough daylight to "dump" the Hercules onto the strip, he "pulled the plug" for a maximum rate of descent. On the way down, falling out of the sky like a rock, the crew could see the flashes of gunfire from the jungles and fields—and learned later that some of that fire was being directed at the Hercules. The airplane didn't receive any damage, and Colonel White dropped the GV-1 onto the strip as though it were a liaison plane.

The Hercules screeched to a halt with full reverse thrust from the propellers, and Marines came pouring out of the airplane.

Preparing to chop power, dump the flaps and gear—and fall out of the sky "like a rock"

They came out with rifles, machine guns, and other rapid-fire-fight weapons and troubleshooting maintenance equipment to remain on the field. A Lockheed technician went in with the airplane to set up the equipment (and was ordered out of the strip aboard Colonel White's Hercules. A Marine lieutenant with a submachine gun dangling loosely in his hands asked him: "You think these guerrillas are going to read that noncombatant card you're carrying? Get your tail on that bird. . . ."). With the troubleshooting equipment on hand, and strict orders to keep one engine of the airplanes running at all times during the quick offloading, "extra caution" paid off—with no delays experienced during the airlift.

By the time the first Hercules was roaring down the strip for an assault takeoff, the perimeter of the field was lined with Marines dug in with heavy machine-gun emplacements and backed up by carefully selected South Vietnamese troops. One after the other the Hercules came over at altitudes of from 22,000 to 26,000 feet, and "pulled the plug" in stomach-wrenching descents—a neat maneuver for a transport airplane to use to avoid ground fire during its approach. "You came straight in over the trees," explained a crew member, "and the sink rate was unbelievable, and the pilot would just slam it onto the ground. Then hell broke loose as the troops poured out and the ground people dragged the guns and supplies from the airplane and *bang*, just like that, we were plowing up the runway again and making maximum climbouts, going for altitude in a hurry."

And then the rains started. Every day the skies poured torrents of water into the jungle and onto the airstrip, and what had been "comparatively smooth" turned into a nightmare. The old concrete was soft to begin with, but held up under the big tires of the Hercules. Now, with water everywhere, "the continued operations just tore the hell out of that strip." The strip wasn't level and the water collected in great pools, and the airplanes went smashing into the water and the broken concrete. One time it damaged an airplane, and the Marines were so surprised they were apologetic about it; they'd flown their Hercules with an in-commission rate the like of which has never been seen. But the Hercules wasn't an amphibious airplane. When it barreled down the airstrip at 90 to 100 miles per hour, the water smashed back with jackhammer pressure against the nose-well doors and twisted the metal out of shape.

Colonel White landed once with his nose-gear system so battered (after taking off from another jungle strip for the primary unloading point) that the nose gear wouldn't drop down. In a beautiful control job he held the airplane on its main gear as long as possible, and then dropped the nose. The jagged concrete ripped the bottom of the airplane. The Marines swarmed forward, jacked up the nose, and heaved mightily to force the damaged door out of the way. They lowered the nose gear, locked it into the down position, and flew it back to the Philippines. The next morning the airplane returned to normal operations.

Many of the stories of the Hercules—flown by Air Force crews into South Viet Nam—must wait until the mantle of secrecy covering their operations is lifted. Until then, suffice it to say that the Hercules *is* a battle-proved and battle-scarred veteran.

The two Marine emergency airlifts into Viet Nam in 1962 lasted only two weeks, and the number of aircraft was small. But in those 14 days, operating in jungle conditions, the GV-1 Hercules flew a total distance of 208,034 miles for a flying time of 652 hours. They carried 1,552 "passengers" and brought 1,873,443 pounds of weapons and supplies into the area.

Across the Andes

Peru is a land nearly twice the size of Texas, lying on the Pacific coast of South America. It is a long, roughly rectangular country 1,400 miles long and about 800 miles deep, an area that forms a paradoxical combination of natural riches and barren land. The entire western seaboard of the country is a desert on which rain seldom falls; the rugged backbone of the Andes Mountains towers to more than 20,000 feet. The mountains block the rain-bearing winds from the east, and in the coastal areas where dwell the great majority of Peru's people, nothing grows without irrigation. It is costly, inefficient, and a terrible brake on the economic growth of the nation.

From the narrow coastal shelf rise the towering peaks, the twisting valleys, and the wind-swept plateaus of the Andes. This High Sierra land mass forms one third of the nation's area, and as a formidable natural barrier it isolates the coastal cities and population from the back country of Peru—one of the most fertile agricultural areas of the world, and one of the richest in minerals.

This is the *montaña*, with half of Peru's land area and only 13 percent of its population. The Peruvian government has long known that the only way to tap this vast source of riches was to link all the areas of the nation with a network of roads and, later, rail lines that would end the crippling isolation and allow the burgeoning of the Peruvian economy. But—*how* to do this in a land where physical communications are a problem just as high and formidable as the Andes themselves?

The highways needed to be more than country roads. They must be able to carry modern machinery in an uninterrupted flow to the undeveloped territory, and allow the smooth return of products to the Peruvian markets and seaports for trade. At the same time, the vast areas of Peru's richest lands would be thrown open to her people.

A study showed that construction should begin at three major sites. Heavy earth-moving equipment—bulldozers, scrapers, earth-movers, etc.—must be moved from Lima to Juanjui, Tarapoto, and Yurimaguas, on the far side of the Andes. The existing roads that snaked their way through the mountains reached as high as 16,000 feet, and were considered useless for the task. Thus the machinery must be shipped northward by barge on the Pacific, through the Panama Canal, southward on the Atlantic, and then up the Amazon —a total distance of 7,000 miles, and at the mercy of weather and other conditions which could not be controlled. They not only could seriously delay or cripple the operation, but would raise the cost greatly.

Could the heavy machinery be *flown over the Andes?* If that were possible, the journey would be reduced to 400 miles, and it would be measured in minutes instead of in months. Government officials laughed at the suggestion. Transport the giant bulldozers and earth-movers over mountains 20,000 feet high, and land—yes, land *where?* There were only crude dirt airstrips on the other side of the Andes.

The Peruvian Air Force turned to the United States government for help. The response came in the form of five C-130A Hercules flown by TAC's Blue Eagles of the 773rd Troop Carrier Squadron out of Sewart Air Force Base in Tennessee.

On August 2, 1961, Captain Lewis B. Senter took off from Lima with the first load of construction equipment, bound for an unprepared jungle strip at Tarapoto. Aboard the airplane were Peruvian pilots serving as guides. Sailing across the Andes at 25,000 feet in a heated, comfortable, pressurized aircraft, the Peruvian officers' sighs could be heard across the flight deck. They had never flown over these mountains, but only *through* their narrow passes, fighting violent turbulence in airplanes that staggered in the thin air.

The other Hercules followed in rapid-fire succession. From Lima into the jungle strips—also at Juanjui and Yurimaguas—the flights averaged 66 minutes. Before returning to the coastal area, the crews loaded the airplanes with coffee and other cargo "just so we wouldn't waste all that airlift going in the other direction."

Six days after the operation began, more than 300 tons of construction machinery were in the Amazon basin interior, and hun-

Hercules in assault takeoff booms off rough grass strip in Peru, carrying heavy road-building equipment for a flight across the Andes, to open up rich undeveloped inland areas. (*Lockheed-Georgia*)

dreds of men were hard at work on Peru's "bootstrap" operation.

Cost to the Peruvian government: $200,000 obtained from international development funds.

There were some post-mission comments to remember. Lieutenant General G. Van Oordt, the Peruvian Air Force Chief of Staff, said that "the airlift will hasten this road-building project by *three years* and open up this previously inaccessible area."

As for the pilots—to them it was a "heads-up type of mission," with the most difficult part of a flight being the plunge down the sides of mountains to make assault-type crash landings into the jungle strips.

Lieutenant Colonel Frank L. Weatherbee, who commanded the operation, comments: "I won't pretend it was a soft touch; it *wasn't*. But the success of the mission proves two things conclusively. We can operate from unprepared strips if we have to, and our planes can be used to as great an advantage for peace as they can for defense."

There are Hercules today flying throughout South America on a bewildering variety of missions. The writer wishes that more people

On the "other side of the Andes," Peruvian driver moves heavy bulldozer out of Hercules that has landed on unprepared grass field. (*Lockheed-Georgia*)

knew of one of the assignments of a Hercules, aside from its regular
duties of aerial surveying for new maps of the continent. The
"combat cargo" transport flies a regular run into a remote and
impoverished area of Peru. The airplane is unbelievably popular
and the crews are showered with adulation.

Their cargo: Two hot meals every day for 70,000 young schoolchildren.

And in the Himalayas . . .

The Andes were rough; the Himalayas were considered by many
to be impossible. The problem was not in flying over the highest
mountains in the world, for the Hercules can soar 10,000 feet and
more above *the* highest. It was to operate with safety from the
rugged and crude strips of dirt and rock hacked out along the
slopes of mountains and in short valleys from 11,000 to 14,000 feet
above sea level—and with heavy cargo loads under "combat pressure" conditions.

In response to appeals of the Indian government for assistance in the late-1962 invasion of Chinese Communist forces, the 322nd Air Division moved a force of 12 Hercules from France to India to begin a day-in, day-out combat airlift operation. Many of the pilots and crewmen had seen these Himalayas before when flying the Hump in World War II with two- and four-engined piston transports. But none of them had flown as high, as far, as fast, carried the loads, or operated anywhere near the airfield heights of the Hercules.

Many of the landings were made at Leh, behind the main ridge of the Himalayas in the barren and cruelly bleak region of Ladakh in northwest India. Maintenance crews at a base near New Delhi worked around the clock to keep the Hercules operating under conditions that exceeded even the worst of Antarctica.

In the period of one week, flying into crudely improvised mountain airstrips that lay up to some 14,000 feet or more above sea level, the 12 airplanes airlifted 5,000 equipped soldiers and a million pounds of combat supplies to the fighting zones.

Here, too, durability proved its worth—as it had already done so many times in the past. One Hercules landed at an unusually rough airstrip three miles above sea level. At the touchdown end of the strip the ground dropped in a long and steep depression. Then it rose again, and abruptly dipped into a second depression. Dozens of flights had been made into the area, *not* without difficulty and some "wild and hairy moments," but definitely without any accidents.

Then one Hercules got snagged between the shock-absorbing action of its nose gear and the hazards of the airstrip conditions. As it landed, the nose depressed the shock-absorber strut in the gear to its maximum distance. Then the airplane lunged out of the depression; the nose came down again and immediately afterward the nose slammed into the second depression. A tremendous ramrod force smashed the gear upward, and it was all that even the Hercules could take. Steel forgings collapsed, metal ripped with a high, screeching sound, and the airplane plowed forward on its nose with the gear mangled into junk.

The scene that ensued rivaled the most fabulous improvisations of World War II. Mechanics and crewmen, with the assistance of Indian Air Force personnel, working at such high altitude that great exertion meant flaming red spots before the eyes and dizzy spells, and sometimes even unconsciousness, jacked up the nose of the Hercules. Then they cannibalized the nose-gear sections from two wrecked airplanes on the strip—that had attempted landings and failed. One was an American C-119 twin-engine transport, the

Refugee Tibetan orphan children (their families killed by Communist attacks from China) being moved into Hercules transports for evacuation. The 104 orphans had found refuge in the frozen mountains at Leh in northern Kashmir. (*Lockheed-Georgia*)

other a brand-new Anatov four-engine turboprop transport sold by Russia to the Indians (who lost almost all their Anatov force in crashes within two weeks of mountain operations).

The crewmen assembled a Rube Goldberg landing gear from the wrecked C-130 system and parts of the C-119 and the Anatov, and installed it on the Hercules. An hour later the airplane was on its way to New Delhi for a new nose gear—and the following day it returned to the airlift operations.

Kaleidoscope

It would be an impossible task to try to give between the covers of any one book a complete list of the extraordinary range and variety of operations carried out by the amazing Hercules—impossible for two reasons: whenever one attempts to compile such a list, one discovers quickly that many of the missions being flown simply have never been reported, and that many remarkable recent performances of the airplane have in fact been exceeded many months before. Then, also, by the time the list could ever reach print, new mission assignments would have been added, with more upcoming.

When I began the many months of extensive research for this story of a unique aircraft, there were 15 major versions of the Hercules in global operations. By the time I had completed thousands of miles of flying in the Hercules, including a good many hours spent at the controls, three new additions to the Hercules family were already in the air and operational.

It is a trying process to deal with a giant airplane that by virtue of its own yet-undiscovered capabilities continues to frustrate the chronicler of its missions by adding to them without pause. To say nothing of the difficulty in cataloguing the spectrum of the past.

I have been singularly fortunate in being the only civilian ever to live, work, and fly with the famed Thunderbirds jet aerobatic precision team. I spent six weeks with these spectacular pilots, who through every attitude, low and high above the earth, in razor-sharp formations, imbue one with a deep and profound respect for their skill in carrying out such fabulous precision maneuvers with four airplanes flying as one. I stand on my ground as an individual who knows this facet of flying far better than most because of my advantage in having lived as a member of that exclusive fraternity.

Thus it is not only with admiration but astonishment that I have viewed the performance in flight of four Hercules transports in what has been aptly described as the "Dance of the Heavies." A team of four Hercules flying out of Sewart Air Force Base, and dubbed the "Four Horsemen" by their fellow crews, turned in dazzling performances as the world's only four-engine (per plane, that is) precision flying team. Their aerial demonstrations delighted and astounded onlookers from Denmark to Japan.

Their maneuvers—with airplanes each weighing 100,000 pounds—followed a series of elaborate and precisely executed aerobatics that left veteran transport pilots shaking their heads in wonder. Precision is not only a requisite but a key to survival when you fly these behemoths with the fluidity of a ballet presentation at speeds of 340 miles per hour—*with the wingtips only six feet apart.*

There is one group of Hercules crews who are possessed of the gall to try to shift the land masses of this planet—*and they are succeeding.* This is the specific assignment of the "Seeing Eye" Hercules version—the RC-130A—which carries millions of dollars of photographic, electronic, and computer equipment in the greatest aerial survey and mapmaking (or correcting) mission in history.

Within months of beginning their assignments, the crews (who turn over their photographs and electronic data to the U.S. Army Map Service and record data such as contours, altitudes, and positions with an accuracy hitherto unknown) were able to do some appreciable shifting about of the global real estate. They proved, for example, that Iceland is 600 feet distant from where it is shown on the most accurate maps of the world. Cuba is 1,200 feet out of position, and its southern coastline curves quite differently than our maps show. Most surprising of all, even Grand Bahamas Island, so close to the United States, is more than 32,000 feet from where it is "supposed to be."

Correcting errors of lesser and greater magnitude (many of them greater) is vital both to international transportation facilities and to the military strategists of the nation. Errors which meant little in the past have assumed critical proportions in the contemporary era of great missiles guided by self-contained inertial systems. The fact that one of our tracking stations of the deep-space net, set up to follow probes to and beyond the moon, was "way out of its believed position" had unhappy effects upon tracking activities in the space program. Those inaccuracies have been narrowed down from "many hundreds of feet to only a few feet."

The major geodetic tool carried by the RC-130A fleet is HIRAN, a complex electronic system that weds advanced mathematics with airborne pulse radar. Systematically surveying, charting, and photomapping vast swaths of the earth, the Hercules/HIRAN team, together with precision television and wide-angle overlap cameras, is producing the first detailed profile of the world in which accuracy finally has true meaning.

All circumstances of such missions cannot be forecast. "At one station in the jungle," reported HIRAN operator First Lieutenant William M. Smith, Jr., "the men were warned about tigers, and were armed with pistols or carbines or rifles. During the four months the station was in operation, nobody saw a striped man-eater, until near the end of this period. Walking down a jungle trail, one of the men came face-to-face with a tiger. A *big* tiger.

"The man, understandably, was rattled. He was so rattled that as he fumbled to draw his .45 pistol, he shot himself in the foot. The tiger stared at him, turned, and slowly walked away. . . ."

And did *that* man have a job explaining to hospital authorities how he shot himself in the foot while meeting a tiger face-to-face in the jungle while on photomapping missions at 25,000 feet. . . .

The Hercules years ago won a place as the best airplane in the business for testing equipment and techniques for high-altitude parachute jumps and drops. Literally tens of thousands of jumps with experimental and research equipment have been made from the Hercules, from low altitude to within the stratosphere itself. As the most telling example, this is the airplane that Captain Joseph W. Kittinger, Jr., of the Air Force selected to "prove out" his equipment before making the longest leap in the world from a balloon—a drop from 102,800 feet. In this free fall he reached a speed of more than 700 miles per hour and plunged for more than four and a half minutes before opening his main parachute.

Jumpers from the Hercules are now testing the revolutionary ballute—balloon parachute—developed from Kittinger's equipment, and to be used by our astronauts in the Gemini two-man spaceship program.

The Hercules is linked closely to space projects. When our astronauts are committed to orbital flights around the earth at five miles per second, crack rescue teams with scuba divers able to parachute into the oceans or anywhere else on this planet are

An RC-130A flying over Colombia is photographed from a sister ship during a photo-mapping mission across South America (*Lockheed-Georgia*)

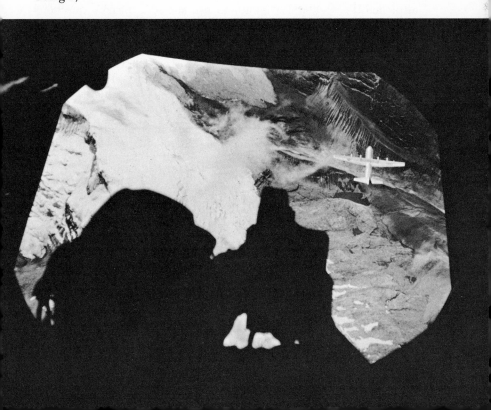

standing by for emergency rescue missions. Their airplane—the Hercules, able to fly at 370 miles per hour to any rescue scene, to slow down to 90 miles per hour for drops, to cruise in the stratosphere with electronic equipment sniffing out a plunging capsule, or to shut down two of its engines and cruise on search missions for from ten to 12 hours.

When the first Hercules flew across the Pacific to Japan—"way back" in 1957—its crew, and that of a companion airplane, volunteered to fly a hazardous over-ocean mission in search of a lost plane and crew.

An Air Force officer who volunteered to join the Lockheed civilian crew aboard the lead Hercules received an initial impression that likely will last him the remainder of his life, and his dazed expression as he told the writer the details of what transpired was something wonderful to behold.

He told me he ran into Operations, grabbed the maps of the search area, and ran out again—through a hard rain, of course. Through the downpour he saw a strange machine the like of which he had never seen before, and in the brief glimpse afforded him he failed to learn into what he had dashed. For a moment he started about him in complete surprise at the huge interior of the airplane. He opened his mouth to ask someone nearby questions about the airplane—at least as to *what* kind of airplane it was— when that someone shoved him rudely into a seat. A terrible din and roar broke out (that ground compressor turbine) and assailed his ears. The man standing in front of him placed his mouth by the officer's ear and screamed at him (he *had* to scream in order to be heard) to strap in tight .

By this time the officer was a bit "shook." The fact that he was not a pilot didn't help matters at all. The next moment an incredible thrumming sound (he described it as "a billion locusts that were loose inside the machine") hammered and rebounded from the walls of the airplane. Unaccustomed to the sonic barrage of the compressor turbine and the rolling thunder of the propeller blades (reflected between the ground and the wing and much worse than when the airplane is airborne), the officer stared about him in a growing daze as the Hercules rocked and heeled. The pilot had chopped the brakes free and was wheeling around in a tight turn, accelerating as he did so, to taxi to the runway.

He looked at the pilot—and his daze became one of complete disbelief. The pilot wore red and white striped socks. He wore a dirty sweatshirt that said "St. Mary's College" or something equally impossible. Atop his head was a crumpled hat of unknown vintage, and the man was nonchalantly blowing thick clouds of smoke from a cigar. The officer again shook his head and looked this time at the copilot. He got as far as a bilious green sport shirt with horrible yellow patterns and then, almost as if seeking mercy, he closed his eyes.

When he looked out again at the world the airplane was trembling from turbulence and every now and then a particularly bad jolt shook everyone in his seat. All he heard was that screaming noise and people shouting at one another; then the pilot turned around in a wreath of cigar smoke and shouted at the flight engineer.

The officer stared aghast as that worthy started hitting switches and killing engines. He held his breath until he turned almost blue, and couldn't believe it when the airplane continued flying just as before—although two engines were now dead.

At this time the Hercules was penetrating the edge of the typhoon then sweeping the Pacific, and the officer made the terrible mistake of looking out at the engines. The rain by now fell from the sky in solid sheets of water . . . the officer stared with jaw agape as a stream of water three or four inches in diameter poured out from the tailpipe of each of the dead engines as though it were under pressure from a firehose.

Panic welled up in our good officer's heart, and for this no one could blame him. He looked back through the airplane to see if anyone else was about to sound an alarm, or do something, and again his jaw fell.

At the rear sides of the airplane, several doors had been removed. Thin rope stretched before a yawning space over what was clearly a wind-lashed fury of liquid oblivion. But there were people standing there, sans parachutes, and leaning out into thin air as they looked for the downed airplane.

It was at this moment that the neophyte to the Hercules, as he explained it to me, "just plain quit thinking." He didn't know whose plane he was on or who was driving it, or what kind of airplane it was, or even what Air Force it was in, and he just didn't give a damn any more.

When the Hercules many hours later returned to solid land he lurched out of the airplane and rushed over to a friend. His eyes were glazed and his voice carried a pleading tone.

"Sam—you'll never believe it. . . ."

Epilogue   The story of the
Hercules is by no means complete. It cannot be, since there
are some 600 of these great machines now flying throughout the
world, many more on the production line, and foreign nations
waiting to join Australia, Canada, Indonesia, and South Africa in
the use of the most versatile transport ever built. For this is the
airplane that has already changed many lands and affected the
course of affairs of the international community.

No one in the fledgling days of the Hercules could have anticipated the heights of versatility to which the turboprop airplane
has ascended. And there are many assignments yet to be accomplished—missions all around the world, impossible of fulfillment by
other aircraft, awaiting only the arrival of the Hercules to push
them forward to successful conclusions.

We have a new national posture—one of great and profound
strength—because of this machine. The reader is well aware by
now of this mission, and it is not necessary at this time to provide
a further summation and rapid recital of superlative deeds accomplished. In any case, to conclude a record when the greatest missions are yet to be flown would be to ignore that wonderful promise
of the coming years.

The Hercules speaks—as it has in these pages—for itself.

There is, however, a thought the writer wishes to leave with
the reader. The performance which we have come to know is the
singular quality of a great machine that impinges deeply upon
the vital interests and concerns of dozens of nations around this
planet that are struggling to raise themselves above economic
conditions and transportation, industrial, and living standards that
they recognize to be inferior to those of the rest of this world's
community of nations. But it is not an easy task to telescope the
efforts of successive generations, and most attempts to do so succumb to the overwhelming demands of such an endeavor.

It is for this reason especially that the Hercules is now receiving
its greatest attention. A golden opportunity to meet the problems
of development peculiar to such nations as Peru is offered by such a

The four Hercules assault transports flown by the "Four Horsemen"—
the only aerobatic team in the world to fly precision formation aerobatic
maneuvers with a four-engine airplane. One of the most telling tributes
to the fame of the Hercules as "truly a pilot's airplane. . . ." (*Stars and
Stripes*)

craft as the Hercules. Vast stores of natural resources, still untapped,
cannot be opened up until physical communications are provided.
Extensive rail and highway arteries are luxuries to be attained only
at fantastic cost and with the passage of many years. Many countries cannot afford either the costs or the time.

There are unbelievable riches in these nations that are strangled
and crippled by geographical barriers that for decades have defied
penetration within the limits of *realistic* economies and national
strength. These nations cannot achieve, through any stretching of
their national resources, the incredible task of smashing the barriers.

Until now . . . when aerial logistics with a meaning never before
known in the history of flight has become a reality.

The law is that the economic growth of any nation is always
proportional to its communications and transportation systems.
Create an arterial system—or several systems—through and over
which goods, products, materials, and people may move with
fluidity, and the country has entered a new, meaningful, and
inevitably prosperous era in its life.

And if the normal systems of steel rails or wide concrete ribbons cannot be built in the near future, or are over the economic rainbow because of staggering costs . . . why, it is possible now to bypass these conventional arteries, to go *over* the barriers to progress—to build a bridge through the sky.

It is in this mission, as yet only started, that the Hercules will best serve not only the United States, but all those nations in this world aspiring to a life that, in order for us to know peace, all men deserve—and which they must have.

The United States is now well into its program to accomplish the third and final phase of its airlift modernization program. The huge winged machine to accomplish this goal so vital to our military and economic strength is the *StarLifter* . . . not an evolution, but a revolution in concept, in performance, and in application to national needs.

Wearing its Air Force colors, it will be known as the C-141A. Operating for Strike Command, within 80 hours a fleet of 200 StarLifters can deploy an entire airborne division nonstop from the United States to any point in Western Europe. And the *entire* globe will be within one-stop range of this great new craft.

But this is only one portion of its breathtaking spectrum of national service. For the StarLifter is the first airplane of its size and performance ever to be designed to conform to *both* the rugged and specialized needs of our military services, and as well to the stringent requirements for meeting all the demands of safety and performance established by the Federal Aviation Agency.

It is not a military transport only; it is not a commercial transport. It is a great logistics weapon created, like the Hercules, to meet *national* airlift requirements.

It is the next of a new breed of great winged craft.

It seems appropriate that the StarLifter should emerge from its chrysalis of design concept and elaborate mockups as the result of the extraordinary success and versatility which has attended the Hercules. The design philosophy of the StarLifter combines the highest aspirations with hardheaded practicality and experience. It represents, in essence, the logistical superiority of an advanced transport designed for cargo . . . without compromise either in the demands placed upon it or in its ability to deliver the corresponding performance.

The Lockheed-Georgia Company received the contractual award for the StarLifter in a competition for logistical aircraft unprecedented in industry history for its importance, a competition in which the best engineering brains of the nation aspired fiercely for success.

The United States government did not lightly award this contract. Initially it stands at a value that exceeds one *billion* dollars. There is nothing more important, however, than proven skill, performance, and intrinsic versatility.

The StarLifter is not revolutionary in aerodynamic design, despite its revolutionary performance and capabilities. A straightforward design, based upon *proven* cargo aircraft engineering knowhow, is the basis of its success: a design mating high sweptback wings and the most powerful turbofan jet engines in the nation, generating at its cruising speed the almost unbelievable energy of 25,000 horsepower.

It is an airplane with a wingspread and a length both of which exceed the total distance of the first flight of the Wright brothers' airplane in 1903. It is a ponderous machine that weighs 316,000 pounds—approximately the combat weight of three fully loaded four-engine B-29 bombers of World War II.

And yet, at its tremendous maximum weight, without any wind blowing down the runway to aid its first moments of flight, it will take off in a distance of only 5,330 feet.

Like the Hercules, the "clear cube" cargo space of the StarLifter is ten feet wide by nine feet high. Unlike the Hercules, this space extends through a length of 81 feet. It is possible to move a train of ten loaded pallets, each weighing 8,000 pounds, and with the airplane's mechanical loading system, winch aboard and lock into place the entire 80,000-pound load in a few minutes.

This is an airplane that is designed to lift from the ground with nearly 100,000 pounds of cargo aboard. Or if the mission is critical, long-distance delivery, it can load 20,000 pounds of cargo and then fly nonstop, even *without* tailwinds, and *with* a substantial fuel reserve, a distance of nearly 7,000 miles.

Up to four miles above the earth its crews will fly at a pressure level equal to that at the ocean surface. If they wish to climb to a desired cruising altitude of 40,000 feet, they will remain in a shirtsleeve environment of only 8,000 feet.

The performance of this new machine—which is not a planned but an *existing* aircraft—is overwhelming. Eight miles above the earth this giant will cruise at 550 miles per hour—200 miles per hour faster than the Hercules. Despite the tremendous bulk and weight of the StarLifter, it will cruise at 40,000 feet with the same speed as the sleek jet airliners now carrying passengers around the world—but which weigh 100,000 pounds *less* than the StarLifter.

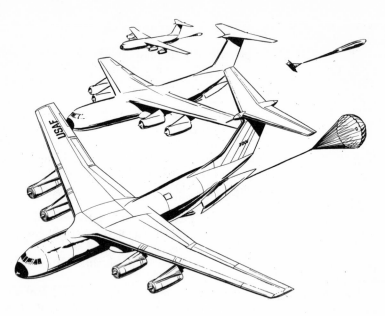

Strategic range, non-stop missions with heavy air drops for the huge StarLifter . . .

Strategic range assault missions with everything—including tanks —for the Hercules . . .

Once again, as has been the case with the Hercules, there is the temptation to succumb to the lure of such glittering statistics. And once again, they tend to obscure the meaningful purpose of this airplane, which can operate from nearly 2,000 airports throughout the world. It will do so without any auxiliary loading aids, it will whip its cargo loads in and out faster than any aircraft save the smaller Hercules, and it will effect a dramatic reduction in costs and in the number of personnel who would ordinarily be required to attend so huge an aircraft.

Three men—no more—can fly this machine. A fourth man—the navigator—will join them for the long-range missions.

Take all the features proved so outstanding in the Hercules, refine them, improve them, add to them the "dream" features of engineers—and you are describing the StarLifter.

If the epilogue is properly to conclude this story—at least for these pages—it must emphasize that the greatest accomplishments, the most outstanding missions, and the most meaningful service to the nation await us in the coming years.

INDEX

Adams, Paul D., 210, 229, 233-34, 243-57, 279
aerial reconnaissance, 254
aerial refueling, 48-51, 206-207, 296-99
Afghanistan, 44
Agadir, Morocco, 301-303
Agena upper-stage rocket, 77-78
Air Commandos, 263-70, 276
Air Development Squadron Six VX-6 (USN), 336
Air Express aircraft, 67
Air Force (magazine), 23
Air Force, United States, 26, 27, 31, 113-18, 120-21, 132-33, 138, 222, 230, 239, 242; Flight Test Center, 128; test pilots, 128-29; pilot training, 129; Hercules assignment specifications, 138; tests Hercules, 159-65; COIN and, 263, 267, 269; South Vietnam and, 267-70; guerrilla air war, 267-70; Vietnamese Air Force and, 268; Operation Ice Flow, 332
Air Police, 9
Air Training Command, 129
Alamo Scouts, 279
Albania, 31
Alert Status, 5
Alison, John R., 264
Allen, Jesse, 168-69, 239-41
alloys, military use of, 250
Altair aircraft, 67, 79
Anatov aircraft, 350
Andring, James H., 282
Antarctica, 327-41
armies, modern day, 21
Army Engineers' Research and Development Laboratory, 178
Army, United States, 222, 230; Fourth Division, 255; Fifth Division, 256; Special Forces Group, 263, 267, 271-72; COIN, 263, 267, 269, 272; Detachment 101, 279

Atlas missile, 21, 77
Avro Lancaster bomber, 127

B-17 (Flying Fortress) aircraft, 66, 72
B-29 attack bomber, 78
B-47 Stratojet, 68
B-57 attack bomber, 205-207
Banyan Tree II, 227-28
Bao Dai government, 38
Bell P-59 Airacomet aircraft, 72
Beltz, Stanley, 60-63, 79
Blue Eagles, 346
Bong, Richard Ira, 71
Bowman, Alfred C., Jr., 281-82, 288-89, 300
Boyd, Albert, 73
Brennan, Bob, 164, 166
Brown, Harold, 24
Bulgaria, 31
Burdick, Jack, 323
Burma, 44, 264-65
Burma Raiders, 264
Byrd, Richard, 334

C-46 Commando aircraft, 263, 267
C-47 (Gooney Bird) aircraft, 66, 263, 267, 270, 339; Dakotas, 325
C-119 Packet aircraft, 197, 325
C-123 Provider aircraft, 197-98, 263, 267, 269
C-124 Globemaster aircraft, 332
C-135 aircraft, 217, 255; Airborne Command Post, 216
C-141 StarLifter, 251, 358-61
Campbell Air Force Base (Kentucky), 224
Cantwell, Bob, 68
Cape Canaveral, 254
Caracas, Venezuela, 222-23
Chambley, Doug, 329, 340-41
Chamoun, Camille, 205
Charleston Air Force Base (South Carolina), 234

Chinese Communist Army, 33
Coast Guard, United States, 131-32
COIN, 263, 267, 269, 272
Collier Trophy, 68
Collyer, C. B. D., 68
combat exercises, 227-28
Comet aircraft, 81-82, 84
commercial airlines, 220, 287
Communists, guerrilla warfare, 24, 29; "limited war" and, 31-32, 47; Greece and, 31-32; Korean War and, 32-33; Indo-China and, 33-34, 37-40; propaganda, 38; objectives of, 44-45; political considerations of, 44-45; Lebanon and, 205, 212-13; Taiwan, 212-13
Composite Air Strike Force (CASF), 51; transport airlift and, 52; Operation Mobile Baker, 53; Operation Mobile Zebra, 53; striking power of, 56, 205-15, 229; Hercules aircraft and, 198; operational procedure, 201-14, 234; STRICOM and, 201-202; Henry Viccellio and, 202, 215-17, 224; Lebanon and, 205-14, 217, 247; Taiwan and, 212-13, 217; Development Control Center, 215; Maurice Preston and, 215-17; Direct Air Support Center, 217; C-135 aircraft, 217-18; Caracas, Venezuela, incident, 222-24; Banyan Tree II, 227-28; Viet Nam jungle warfare, 268
Congress, United States, reorganization of Department of Defense, 254-55
Constellation aircraft, 72, 74-75, 79
Constitution aircraft, 74-76, 79
Continental Army Command, 230
Cook, Pyatt H., 282
Councill, Bill, 73
counter-guerrilla operations, 276-79
Counter-Guerrilla Warfare School (USMC), 277
Counterinsurgent Forces (COIN), 263, 267, 269, 272
Curth, Henry, 282

"Dance of the Heavies," 351
Dees, Hank, 328
demolition, 273
Department of Defense, 178; reorganization of, 254-55
Detachment 101, United States Army, 279

Dienbienphu, 34, 39
Direct Air Support Center (DASC), 204, 217
Division Ready Force, 252-54
Division Ready Force Alert, 252
Donlon, Jocko, 135-37
Doolittle, James, 68
Doris, Harry W., Jr., 49
Douglas DC-3 aircraft, 65
Drogue Inflight Refueling Project, 49, 51

82nd Airborne Division, 271
839th Air Division, 5, 9, 11, 260, 312-14, 316, 321
Earhart, Amelia, 67-68
Edwards Air Force Base (California), 63, 79
Eglin Air Force Base (Florida), 263
Egypt, 44
Eielson, Ben, 67
El Centro, California, 184
Electra aircraft, 68, 79, 287
Electra Jr. aircraft, 68
energy-absorption system, 261
Evreux-Fauville Air Base (France), 3, 182, 197, 281, 304, 313; 839th Air Division at, 5, 9; flight operations, 6, 7, 9, 11; 322nd Air Division at, 9; Hercules system at, 9; Air Police vehicles, 9; personnel at, 10
Evreux, France, 3
"Examples of Limited War" (Air University of the Air Force), 31
Exercise Sagebrush (1955), 199
extraction drops, 258-62

F-80 Shooting Star, 49
F-84G Thunderjet, 51
F-84F fighter-bombers, 51
F-86D Sabre aircraft, 209
F-94 Starfire aircraft, 76
F-100D Super Sabre aircraft, 206-207
F-104 Starfighter aircraft, 73, 76
405th Fighter Bomber Wing, 50-51
463rd Troop Carrier Wing, 238
508th Fighter Escort Wing, 49
Fahy, Herb, 68
Faisal II (King of Iraq), 205
Far East Air Forces Probe, 49, 51
Felt, Harry D., 29
Ferguson, W. E., quoted, 54
Fifth Air Force, 48

fighting man, individual, 18-19, 21, 24-26
First Combat Applications Group, 263-64
First Special Group (Airborne), 275
Fisher, Thomas L., II, 42, 45, 54; quoted, 29-30, 35
Fort Carson (Colorado), 256
Fort Bragg (North Carolina), 201, 272-73
"Four Horsemen," 351
French Air Force, 34
French forces (Indo-China), 34, 37-39

Gardner, Hugh H., 279
Gatty, Harold, 67
Gilley, Jack G., 123
Goebel, Art, 68
gravity, negative g, 105; positive g, 105; weightlessness, 106
Great Britain, 187
Greece, 31; Communists in, 32; methods of combat, 32
Greek Army, 32
Griffin, Bennett, 67
Griffin, Herman, 296-97
guerrilla warfare, 19, 24, 28-29, 31-34, 37-39, 254, 267-70, 277-79

Hammarskjöld, Dag, 303
Hawkins, Willis M., 56-57
Hawks, Frank, 68
Hensleigh, Walt, 125-26
Hercules aircraft, cargo compartment, 4, 6, 10, 14, 16-17, 82-83, 96, 224; appearance, 7-8, 58-59; flight procedure, 8-9; disaster areas and, 10-11, 17; capabilities of, 12-17; performance, 13-17, 238-39; test flights of, 60-63, 79, 238-40; ancestry of, 66, 68-69, 71, 72-75; design philosophy, 80, 82, 92, 94; hydrostatic pressure fatigue tests, 82-85; inspection tests, 85-92; metal testing, 89-92; Immerscope, 91; repetition concept, 92; hydraulic system, 92-93; electrical power systems, 93; refueling, 95-96; air pressure tests, 96; static tests, 96; landing gear, 97; flight-testing, 98-111, 238-39; gravity tests, 105-107; structural integrity, 105-11; zero-g flights, 106-107; air-drop tests, 110; cargo release, 110-11; operational

flight tests, 113-14; versions of, 116; E model, 116-18, 234-35, 242, 252, 262; A model, 116-18, 132-33, 135, 140, 150, 157, 178, 187, 224-25; B model, 116-18, 135, 147, 152, 225-27, 234-52, 281; lifting capability, 116, 118, 120-21; range, 117-18; noise, 117; engines, 117-18, 124-25, 132-37; short-field characteristics, 118, 122; speed, 118; GV-1 model, 118; KC-130F model, 118; U.S. Marine Corps and, 118-19; U.S. Navy and, 118; commercial potential, 119-20; early incidents, 122-23; stability, 125-26, 132-33; control characteristics, 127; rescue operations, 131; U.S. Coast Guard and, 131-32; two-engine use, 132-35; three-engine use, 132; one-engine use, 136-37; variety of missions, 176, 222-23; equipment drops, 176; Project SLIDE, 176-77; skis developed for, 177; Arctic flying, 178; C-130D, 178, 321; heavy equipment tests, 178; rescue operation, 180-81; bulk cargo tests, 181-83; mechanical loading, 183; air-drop tests, 184-88; world records, 186-87; world-wide service, 188-89; Lebanon incident and, 207; KC-97 "Talking Bird," 217-18; portable gas stations, 226-27; Banyan Tree II and, 227-28; extraction drops, 258-62; flight deck, 282, 285, 287-89, 292; sound, 287; hold, 287; navigator cubicle, 288-89; storms and, 289-91; radar system, 292-93; KC-130F tanker, 297; GV-1 tanker, 297-98; nonstop in formation record, 299; Agadir rescue, 301-303; Congo mission, 303-10; safety record, 304; "Helping Hand Missions," 310-12; East Pakistan mission, 310; Moscow assignment, 316-20; Greenland assignment, 320-25; C-130BL, 324; LC-130F, 324; Arctic mission, 325-27; Antarctica mission, 332-41; Operation X-Ray, 342-45; Andes mission, 345-48; Himalaya mission, 348-50; precision flying, 351; RC-130A, 351-52; aerial survey mission, 352; high-altitude equipment tests, 353; space projects and, 353-54
Hershberg, Sidney S., 204

Hibbard, Hall L., 58, 67, 72
Himalayas, 263
Ho Chi Minh, 34
Holloway, B. K., 234
Hudson aircraft, 70, 79
Hughes, Howard, 71, 74
Hump operations, 263

ICBM, 21
Immerscope, 91
Incirlik Air Base (Turkey), 6, 10, 207
India, 349-50
Indians, American, 279
Indo-China, guerrilla warfare, 24, 29, 33; methods of combat, 34; terrain, 36-37; French forces in, 37-38; Communist propaganda, 38
Indonesia, 44
Ingalls, Laura, 67
Invader attack bombers, 263, 267
Iran, 44
Iron Curtain, 192

Jackson, Charles, 187
Johnson, C. L. Kelly, 67, 72-73, 274
Joint Operations Center (Saigon), 267
Jungle Warfare Training Center (Fort Sherman, Canal Zone), 273
Jupiter missile, 21

KC-97 "Talking Bird" aircraft, 218-19
Kaufman, William W., quoted, 43
Kindley Air Force Base, 206
Kingsford-Smith, Sir Charles, 67
Kissinger, Henry A., 44
Kittinger, Joseph W., Jr., 353
Khrushchev, Nikita, 19
Korean War, 26, 29-32, 42, 47; methods of combat, 33; U.S. cost in, 41-42; aircraft used during, 76
Kuperov, Leonid, 337

L-28 liaison aircraft, 213
Langley Air Force Base (Virginia), 50; TAC Headquarters Command Post, 216-17, 219-22
Lead Sled, 171
Lebanon, 205, 207-14, 247
LeMay, Curtis E., 194, 235-36
Leopoldville, Congo, 302-303
LeVier, Tony, 73
"Limited war," 26-30, 34-35; Lebanon incident, 205-14; Taiwan incident, 212-13

Lindbergh, Anne, 68
Lindbergh, Charles, 68
Lockheed Aircraft Corporation, 27, 56, 58; aircraft production, 67-68, 78, 238; manufacturing growth of, 68-69; supplies England during World War II, 70; fighter planes of, 70-71; robots, 77; modifications of Hercules aircraft, 226-27, 234, 238-39; C-130E model Hercules, 234-35, 242, 251, 255; C-141 StarLifter, 251
Lockheed, Allan, 67
Lodestar aircraft, 71-72, 79
Loosbrock, J. F., quoted, 23

M-1 rifle, 250
M-14 rifle, 250
MacDill Air Force Base (Florida), 219
McDonnell Phantom II aircraft, 194
McGuire, Thomas B., Jr., 71
McNamara, Robert, 257
McReynolds, James S., 281-82, 288, 300
Malaya, 44
Marine Corps, United States, 118-19
Mariner II (robot), 77-78
Marion, Francis, 278
Martin, Bud, 116
Mattern, Jimmy, 67
medical aides, 273
Merrill's Marauders, 274, 279
metals, military use of, 250
microjet rocket, 277
Middlewood, R. W., 79
Military Air Transport Service (MATS), 140, 212, 220, 234-35, 248
Minute Men, 278
Mobile Tactical Strike Force, 50
Moore, William G., 313
Morcock, D. S., 85
Mosby, John S., 278
Mule Train operation, 269
Myrtle Beach Air Force Base (South Carolina), 206

19th Air Force, 201-202; purpose, 203-205, 233-34; Direct Air Support Center of, 204; missions, 205-14; Lebanon and, 205-14; Taiwan incident, 212; operational procedure, 215-17; KC-97 communication flights, 218
National Science Foundation, 331

Navy, United States, 44; Hercules order, 324; Operation Deep Freeze, 331-41; Air Development Squadron Six VX-6, 336
Nepal, 44
Newcomer, Lloyd E., 337-38
Nichols, Ruth, 68
Nixon, Richard, 222; visit to Caracas, Venezuela, 223-24
"normal alert," 10
North American Air Defense Command (NORAD), 229
North Korean Army, 33
North Viet Nam, 34, 269
Northrop, John, 67
nuclear weapons, 19-24, 55-56

116th Fighter Bomber Wing, 48
1700th Test Squadron, 140-41
Operation Boxkite (1954), 50
Operation Deep Freeze (USN), 331-41
Operation Ice Flow (USAF), 332
Operation Longstride (1952), 49
Operation Mobile Baker (1956), 53
Operation Mobile Zebra (1957), 53
operational flying, 112; purpose, 113
Orion aircraft, 68

P2V Neptune aircraft, 73-74, 79
P-38 Lightning aircraft, 70-71
Pacific Air Forces (PACAF), 270
Pakistan, 311
pallets, extraction drop, 259; people drop, 261-62
paratroopers, 271-72, 274-76
Peru, 345
Peterson, Vern, 122-24, 164-66
Pickens, Andrew, 278
pilots, troop-carrier, 313-15
Polaris missile, 77
Pole Station (South Pole), 332-41
Portal, Sir Charles, quoted, 43
Post, Wiley, 67
Potsdam Conference, 32
Preston, Maurice A., 203, 215-17
Price, Nathan, 72
Project SLIDE, 175
Pruett, Jack, 304, 306-307, 309
psychological warfare, 38
Puerto Rico, 224
Pulver, W. A., 76, 79

Quarles, Donald A., quoted, 22, 54
Quinn, Homer H., 282, 300

RB-66 reconnaissance bomber, 207
RF-101A Voodoo aircraft, 207
Ranger battalions, 279
Real, Jack, 60
Red China, 22
Republic F-105 Thunderchief aircraft, 194
Rhein-Main Air Base (Germany), 6, 10
Ridings, Ned, 133
Rinn, John R., 282
robots, 77
rocket bottles, 173-74
Royal Air Force (Britain), 187
Royal Canadian Air Force, 324-27

61st Troop Carrier Squadron, 332
773rd Troop Carrier Squadron, 346
Saturn twin-engined airliner, 76
Scott, Robert Falcon, 338
Scott, Winfield, 278
Senter, Lewis B., 346
Sewart Air Force Base (Tennessee), 224, 238, 260, 313
Seymour-Johnson Air Force Base, 201
Sirius aircraft, 68, 79
Sixth Army, United States, 279
Sixth Fighter Squadron, 264
Skyraider fighter-bombers, 267
Slessor, Sir John, quoted, 56
Smith, Bill, 184, 328, 338-40
Smith, William M., Jr., 352
Snark missile, 21
Sondestrom Air Base (Greenland), 321
South American, Banyan Tree II operation, 227-28
South Graham Land Island, 67
South Korea, 33
South Pole, 327-28, 331-32, 334-41
South Viet Nam, guerrilla warfare, 267-70, 277-79; Mule Train operation, 269
Spad XIII fighter aircraft, 263
Special Air. Warfare Center (Florida), 263-67
Special Forces Group, 263, 267, 271-72
Sperry APN/59 Radar System, 292-93
Stanton, R. E., 60
Stearman, Lloyd, 67
Strategic Air Command (SAC), 33, 47-48; aerial refueling, 49; operational procedure, 191-92, 194; Iron

Strategic Air Command (cont.)
Curtain and, 192; based on CASF, 231; "tailormade" striking force, 231, 234; mobility, 231-32; preventative of nuclear war, 231
Strategic Army Corps (STRAC), 201
Strategy for the West (Slessor), 56
Strike Command (STRICOM), 201-202, 263; purpose, 243-44; Hercules aircraft and, 245, 251; weapons, 244-45, 250; conventional forces, 246; troops, 246, 248; modernization problems, 250; equipment, 250-52; mobility control, 251-52; Division Ready Force, 252-54; Division Ready Force Alert, 252-54; aerial reconnaissance, 254; guerrilla combat exercises, 254; meaning of, 254-55; Swift Strike II, 255-56; C-141A StarLifter, 251, 358
Sullivan, Leo, 79, 99-119, 127-28, 138, 156, 173
Sumter, Thomas, 278
Sweeney, Walter C., Jr., 191-94, 219, 230
Swift Strike II, 255-56
Syria, 44

T2V SeaStar aircraft, 76
12th Air Force, 212
31st Fighter Bomber Wing, 50
314th Troop Carrier Wing, 224, 321
315th Air Division, 312
322nd Air Division, 9-11, 302-12, 349
326th Engineer Battalion, 101st Airborne Division, 174
354th Tactical Fighter Wing, 227
388th Fighter Bomber Wing, 50
Tactical Air Command (TAC), 46-49; Mobile Tactical Strike Force, 50-51; aerial refueling, 50-52; operational success of, 53; 18th Air Force, 113; pilot training, 129; cooperates with aircraft manufacturers, 140; tests Hercules, 141; emergency missions and, 142; purpose of, 190-91, 193-94, 197-98, 230; operational procedure, 190-92, 194, 196, 198-217; supersonic fighter wings, 194-96; 19th Air Force and, 201, 203; Lebanon and, 205-14; Headquarters Command Post, 216-22; Banyan Tree II, 227-28; extraction drop techniques, 258-62; people-pallet

system, 261-62; Special Air Warfare Center (Florida), 263; CASF, 263; First Air Commando Group, 263-67; pilots, 293-96; Andes operation, 346-48
Tactical Fighter Squadron, 206
Taiwan, 44, 212-13
Tan Son Nhut Air Base (Saigon), 267
tanker aircraft, 50-51, 206, 296-98
Teller, Edward, quoted, 22
Texas Rangers, 278
Thailand, 44
thermonuclear war, 19-22; second-strike capability, 23-24
Thompson, Llewellyn E., Jr., 316, 318-19
Thor missile, 21, 77
Thunderbirds, 351
Tracy, Joseph P., 114-16
Trojan (trainer) aircraft, 263, 267
Truman Doctrine, 32
turboprop engines (Allison), outboard reduction-gear assembly, 140, 147-48; turbojet, 140; propeller, 140; turboprop, 140; YT56-A-1 (turboprop engine), 140; Military Air Transport Service and, 140; U.S. Air Force and, 140; flight tests, 140-41; official evaluation, 141; major overhauls, 141-42; economy, 142-43; change time, 143; T56, 143, 147, 158; characteristics, 143; versatility, 143, 145; fleet operations, 146; "unscheduled removal rate," 146; safety record, 146-47; T56-A7, 147; horsepower, 147, 158; dimensions, 147; air time, 147; gas turbine assembly, 147-48; power section, 147-56; simplicity, 148; Phase III, 158; T56-M5, 158; T56-M9, 158; icecap tests, 321
Turk, Wilbert, 332, 334-35
Turner, Roscoe, 68
Tyree, David M., 329-32, 336, 338

U-2 aircraft, 73, 76
Union of Soviet Socialist Republics, 46; strategies of, 18, 20-25; nuclear weapons and, 18-19, 21-24; negotiations with United States, 19; Korean War and, 35; military power and, 47, 229; Lebanon and, 205, 207, 247; weather data, 220

United Nations, 29
United States Air Forces Europe (USAFE), 209, 312
United States of America, strategies of, 18, 20-25; nuclear weapons and, 18-19, 21-24, 55-56; negotiations with Soviet Union, 19; strike forces of, 25, 49, 51-53; Korean War and, 30-31, 71; "limited wars" and, 41-42, 45; Indo-China and, 42; Communist tactics and, 45; re-evaluates combat methods, 45-46, 48; air power, 46-47, 49; "massive retaliation" policy of, 47; Lebanon and, 205-14; Taiwan incident, 212-13; weather data, 220; Banyan Tree II, 227-28; command posts, 229

Van Fleet, James, 32
Van Oordt, G., 347
Vega aircraft, 67, 79
Ventura aircraft, 71-72
Viccellio, Henry, 47, 50, 52, 202, 215-17
Viet Cong forces, 267-70, 277
Vietminh forces, 34, 37-40
Vietnamese Air Force (VNAF), 268
Vosburg, Frederick G., 335
Vultee, Gerald, 67

WB-66 weather-reconnaissance aircraft, 207
Wallick, Wilmer S., 281-82, 292, 300
War of 1812, 278
warfare, thermonuclear, 19-24; guerrilla, 19, 24, 28-29, 31-34, 37-39, 254, 267-70, 277-79; psychological, 38; new, 258-62; old style, 262-70
weapons, 244-45, 250; nuclear, 19-24; microjet rocket, 277; gas, 277
Weather Bureau, United States, 220
Weatherbee, Frank L., 347
White, Robert, 343-44
Wilkins, George Hubert, 67
Wilkinson, Spencer, quoted, 43
Williams, Gayle, 280, 296-97
Wimmer, Roy, 60
Winnie Mae (airplane), 67
World War II, 279

X-7 rocket, 77
X-15 rocket aircraft, 180
X-17 hypersonic research rocket, 77
XC-35 aircraft, 68
XP-80 Shooting Star aircraft, 73
XFV fighter plane, 76

Yemen, 44
Yugoslavia, 31